SEMICONDUCTOR CONTROLLED RECTIFIERS:

PRINCIPLES AND APPLICATIONS OF p–n–p–n DEVICES

PRENTICE-HALL SERIES IN ELECTRICAL ENGINEERING

Frontispiece—Semiconductor controlled rectifiers cover a wide range of power ratings and include variations such as light activated switches (lower left of photo) and aircooled types with integral heat sinks (background).

Semiconductor Controlled Rectifiers :

PRINCIPLES AND APPLICATIONS OF p–n–p–n DEVICES

F. E. GENTRY — Manager Advance Engineering
Rectifier Components Dept., General Electric
Company

F. W. GUTZWILLER — Manager Application Engineering
Rectifier Components Dept., General Electric
Company

NICK HOLONYAK, JR. — Professor, Department of Electrical Engineering
University of Illinois

E. E. VON ZASTROW — Consulting Engineer, Semiconductor Applications
Rectifier Components Dept., General Electric
Company

Prentice-Hall, Inc., Englewood Cliffs, N.J.

Current printing (last digit):

12 11 10 9 8 7 6 5 4 3

Library of Congress
Catalog Card No. 64-21172
Printed in the United States of America
   C 80610

PRENTICE-HALL INTERNATIONAL, INC., *London*
PRENTICE-HALL OF AUSTRALIA, LTD., *Sydney*
PRENTICE-HALL OF CANADA, LTD., *Toronto*
PRENTICE-HALL OF INDIA (PRIVATE) LTD., *New Delhi*
PRENTICE-HALL OF JAPAN, INC., *Tokyo*

PREFACE

In recent years, a number of semiconductor devices have been the subject of large-scale popular attention. Although in practice they have not, in many cases, realized their initial promise, the entire family of *p-n-p-n* devices (particularly the semiconductor controlled rectifier—SCR) for some time has been of considerable research interest and has provided some of the work-horses of the electron-device field. Accordingly, and since no single comprehensive account of the *p-n-p-n* family of devices has been previously available, we have attempted to fill what appears to us a gap in the literature by writing a book almost equally divided between the essential semiconductor and device principles, and the more typical and useful applications of *p-n-p-n* devices.

At this writing, most practical *p-n-p-n* semiconductor devices function as switches. Owing, in large part, to their two stable states (ON and OFF) and their low power dissipation in these two states, *p-n-p-n* devices have found unique usefulness in those applications which require latching action and power-handling capability. Other characteristics that have stimulated wide usage of *p-n-p-n* devices are their triggering sensitivity, control-power gain, static operation, and high speed of operation. The best known of the *p-n-p-n* device family is the semiconductor controlled rectifier, known widely as the SCR and in some international circles as the "Thyristor." Around the SCR have sprung many other semiconductor devices that operate on the *p-n-p-n* principle: the gate turn-off switch, the controlled switch, light-activated switches, and bilateral switches (with both two and three terminals), to mention but a few.

No preface to a book of this type would be complete without brief mention of some of the history of the *p-n-p-n* switch, which can be traced

vii

back to Shockley's concept of the "hook" collector. Following Shockley's work, Ebers developed a two-transistor circuit approximation (*n-p-n* and *p-n-p* interconnection) to the *p-n-p-n* switch which served as a useful model of what such an integrated device might be. In 1954 and 1955 perhaps no one more than John Moll appreciated what a *p-n-p-n* switch would be and in what material (silicon) it should be constructed. Following the guidance and urging of Moll, a group under his direction at the Bell Telephone Laboratories built the first working *silicon p-n-p-n* devices. This work and the principles underlying the operation of *p-n-p-n* devices were described in a *Proc. I.R.E.* article† which has served as the basis for all succeeding work in this field.

As has been true of some other devices, the *p-n-p-n* switch was not well understood and fully appreciated by many workers in 1956 and 1957, and might have been ignored as a practical device. However, R. A. York (of the General Electric Company), aware of the work at Bell Labs and the need for a semiconductor "thyratron," initiated a successful project to build high-current versions of the silicon *p-n-p-n* switch (SCR). York and his associates, followed later by many others, sensed what the acceptance would be to a semiconductor thyratron-like device, and that not only were *p-n-p-n* devices destined to work at signal levels but were also capable of handling hundreds of kilowatts. (This fact was indicated in the published BTL work, but was either overlooked or not understood by most readers.) Since the commercial introduction of the SCR, the future of the *p-n-p-n* switch in its many forms, varieties, sizes, speeds, and power levels has become assured; no longer is research on such devices subject to pessimistic scrutiny. In the SCR field today, devices are available with current ratings from a few milliamperes to hundreds of amperes, and the blocking voltage ratings of power SCR's extend above 1000 v (see frontispiece).

Probably because of some superficially simple features of SCR's, there has been some tendency to underestimate the subtlety, complexity, and potential variety of *p-n-p-n* devices. This class of devices represents a more general form of "transistor" than the commonly known transistor. As such, at this stage of development, though sophisticated, it offers in many respects greater potential for further study, development, and application than its simpler progenitor. We have, thus, adopted the point of view in writing this book that both device and application principles deserve equal treatment. Although most readers may be interested in applications, no full realization of potential applications is possible unless the reader understands certain device features of *p-n-p-n* switches. Also, many individuals interested solely in applications will find that ultimately they would like to understand more concerning the device and will be equipped to do so. Furthermore, some treatment of devices must be at hand if one is to be able to understand and

† Moll, Tanenbaum, Goldey, and Holonyak, "*p-n-p-n* Transistor Switches," *Proc. IRE*, Vol. **44** (September, 1956), pp 1174–1182.

use the whole host of devices that are in development and that will be developed in the future (both at signal and power levels).

We have outlined application principles for their own sake; we hope, however, that the reader interested in devices may learn from the applications section what features in devices are limiting, are circumscribed, and are weaknesses which should afford challenge for improvement and change. (To this point, we should mention that it was the needs and problems of the application engineer that led directly to the development of the bilateral, or a-c, *p-n-p-n* switch.) We have tried to provide the device engineer, and others, with an introduction and summary of semiconductor principles directly applicable to *p-n-p-n* device problems. This has led us to repeat some material already in certain books, but has allowed us the advantage of presenting a largely self-contained treatment and the further advantage of being able to emphasize what we think are some of the key ideas in *p-n-p-n* switch operation.

We should caution the reader that he will find many things missing in this book. These are largely the newer devices and newer applications which perforce continue to grow around a device principle so unique and broad as that inherent in a "more general transistor," i.e., in the *p-n-p-n* switch mechanism. An intuitive "feel" for these statements can be gained by remembering that, of all active semiconductor devices, only the *p-n-p-n* switch works a range from the very lowest power levels to the very highest power levels. Because the development of signal-level devices and also the more general four-terminal *p-n-p-n* switch have tended to lag behind power devices and three-terminal devices, it has been necessary for us to slight these areas. However, if the reader finds comprehensible what is contained herein, he will experience no problems in understanding and using newer *p-n-p-n* devices.

Letter symbols for electrical ratings and characteristics of devices discussed in this book are taken from the proposed *IEEE Standards on Solid-State Devices: Letter Symbols for Semiconductor Devices* as it stands at this time. Circuit symbols are from ASA Standard Y32.2-1962 with the notable exception of the symbol for the SCR. Here the authors have used instead the SCR symbol that is in general usage today. The official *p-n-p-n* triode circuit symbol has been reserved for *p-n-p-n* devices with useful gate turn-off characteristics in order to differentiate between the two types of devices.

We owe a considerable debt to a number of our associates and colleagues for help in preparing this book. Among these are R. A. York, D. Bisson, U. Faubion, R. E. Hysell, R. Kokosa, A. Schmidt, and the General Electric Company for having made much of the work described herein possible. One of us (N.H.) owes much to B.T.L. and J. L. Moll for introducing him to the challenges of *p-n-p-n* switches and the uniqueness of silicon. All of us appreciate the patience and understanding of our wives so necessary for completion of this work.

CONTENTS

CHAPTER 1

SEMICONDUCTOR AND *p-n* JUNCTION PROPERTIES

1.1 Introduction

The *p-n-p-n* switch, the three-terminal version of which we shall frequently refer to as the semiconductor controlled rectifier or SCR, is similar in many respects to the junction transistor.[1] The operation of both of these classes of devices depends very essentially upon minority-carrier injection, efficient transport of injected minority carriers across an appropriate base region or base regions, and finally minority-carrier collection at a collector junction. In the *p-n-p-n* switch, unlike the transistor, a hole emitter and an electron emitter are present at either end of the device. Both emitters are operative in injecting minority carriers, electrons and holes, into two base regions which are disposed on either side of a common collector junction. Thus, in contrast to a transistor, the collector or central junction of a *p-n-p-n* switch collects both electrons and holes as a normal and essential part of its operation.

If the efficiency with which electrons and holes are injected and transported across each base region to the common collector can be made to increase by increasing the current through the device, or by light shining upon the device, or by any similar mechanism, the total collector current (absolute sum of collected hole and electron currents) will tend to become larger than the current flowing through either end of the device through the emitters. A situation would exist momentarily that would tend to violate continuity of current through the device. When this occurs, some of the fixed space charge of the reverse-biased collector is discharged, and the collector switches to forward bias, and low voltage. This allows the collector junction, according to superposition, to reinject into both base regions just sufficient minority

1

carriers in opposition to emitter-injected minority carriers to maintain continuity of current in the device. In terms of the familiar concept of transistor *alpha*, the sum of the alphas α_n and α_p, in the *p-n-p-n* switch becomes equal to unity when switching occurs. The unique manner in which the collector of a *p-n-p-n* device switches from reverse to forward bias is the distinguishing characteristic which makes it similar to a thyratron.

We have described above the operation of a regenerative, self-latching switch which turns off if the current through it is reduced below a certain minimum value or if base current and transistor action are employed to drive the *p-n-p-n* OFF. The device we have described switches from high to low impedance because a reverse-biased collector, which can sustain high voltages, switches to forward bias and low voltage. In a transistor this occurs only so long as a large external current drive is maintained on the base, and instead of requiring base current to drive OFF the transistor, base current is needed to keep it ON. As we shall see later, one of the methods of analyzing a *p-n-p-n* switch is to consider it as two transistors connected in such a way that the collector of one drives the base of the other, and vice versa. Without considering at this point the details of this analysis, we see already that the collector output of one transistor section provides the base drive which holds the other transistor ON and vice versa, and thus no external base drive is required to keep the device ON. Hence, once turned on, the *p-n-p-n* switch (SCR) tends to stay ON and requires external base drive (of proper polarity) or a sufficient reduction in load current to be turned off.

Thus far, we have presented a loose description of the operation of the *p-n-p-n* switch. Also, we have introduced a number of undefined terms and concepts which are to be more carefully treated in later chapters. Our purpose in the remainder of this chapter will be to review only those semiconductor fundamentals required later for description, analysis, and design of *p-n-p-n* devices (SCR's). Since there are now many excellent books concerning semiconductors and transistors, we shall assume that the reader already has some general understanding of this field or can easily turn to a standard reference for a more detailed discussion of semiconductor principles than we shall provide.[2,3,4,5] We shall resort to a number of qualitative arguments in this chapter but shall develop as much quantitative material as we shall need in later chapters to give a rather complete discussion of the device aspects of *p-n-p-n*'s.

1.2 Energy Levels, Electrons, and Holes in Semiconductors

Perhaps the material most universally employed in semiconductor devices nowadays and in the foreseeable future is silicon. For concreteness we shall, therefore, present arguments and quote data which apply mainly to silicon. By doing so, however, we shall lose little in the generality of our treatment.

In a silicon crystal, individual atoms are arranged in a more or less perfect three-dimensional periodic array, the diamond crystal structure of Fig. 1.1 in which each atom is surrounded by four neighboring atoms. The four valence or outer electrons of each silicon atom are shared in four covalent bonds in which the four neighboring atoms also contribute one electron to each bond. This electron bond structure, which may be visualized as the connecting links between atoms in Fig. 1.1, leads to a particularly stable crystalline lattice. At low temperatures no electrons are available for conduction, and the crystal appears to be an insulator. From the standpoint of quantum mechanics, all of the energy levels available to valence electrons are filled, and thus no nearby energy levels are left to which electrons can be accelerated by,

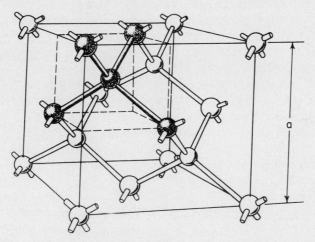

Fig. 1.1 Diamond structure, characteristic of germanium and silicon, with connecting links representative of covalent bonds between each atom and its four nearest neighbors.

let us say, conduction in an applied electric field. This situation in a pure crystal is represented in Fig. 1.2 by a series of closely spaced energy levels which, at low temperature, are filled to an energy E_v, called the valence-band edge. Above the energy E_v lies the forbidden gap, a region of width E_g in which, for a pure crystal, there are no allowed energy levels. Heat energy, i.e., lattice vibrations, or light of proper wavelength can break a number of the electron bonds and excite electrons from the valence band (from below or at the energy E_v) to the conduction band, i.e., to an energy at or above E_c. In silicon at room temperature an energy E_g of approximately 1.1 ev is required to excite an electron directly from the valence to the conduction band, or, in other terms, to break an electron loose from one of the bonds and set it loose to wander or to be accelerated in the crystal lattice.

When an electron is excited from the valence band to the conduction band, a *hole* is created in the valence band. That is, a net positive charge, a *hole*, is left in the valence band to wander or drift just as does an electron in the conduction band. In the atomic picture, after an electron has been broken free from a bond, a net positive charge remains, owing to uncompensated positive charge on the atom which contributed the electron. An electron in an adjacent bond can "hop" into the vacant bond and leave behind another vacant bond, which again has a net positive charge and in fact represents the hole—a hole which has moved.

In Fig. 1.2 we have represented symbolically a hole in the valence band as a circle and an electron in the conduction band as a solid circle. In diagrams such as that of Fig. 1.2 increasing energy for electrons is upward; increasing energy for holes is downward.

The reader will notice that we have tacitly assumed that semiconductors may be described by what is known as band theory. A solution of the problem

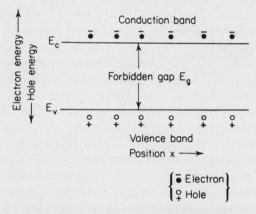

Fig. 1.2 Energy level diagram of a "pure" crystal with schematic representation of electrons and holes, $T > 0°K$.

of wave propagation or particle motion in certain types of periodic structures inherently leads to a solution consisting of allowed bands of energy or frequency, separated by unallowed bands. For example, frequently in the case of a transmission line having a periodic structure, signals in certain frequency bands will propagate down the line. Between these bands exist stop bands such that signals with stop-band frequencies will not propagate. We should mention that, fundamentally, existence of energy bands in solids arises because of close spacing of atoms and resultant splitting of discrete levels into bands of energy levels. Thus an amorphous material such as selenium can exhibit band properties. Nevertheless, it is convenient to use the periodicity properties of semiconductors to establish and analyze energy level and band properties.

The problem of calculating energy-band structure, generally electron energy as a function of momentum or wave number, in solids is an intricate and highly developed science which shall not concern us.[6,7] Let us just mention that this is a three-dimensional problem that generally leads to complicated, curved energy surfaces in momentum or wave number space. In regions where the surfaces are essentially spherical, a free-particle approximation can be established to describe the motion of electrons and holes. It follows that an effective mass m_n can be ascribed to electrons and an effective mass m_p to holes. The effective mass of either electrons or holes can be quite different from that of a free electron, and ordinarily is not isotropic. Near the band edges, E_c and E_v of Fig. 1.2, the free-particle approximation is particularly good. In most subsequent discussions we shall assume this approximation to hold and shall deal with electrons and holes as though they indeed are particles.

1.3 Doping Impurities and Impurity Levels

Figures 1.1 and 1.2 represent the situation in a pure crystal, an *intrinsic* crystal. For most device purposes crystals must be doped with impurities to cause a preponderance of either electrons, *n-type* crystals, or holes, *p-type* crystals. The designation *n* represents *negative* charge carriers or conductivity; the designation *p* represents *positive* charge carriers or conductivity. We shall also use these letters as subscripts in the sense defined above.

If we consider the crystal of Fig. 1.1 and substitute a phosphorus atom, a *donor* atom, with its five valence (outer) electrons for a silicon atom, four of the phosphorus atom's valence electrons participate in the four covalent bonds surrounding the atom. The fifth electron is loosely bound and can be readily shaken loose by thermal energy to wander in the crystal lattice and conduct. We may think of the phosphorus atom with its fifth electron as being somewhat like a hydrogen atom buried in a medium, the silicon lattice, of dielectric constant considerably higher than that of free space. From the usual simple treatments of the Bohr-atom model of hydrogen, we see that the ionization energy of the donor (energy to shake loose the fifth electron) is very low, approximately the ionization energy of hydrogen (13.6 ev) divided by the square of the dielectric constant of silicon (139). We have ignored an effective mass correction which improves the approximation.[3]

Similarly, in Fig. 1.1 we may substitute a boron atom, an *acceptor* atom, with its three valence electrons in place of a silicon atom. This results in a shortage of one electron to complete the four covalent bonds surrounding the boron atom. An electron from an adjacent covalent bond can be ionized to complete the bond on the boron atom. This creates a hole in the lattice, in the valence band, and results in a negative charge surrounding the site of the boron atom. The hole which results in this situation tends to stay bound to the negatively charged acceptor, but, just as for an electron bound to a donor, it is readily ionized by heat energy and can be set free to wander and conduct. The localized levels introduced by donors and acceptors are shown schematically in Fig. 1.3.

Since the fifth electron introduced by a donor cannot participate in one of the covalent bonds, no levels are available to it in the valence band. Also, because it is weakly bound by coulombic forces to the donor atom (unless a weak ionization energy is supplied to excite it to conduction-band levels), the levels associated with donors are not found in the conduction band. Hence, the levels in question fall a small distance (energy) below the conduction-band edge E_c; these are designated by the energy E_d in Fig. 1.3. Similarly, acceptor levels, as shown at energy E_a, are a small distance (energy) above the valence-band edge E_v. In the preceding paragraphs we have described the hydrogen-atom approximation which indicates roughly the magnitude of the energy required to excite electrons from donor sites and holes from acceptor sites.

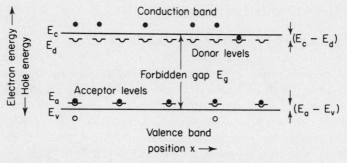

Fig. 1.3 Energy levels, including donor E_d and acceptor E_a levels, in a semiconductor, $T > 0°K$.

In pure crystals, *intrinsic* crystals, excitation of an electron into the conduction band leaves a hole in the valence band. Hence, in an intrinsic crystal an equal number of electrons and holes are present in, respectively, the conduction band and the valence band. In a crystal doped with donors, e.g., silicon doped with phosphorus, thermal energy at room temperature and considerably below (and above) is sufficient to ionize almost all donor sites, which then contribute essentially an electron per donor atom to levels in the conduction band. This results in an *n*-type crystal in which more electrons than holes are available for conduction. In such a crystal, electrons are *majority* carriers, and holes are *minority* carriers. Likewise, a crystal doped with acceptors, e.g., silicon doped with boron, has in the valence band almost one hole per acceptor atom. This results in a *p*-type crystal in which the hole population is greater than the electron population and conduction is due mainly to holes. Holes in this case are majority carriers, and electrons are minority carriers. In all real situations both donors and acceptors are present in a crystal. If the density of donors N_d is greater than the density of acceptors N_a, the crystal will be *n*-type with an effective donor concentration N of

$N_d - N_a$. Electrons from N_a donor sites drop into the N_a acceptor sites and compensate out the acceptor doping. The reverse situation occurs when N_a is larger than N_d; then the crystal is p-type.

Besides the shallow donor and acceptor levels which we have described, deeper levels may be introduced into the forbidden gap by numerous impurities. These levels, as well as levels contributed by flaws and imperfections of many types, play a dominant role in determining minority-carrier recombination processes and lifetime. We shall return to this topic later.

1.4 Form of Energy Bands and Density of States

In Figs. 1.2 and 1.3 the positions of the valence band, conduction band, and donor and acceptor levels in a semiconductor are shown schematically. The densities of donor and acceptor levels are controlled, in a given crystal, by

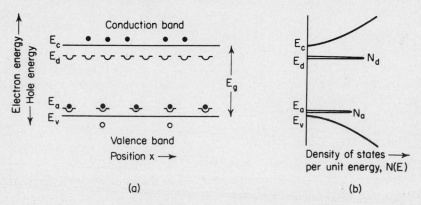

Fig. 1.4 (a) Energy levels in a semiconductor; (b) density of states in a semiconductor.

the amount of donor or acceptor impurities which are grown into the crystal or diffused into the crystal. The density of states per unit energy in the valence band and the conduction band are parabolic in form, as shown in Fig. 1.4. This follows as a consequence of the free-particle approximation (Sec. 1.2), which can ordinarily be utilized near band edges such as E_c and E_v.

If the magnitude of the energy E_c is arbitrarily set equal to zero, then the energy of an electron above the conduction band edge is given as

$$E = \frac{1}{2m_n} (P_x^2 + P_y^2 + P_z^2), \tag{1.1}$$

where m_n is the electron effective mass and P_x, P_y, and P_z are the momenta (crystal momenta) in the x, y, and z directions. According to the Heisenberg uncertainty principle, only two electrons, one of one spin and the other of oppositely directed spin, can occupy a volume in phase space (position–momentum space) given by

$$\Delta x \, \Delta y \, \Delta z \, \Delta P_x \, \Delta P_y \, \Delta P_z = h^3, \tag{1.2}$$

where h is Planck's constant. Hence, in a region of unit volume, the incremental number of allowed states $dN'(P)$ between P_x and $P_x + dP_x$, P_y and $P_y + dP_y$, and P_z and $P_z + dP_z$ is given as

$$dN'(P) = \frac{2 \, dP_x \, dP_y \, dP_z}{h^3}, \tag{1.3}$$

where the factor 2 accounts for particles of either spin. Notice that the momenta increments in (1.2) and (1.3) are not the same. In (1.2) we have the size of a "box" that accommodates a particle of either spin. In (1.3) we use this information to find how many "boxes" of this size fit into a "small" volume $dP_x \, dP_y \, dP_z$ in momentum space.

Since

$$P^2 = P_x^2 + P_y^2 + P_z^2, \tag{1.4}$$

we can replace $dP_x \, dP_y \, dP_z$ in (1.3) by

$$4\pi P^2 \, dP, \tag{1.5}$$

which is the incremental volume in momentum space between a sphere of radius P and a sphere of radius $P + dP$. Thus,

$$dN'(P) = 2 \, \frac{4\pi P^2 \, dP}{h^3}. \tag{1.6}$$

Instead of retaining the number of states as a function of momentum, we may use equations (1.4) and (1.1) to convert (1.6) to the number of states (in the conduction band) between the energy E and $E + dE$. By substituting (1.4) into (1.1), we obtain

$$E = \frac{P^2}{2m_n},$$

and

$$dE = \frac{P}{m_n} \, dP. \tag{1.7}$$

Hence, the number of states per unit volume, $dN'(E)$, is given as

$$dN'(E) = \frac{4\pi}{h^3} (2m_n)^{3/2}(E)^{1/2} \, dE \equiv N(E) \, dE. \tag{1.8}$$

In equation (1.8) we have defined as a function of E a quantity $N(E)$;

$$N(E) \equiv \frac{4\pi}{h^3} (2m_n)^{3/2}(E)^{1/2}, \tag{1.9}$$

which gives the density of states per unit volume per unit energy.

If the zero of energy is not taken at E_c, equation (1.9) can be rewritten as

$$N(E) = \frac{4\pi}{h^3} (2m_n)^{3/2}(E - E_c)^{1/2}. \tag{1.9a}$$

Similarly, the density of allowed states in the valence band is given as

$$N(E) = \frac{4\pi}{h^3} (2m_p)^{3/2}(E_v - E)^{1/2}. \tag{1.10}$$

Equations (1.9a) and (1.10) account for the parabolic shape of the conduction and valence bands shown in Fig. 1.4(b). The donor and acceptor levels in Fig. 1.4(b) are shown somewhat broadened, in order to indicate that these levels may become broadened at higher doping levels.

The results presented above are correct. However, the arguments used are not to be considered rigorous. A rigorous development of the above expressions is much more involved and requires greater attention to many of the finer and more important aspects of the quantum mechanics of solids.[2,3,4,5,7]

1.5 The Fermi–Dirac Distribution Function and the Densities of Electrons and Holes in Semiconductors

Thus far we have described the energy levels in a semiconductor and the density of states associated with the various levels and allowed bands. Not all of the levels and states associated with a semiconductor are necessarily populated with electrons or holes. The filling of the various states and levels with electrons and holes is governed by the Fermi–Dirac distribution function $f(E)$.[2,5]

$$f(E) = \frac{1}{\exp\left[(E - E_f)/kT\right] + 1}, \tag{1.11}$$

where E_f is the so-called Fermi level, k is Boltzmann's constant, and T is the absolute temperature. The Fermi function $f(E)$ gives the probability that a level of energy E is occupied by an electron; it is shown in Fig. 1.5 at $0°K$ and at $T > 0$, e.g., $300°K$.

At $T = 0°K$, $f(E) = 1$ for $E < E_f$ and $f(E) = 0$ for $E > E_f$. In other words, below E_f all allowed levels are occupied (with electrons), whereas at energies greater than E_f all allowed levels are unoccupied. At temperatures

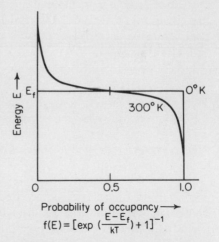

Fig. 1.5 Fermi–Dirac distribution function for electron occupancy of energy levels E.

above $0°K$ the Fermi function does not change abruptly from unity to zero at the Fermi level E_f. The function is symmetrical around $(\frac{1}{2}, E_f)$ and changes more gradually from unity below E_f, to $\frac{1}{2}$ at E_f, and gradually to zero above E_f. At an energy E', $E' > E_f$, $f(E')$ has the same value as does $1 - f(E'')$, where E'' is as far below E_f as E' is above E_f, i.e., $E' - E_f = E_f - E''$. That is to say, for a given energy increment above E_f, the probability that a level (if one exists) is occupied is the same as the probability that a level at the same energy increment below E_f is unoccupied.

By multiplying the density of states expression (1.9a) by expression (1.11) giving the probability $f(E)$ that a state at energy E is occupied, and by integrating from E_c to E, we obtain the expression

$$n(E) = \int_{E_c}^{E} f(E)N(E) \, dE = 4\pi(2m_n)^{3/2}h^{-3} \int_{E_c}^{E} \frac{(E - E_c)^{1/2} \, dE}{\exp\left[(E - E_f)/kT\right] + 1} \quad (1.12)$$

for the total number of electrons in the conduction band (per unit volume) in the energy interval from E_c to E. The total number of electrons n in the conduction band is obtained by allowing the upper limit in (1.12) to run to the top of the conduction band, which practically can be taken to approach ∞, since the Fermi function decreases rapidly at energies $E > E_f$, and dominates in the integral given in (1.12). Hence, the total number of electrons per unit volume in the conduction band becomes

$$n = 4\pi(2m_n)^{3/2}h^{-3} \int_{E_c}^{\infty} \frac{(E - E_c)^{1/2} \, dE}{\exp\left[(E - E_f)/kT\right] + 1}. \quad (1.12a)$$

If E_f is well below the conduction-band edge so that $(E - E_f)/kT \gg 1$, then the Fermi function can be approximated as an exponential and

$$n = 4\pi(2m_n)^{3/2}h^{-3} \exp\left[-\frac{(E_c - E_f)}{kT}\right]$$

$$\times \int_{E_c}^{\infty} (E - E_c)^{1/2} \exp\left[-\frac{(E - E_c)}{kT}\right] dE \quad (1.13)$$

$$= 4\pi\left(\frac{2m_nkT}{h^2}\right)^{3/2} \exp\left[-\frac{(E_c - E_f)}{kT}\right] \int_{0}^{\infty} x^{1/2} \exp(-x) \, dx$$

$$= 2\left(\frac{2\pi m_nkT}{h^2}\right)^{3/2} \exp\left[-\frac{(E_c - E_f)}{kT}\right] = N_c \exp\left[-\frac{(E_c - E_f)}{kT}\right]. \quad (1.14)$$

The quantity N_c in (1.14) is the effective density of states in the conduction band. The Boltzmann factor in (1.14), i.e., the exponential, may be interpreted as giving the probability of filling of N_c states effectively all located at energy E_c.

If we assume that E_f is well into the forbidden gap, then we may make the same approximations as above and integrate (over the valence band) the product of the density of states (1.10) in the valence band and the probability that a state is empty, $1 - f(E)$, (i.e., occupied by a hole) and obtain for the density of holes in the valence band the expression

$$p = 2\left(\frac{2\pi m_p kT}{h^2}\right)^{3/2} \exp\left[-\frac{(E_f - E_v)}{kT}\right]$$

$$\equiv N_v \exp\left[-\frac{(E_f - E_v)}{kT}\right]. \tag{1.15}$$

The quantity N_v in (1.15) is the effective density of states in the valence band. The Boltzmann factor in (1.15) may be interpreted as giving the probability that N_v hole states, effectively at E_v, are filled. From (1.14) and (1.15) the product of electrons n in the conduction band and holes p in the valence band is

$$np = N_c N_v \exp\left[-(E_c - E_v)/kT\right]$$
$$= N_c N_v \exp\left(-E_g/kT\right)$$
$$= 1.5 \times 10^{33} T^3 \exp\left(-1.21/kT\right) \quad \text{(in silicon)}$$
$$= 2.25 \times 10^{20}/\text{cm}^6 \qquad \text{(at room temperature).} \tag{1.16}$$

From (1.16) we see that the electron–hole product np is independent of the position of the Fermi level.

In an intrinsic semiconductor the electron concentration n_i and hole concentration p_i are equal, and from (1.14) and (1.15)

$$n_i = p_i = N_c \exp\left[-\frac{(E_c - E_f)}{kT}\right] = N_v \exp\left[-\frac{(E_f - E_v)}{kT}\right] \tag{1.17}$$

Also,

$$np = n_i p_i = n_i^2 = N_c N_v \exp\left(-\frac{E_g}{kT}\right), \tag{1.18}$$

which is the same as (1.16) but indicates explicitly that the electron-hole product is equal to the square of the intrinsic concentration of electrons (or holes). If we take the square root of (1.18) and substitute the constants defining N_c and N_v, the intrinsic concentration n_i becomes

$$n_i = 2\left(\frac{2\pi kT}{h^2}\right)^{3/2} (m_n m_p)^{3/4} \exp\left(-\frac{E_g}{2kT}\right)$$

$$= 1.5 \times 10^{10}/\text{cm}^3 \quad \text{(in silicon at room temperature).} \tag{1.19}$$

From the latter part of expression (1.17), the Fermi level E_f in an intrinsic semiconductor is given as

$$E_f = E_v + \frac{E_g}{2} + \frac{kT}{2} \ln \frac{N_v}{N_c}$$

$$= E_v + \frac{E_g}{2} + \frac{3kT}{4} \ln \frac{m_p}{m_n}. \tag{1.20}$$

From (1.20) we see that if the electron and hole effective masses are equal, the Fermi level lies at the middle of the forbidden gap in an intrinsic semiconductor. This situation is shown schematically in Fig. 1.6, where we have also indicated schematically the derivation of expressions (1.14) and (1.15).

In a semiconductor doped with N_d donors, at room temperature most of the donor impurities are ionized and contribute essentially N_d electrons to the conduction band. The Fermi level in this case moves upwards toward the conduction-band edge from its position near the middle of the forbidden gap in an intrinsic semiconductor. An examination of Fig. 1.6 shows immediately

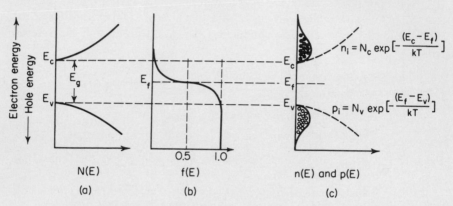

Fig. 1.6 Electron and hole concentrations (per unit energy) $n(E)$ and $p(E)$ in an intrinsic semiconductor, (c) [product of density of states $N(E)$ and Fermi function $f(E)$ shown respectively in (a) and (b)].

that the entire Fermi function must shift upwards in order to give a density of conduction band electrons $n \approx N_d > n_i$. The electron-hole product

$$np = n_i^2 \tag{1.18}$$

remains constant and indicates that when

$$n \approx N_d > n_i,$$

then

$$p \approx \frac{n_i^2}{N_d} < n_i \tag{1.21}$$

and holes are minority-charge carriers. This is shown schematically in Fig. 1.7. A more accurate and general expression for n (with $N_c > n > n_i$) can be derived by substituting equation (1.18) into the electrical neutrality condition[2,5]

$$p - n + N_d - N_a = 0,$$

which applies quite generally in regions other than the actual transition region of a *p-n* junction. By making use of the quadratic formula, we obtain

$$n = n_n = \frac{N}{2}\left[\left(1 + \frac{4n_i^2}{N^2}\right)^{1/2} + 1\right] \qquad (1.21a)$$

and

$$p = p_n = \frac{N}{2}\left[\left(1 + \frac{4n_i^2}{N^2}\right)^{1/2} - 1\right], \qquad (1.21b)$$

where we have defined $(N_d - N_a)$ as N, the number of donors uncompensated

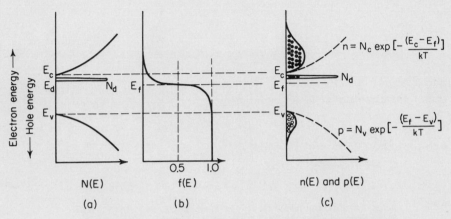

Fig. 1.7 Electron concentration n (majority carriers) and hole concentration p (minority carriers) in an *n*-type semiconductor.

by acceptors. For large donor concentrations (however, N still less than N_c), equation (1.21b) reduces to (1.21). The electron concentration, in this case, is more accurately given as

$$n = N + n_i^2/N.$$

Since in simple cases

$$n \approx N_d,$$

the position of the Fermi level is given by

$$n_i < N_d \approx n = N_c \exp\left[-\frac{(E_c - E_f)}{kT}\right]$$

and

$$E_f = E_c - kT \ln \frac{N_c}{N_d}. \qquad (1.22)$$

The various approximations we have used above begin to break down as the doping level N_d approaches and exceeds N_c, and the Fermi level approaches and crosses above the conduction-band edge E_c. For the large part our work will not be concerned with this case, a situation that does apply in degenerate semiconductors and tunnel junctions.

Arguments analogous to those above may be used to describe p-type semiconductors, in which the Fermi level is found near the valence-band edge and

$$n_i < N_a \approx p = N_v \exp\left[-\frac{(E_f - E_v)}{kT}\right].$$

Since

$$np = n_i^2 \tag{1.18}$$

and

$$p \approx N_a > n_i,$$

then

$$n \approx \frac{n_i^2}{N_a} < n_i \tag{1.23}$$

and electrons in this case are minority carriers. As before, if we make use of (1.18), the electrical neutrality condition

$$p - n - (N_a - N_d) = 0$$

and the quadratic formula, we obtain

$$p = p_p = \frac{N}{2}\left[\left(1 + \frac{4n_i^2}{N^2}\right)^{1/2} + 1\right] \approx N + \frac{n_i^2}{N} \tag{1.23a}$$

and

$$n = n_p = \frac{N}{2}\left[\left(1 + \frac{4n_i^2}{N^2}\right)^{1/2} - 1\right] \approx \frac{n_i^2}{N}, \tag{1.23b}$$

where we have now redefined $(N_a - N_d)$ as N, a positive quantity giving the number of acceptors uncompensated by donors.

Since n_i^2 at a given temperature is a constant characteristic of the particular semiconductor, it is obvious that once the net donor concentration $N = N_d - N_a$ in an n-type semiconductor is given, the minority-carrier (hole) concentration p (or p_n) is determined by equation (1.21) or (1.21b). Likewise, in a p-type semiconductor in which the net acceptor concentration $N = N_a - N_d$ is known, the electron (minority carrier) concentration is given by equation (1.23) or (1.23b). Often it is convenient to have available the minority-carrier concentration p_n or n_p as a function of the net donor or acceptor concentration N, with temperature a parameter. These data for silicon, calculated from (1.21b) and (1.23b), are presented in Fig. 1.8.

We have simplified above the problem of how to determine where the Fermi level E_f is located in a semiconductor. Ordinarily the problem is more difficult than we have assumed and requires a calculational procedure, as partially indicated above, based on summing the total negative charge contributed by conduction-band electrons and ionized acceptors and equating to the total positive charge contributed by holes and ionized donors so that electrical neutrality is preserved in the semiconductor. In addition to arriving at the expressions of electron and hole densities which we shall need, it is useful to remember from our earlier discussions that the Fermi level lies near the middle of the forbidden gap in an intrinsic semiconductor, is near the

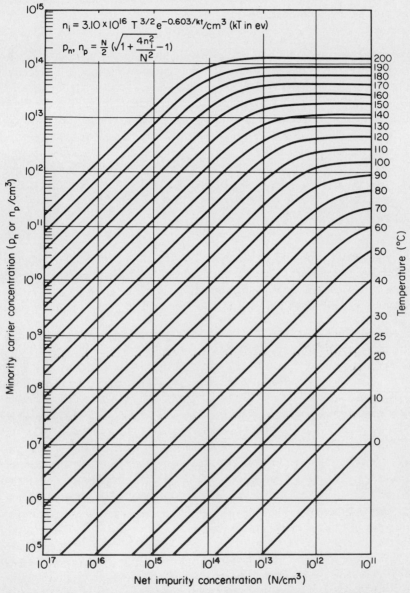

Fig. 1.8 Minority carrier concentration in silicon as a function of doping and temperature.

conduction-band edge in an *n*-type semiconductor, and is near the valence-band edge in a *p*-type semiconductor.

Often it is convenient to have expressions (1.14) and (1.15) for the electron and hole densities in a somewhat different form. Instead of expressing the electron and hole densities in terms of various energy levels, we can develop expressions which give the densities in terms of the electrostatic potential ψ in the crystal. By definition

$$-q\psi \equiv E_i, \tag{1.24}$$

where the zero of potential (arbitrary) is so chosen that $-q\psi$ coincides with an energy E_i equal to the Fermi level E_f in an intrinsic crystal. If the electron and hole effective masses are nearly equal, then, as is evident from equation (1.20), E_i and $-q\psi$ lie near the middle of the forbidden gap, as does the Fermi level E_f in an intrinsic semiconductor. The quantity q, the magnitude (positive) of the electron charge, is needed to convert potential to electron energy. Since we have taken electron energy to increase upward on the various diagrams we have used, potential in similar diagrams increases downward, i.e., increases in the same direction as hole energy or opposite to electron energy, as is clear from expression (1.24). In correspondence to the Fermi level E_f we define a Fermi potential φ given by

$$-q\varphi \equiv E_f. \tag{1.25}$$

As previously noted, E_f and φ change with doping; the electrostatic potential, as defined, remains near the middle of the forbidden gap and does not change in vertical position but does change or vary relative to E_f or φ.

From the definitions above and the fact that $E_f = E_i$ in an intrinsic semiconductor

$$n_i = N_c \exp\left[-\frac{(E_c - E_i)}{kT}\right] = N_c \exp\left[-\frac{(E_c + q\psi)}{kT}\right], \tag{1.26}$$

and

$$N_c = n_i \exp\left[\frac{(E_c + q\psi)}{kT}\right]. \tag{1.27}$$

Also,

$$p_i = n_i = N_v \exp\left[-\frac{(E_i - E_v)}{kT}\right] = N_v \exp\left[\frac{(q\psi + E_v)}{kT}\right], \tag{1.28}$$

and

$$N_v = n_i \exp\left[-\frac{(q\psi + E_v)}{kT}\right]. \tag{1.29}$$

By substituting equation (1.27) in (1.14) and equation (1.29) in (1.15) and by making use of (1.25), we obtain

$$n = n_i \exp\left[\frac{q(\psi - \varphi)}{kT}\right], \tag{1.30}$$

and

$$p = n_i \exp\left[\frac{q(\varphi - \psi)}{kT}\right]. \tag{1.31}$$

With the assumptions we have made that the Fermi level be appreciably into the forbidden gap and several kT away from the band edges, equations (1.14) and (1.15) for the electron and hole densities are given by rather large quantities N_c and N_v (effective density of states) multiplied by fractions less than unity. On the other hand, equations (1.30) and (1.31) for the electron and hole densities are given by relatively smaller quantities n_i multiplied in one case by a fraction greater than unity and in the other case by its reciprocal, a fraction less than unity. From equation (1.30) we see immediately that as a semiconductor is doped heavier n-type and E_f rises above $E_i(\psi > \varphi)$, the exponential in (1.30) increases steadily from unity and the electron concentration increases from n_i toward N_c. Simultaneously, the exponential in (1.31) decreases steadily from unity, and the hole concentration (minority carriers) decreases steadily below n_i. As a semiconductor is doped p-type more heavily from intrinsic, the Fermi level E_f moves steadily below $E_i(\psi < \varphi)$, and the above statements are reversed. The electron concentration decreases below n_i and the hole concentration increases steadily from n_i. The exponentials in (1.30) and (1.31) show, as expected, that electrons tend to populate regions of greater electrostatic potential and holes to populate regions of lesser electrostatic potential. From this we can already infer that in a p-n junction the n-type side is at higher electrostatic potential than the p-type side.

1.6 Minority-carrier Generation, Recombination, and Lifetime

Although we did not draw attention to this matter earlier, the expressions developed in the preceding section for the densities of electrons and holes represent equilibrium magnitudes. Under conditions of thermal equilibrium, the rate of excitation of electrons to the conduction band and holes to the valence band just equals the rate of mutual decay of electrons and holes by recombination, and the net carrier concentrations remain constant. It is possible to upset the equilibrium electron and hole concentrations by such means as electrical or optical injection, i.e., by such means as carrier injection in a p-n junction or by excitation with incident light of wavelength corresponding to an energy equal to or greater than the band gap E_g. When the external injecting excitation is removed, the carrier concentrations decay from the perturbed values to their thermal equilibrium values. As is true in many physical processes, excess carriers tend to decay at rates proportional to the deviation from equilibrium and are therefore represented by a decaying exponential. Thus

$$n - n_0 = \delta n_0 \exp\left(-\frac{t}{\tau_n}\right), \tag{1.32}$$

where n is the perturbed (total) electron concentration, n_0 is the thermal equilibrium electron concentration, δn_0 is the excess electron concentration just when the external excitation is removed, t is time, and τ_n is a characteristic decay constant known as *lifetime*. If equation (1.32) is differentiated, then the equation

$$\tau_n = \frac{-(n - n_0)}{dn/dt} = \frac{\delta n}{-dn/dt} \qquad (1.33)$$

is obtained. If $-dn/dt$ is recognized as the excess of the recombination rate over the generation rate, by definition R_n, then

$$\tau_n = \delta n / R_n. \qquad (1.34)$$

Likewise, for holes

$$\tau_p = \delta p / R_p, \qquad (1.35)$$

where τ_p is the hole lifetime, δp is the excess hole concentration above equilibrium, and R_p is the excess of the hole recombination rate over the generation rate. We see that finding the lifetime of carriers in a semiconductor becomes a problem of determining R_n and R_p.

At this point, it is perhaps well to digress and to mention that the issue of lifetime and the physical mechanisms governing lifetime are important in understanding several aspects of the behavior of *p-n* junctions and *p-n-p-n* switches. The speed properties of *p-n* junctions and *p-n-p-n* switches are both influenced by carrier lifetime. Also, in the case of the *p-n-p-n* switch, at least one of the mechanisms to which the switching behavior of the device has often been attributed is related to the generation-recombination mechanisms governing lifetime. We shall return to these topics later.

Three types of recombination processes may be considered. The first is direct recombination of an electron and a hole, i.e., radiative recombination in which the energy lost in the electron-hole recombination is carried away by a photon. The second, known as Auger recombination, occurs when a third carrier is excited to some higher energy by the energy released in the recombination of an electron and hole. The third is multiphonon recombination, in which the energy is dissipated by creation of phonons (quanta of lattice vibrational energy). Since multiphonon recombination predominates in materials such as germanium and silicon ("indirect" semiconductors), we shall confine our attention to this case, in which excess electrons and holes recombine indirectly via energy levels (flaw or trap states) relatively deep in the forbidden gap.

In more or less civilized societies, a male-female encounter—with capture —is not often a direct process; rather, one party and the other, with a somewhat greater or lesser likelihood, are drawn to a store, school, work, or some other capture center or "trap" at which the encounter and "capture" process are facilitated. Likewise, in the case of an excess electron in, let us say, a *p*-type semiconductor, the electron first drops into a recombination center with energy relatively deep in the forbidden gap. This increases the negative charge at the center and tends to attract a majority carrier, a hole, which readily "drops" (upward) into the recombination center and annihilates the electron, thus leaving the recombination center free for repetition of the process. The same type of argument applies to an n-type semiconductor. Both the electron and the hole in dropping to a lower energy state give energy to phonons (create phonons). The recombination centers, or traps, which promote this process are formed by impurity atoms, lattice defects, or, in general, flaws of any type. In silicon devices gold is often deliberately introduced to create deep levels (flaws) to promote recombination purposely and lower lifetime.

The processes described above may be treated quantitatively to obtain R_n and R_p, and the well-known Hall–Shockley–Read[8,9] expression for the lifetime. For simplicity, let us assume a semiconductor with the usual shallow doping impurities which determine n_0 and p_0, where the zero subscripts indicate thermal equilibrium magnitudes. Also, let us assume N_t deep-level impurities (flaws, recombination centers) whose concentration is small relative to the net concentration of doping impurities, so they have little effect on the carrier distributions. The fraction f_t of recombination centers which are occupied by electrons will be determined, in the usual manner, by the position of the Fermi level E_f relative to the energy E_t of the recombination centers (traps). From Fig. 1.9 we see that the following four processes must be considered in order to determine R_n and R_p, and lifetime:

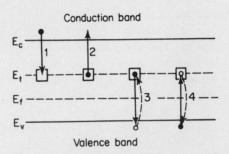

Fig. 1.9 Indirect (electron-hole) recombination by means of deep-level flaws or traps in a p-type semiconductor.

1. Electron capture by an empty center, probability $= C_n$.
2. Electron emission from a filled center to the conduction band, probability $= G_n$.
3. Hole capture by a filled center, probability $= C_p$.
4. Hole emission from empty center into valence band, probability $= G_p$.

The net recombination rate for electrons, R_n, is equal to the capture rate less the emission or generation rate. The capture rate is proportional to the density of free electrons n, the density of empty traps $N_t(1 - f_t)$, and the electron-capture probability C_n, where we have further assumed that C_n is not dependent upon the energy of the electron, i.e., does not depend upon the energy of an individual electron in the conduction band. The electron-emission rate is equal to the product of the filled traps $N_t f_t$ and the electron-emission probability G_n. Hence, from the preceding two statements

$$R_n = C_n n N_t (1 - f_t) - G_n N_t f_t. \qquad (1.36)$$

Later, it will be necessary for us to eliminate C_n or G_n from the expressions for the net recombination rate. Under equilibrium conditions when $n = n_0$ and $R_n = 0$, equation (1.36) may be solved for f_{t0} and gives

$$f_{t0} = \frac{1}{1 + G_n/n_0 C_n}. \tag{1.37}$$

Instead of determining G_n in terms of C_n and f_{t0}, we know that for a very particular doping such that $n_0 \equiv n_1$ and $p_0 \equiv p_1$, the Fermi level E_f may be made to coincide with the trap energy E_t. For this case (i.e., $E_f = E_t, n_0 = n_1$, and $p_0 = p_1$) the Fermi function f_{t0} (1.37) equals one-half, and

$$G_n = n_1 C_n. \tag{1.38}$$

Determining G_n in this manner is a matter of convenience and in no way compromises the generality of our arguments. From a knowledge of how we have doped our crystal, we know the position of E_f, we know n_0 and p_0 (see Sec. 1.5), we know E_t, and we could—if we chose to do so—calculate f_{t0} from (1.11) and write the expression for G_n in terms of a conduction-band electron density other than n_1, the density of conduction-band electrons when $E_f = E_t$.

Arguing as above, we can show that the net recombination rate for holes is given by the capture rate $C_p p N_t f_t$ less the generation rate $G_p N_t (1 - f_t)$ or

$$R_p = C_p p N_t f_t - G_p N_t (1 - f_t). \tag{1.39}$$

At equilibrium, as before, $p = p_0$, R_p is zero, and

$$f_{t0} = \frac{1}{1 + C_p p_0/G_p}. \tag{1.40}$$

By making use again of our choice of convenience that $E_f = E_t$, i.e., that the conduction-band electron density n_0 be equal to n_1 and the valence-band hole density p_0 be equal to $p_1 (n_1 p_1 = n_t^2)$, we obtain

$$G_p = p_1 C_p. \tag{1.41}$$

For steady-state, nonequilibrium conditions, excess electrons and holes are removed at a rate $R = R_n = R_p$, and from (1.36) and (1.39)

$$R = C_n n N_t (1 - f_t) - G_n N_t f_t = C_p p N_t f_t - G_p N_t (1 - f_t). \tag{1.42}$$

Because the capture probabilities C_n and C_p and emission probabilities G_n and G_p are independent of equilibrium or nonequilibrium conditions, equations (1.38) and (1.41) may be used to eliminate G_n and G_p from (1.42) to give

$$R = C_n n N_t (1 - f_t) - C_n n_1 N_t f_t = C_p p N_t f_t - C_p p_1 N_t (1 - f_t). \tag{1.43}$$

From (1.43)

$$f_t = \frac{1}{1 + (n_1 C_n + p C_p)/(n C_n + p_1 C_p)}, \tag{1.44}$$

and substitution into either part of (1.42) gives a net recombination rate of

$$R = \frac{np - n_1 p_1}{(1/N_t C_p)(n + n_1) + (1/N_t C_n)(p + p_1)}$$

$$= \frac{np - n_i^2}{(1/N_t C_p)(n + n_1) + (1/N_t C_n)(p + p_1)}.$$

(1.45)

Because of our initial assumption of small concentration N_t of recombination centers, we may ignore the charge stored in the traps. Thus, in order to maintain space-charge neutrality in the crystal, any increase δn in electrons must be accompanied by an equal increase $\delta p = \delta n$ in holes. The electron and hole concentrations n and p may then be written

$$n = n_0 + \delta n \quad \text{and} \quad p = p_0 + \delta p = p_0 + \delta n$$

or

$$np - n_i^2 = (n_0 + p_0)\,\delta n + (\delta n)^2 + n_0 p_0 - n_i^2 \approx (n_0 + p_0)\,\delta n.$$

Hence,

$$R \approx \frac{(n_0 + p_0)\,\delta n}{(1/N_t C_p)(n_0 + n_1) + (1/N_t C_n)(p_0 + p_1)}.$$

(1.46)

If (1.46) is substituted into equation (1.34) or (1.35), the expression

$$\tau = \frac{(1/N_t C_p)(n_0 + n_1) + (1/N_t C_n)(p_0 + p_1)}{(n_0 + p_0)}$$

(1.47)

is obtained for the lifetime in a semiconductor with a relatively small trap concentration. This is the Hall–Shockley–Read expression for the lifetime under low-level injection conditions.

In strongly p-type material, electrons are minority carriers, readily drop into nearly empty traps, and recombine quickly with holes, which are much more numerous. For this situation (1.47) reduces to

$$\tau = \tau_{n0} = \frac{1}{N_t C_n}.$$

For the case of strongly n-type material, holes are minority carriers, readily drop (upward) into filled traps, and recombine rapidly with electrons. In this case (1.47) becomes

$$\tau = \tau_{p0} = \frac{1}{N_t C_p}.$$

Hence, (1.47) may be rewritten as

$$\tau = \frac{\tau_{p0}(n_0 + n_1) + \tau_{n0}(p_0 + p_1)}{(n_0 + p_0)}.$$

(1.48)

If the lifetime τ is plotted as a function of doping level from strongly p-type to intrinsic to strongly n-type, the lifetime increases from a limiting value of τ_{n0} to some maximum value at intermediate doping levels and down to a limiting value of τ_{p0}.[8]

The physical processes and models which account for carrier recombination also can account, in certain circumstances, for carrier generation. In regions which are depleted of free electrons and holes, e.g., *p-n* junctions under some conditions, n and p are both near zero, and equation (1.45) becomes

$$R = \frac{-n_i^2}{n_1/N_t C_p + p_1/N_t C_n}. \tag{1.49}$$

The negative sign in (1.49) indicates that the "net recombination rate" is really a generation rate

$$G = \frac{n_i^2}{n_1 \tau_{p0} + p_1 \tau_{n0}}, \tag{1.50}$$

where (1.50) is (1.49) rewritten in terms of the limiting lifetimes. If the trap levels are near the middle of the forbidden gap so that $n_1 = p_1 = n_i$ and it is assumed that $\tau_{p0} = \tau_{p0} = \tau_0$,

$$G = \frac{n_i}{2\tau_0}. \tag{1.51}$$

This is the number of electron-hole pairs which are generated each second per unit volume in the depleted region. If the region has unit cross section and a width W, the current owing to generation from traps at the middle of the forbidden gap is

$$J_g = \frac{q W n_i}{2\tau_0}, \tag{1.52}$$

where q is the charge of an electron.

If equations (1.38) and (1.41) are substituted in the expression for the generation rate ($G = -R$), we obtain

$$G = \frac{N_t G_n G_p}{G_n + G_p}. \tag{1.53}$$

The probability G_n with which electrons are generated from traps is proportional to a Boltzmann factor depending upon the distance of the traps below the conduction-band edge. Likewise, the hole-generation probability G_p is proportional to a similar exponential factor depending upon the distance of the traps from the valence-band edge. Thus,

$$G_n \sim \exp\left[-\frac{(E_c - E_t)}{kT}\right]$$

and

$$G_p \sim \exp\left[-\frac{(E_t - E_v)}{kT}\right].$$

From these equations and (1.53) it can be shown that the generation rate G is greatest for generation-recombination centers (traps) located near the middle of the band gap. This shows why certain deep-level flaws (i.e., those near the middle of the energy gap) are most effective as charge-generation centers.

1.7 Carrier Drift, Diffusion, and the Continuity Equation

In previous sections we have derived the expressions giving the equilibrium densities of electrons and holes in a semiconductor [equations (1.14) and (1.15) or (1.30) and (1.31)] and have also considered the recombination processes which tend to restore equilibrium when the carrier densities have been disturbed from equilibrium by light, heat pulses, or injection at a junction or metal contact. In the study of *p-n-p-n* devices and, in fact, almost all junction devices, carrier motion and the nature of current flow in the devices are the central issues. In this section and the rest of this chapter these shall be our main concern.

Electrons and holes in a crystal are in a constant state of thermal agitation, move in one direction, suffer a collision, and then move in another random direction only to repeat the process. The carrier motion is so chaotic, so random, that on the average there is no net current flow. If an electric field $\mathscr{E}$ is applied to the crystal, holes will have superimposed on them a tendency to drift in the direction of the field and electrons a tendency to drift opposite to the field, so the net drift current (because of the negative charge of the electron) is the absolute sum of hole and electron currents. Because the carriers suffer collisions, either with lattice vibrations (phonons) or with impurity atoms, and restart their drift after each collision, their velocities at moderate field strengths are proportional to the field. The proportionality factor is known as *mobility*, μ_n for electrons and μ_p for holes, and is a function of impurity concentration, temperature, and the type of scattering processes that the carriers undergo. Electron and hole velocities can be written as

$$\mathbf{v}_n = \mu_n \mathscr{E} \quad \text{and} \quad \mathbf{v}_p = \mu_p \mathscr{E}. \tag{1.54}$$

Since drift current density is given by the familiar expression

$$\mathbf{J} = \mathbf{J}_n + \mathbf{J}_p = qn\mathbf{v}_n + qp\mathbf{v}_p,$$

from (1.54)

$$\mathbf{J} = q(n\mu_n + p\mu_p)\mathscr{E} = \sigma\mathscr{E} = \frac{1}{\rho}\mathscr{E} \tag{1.55}$$

or

$$\sigma = \frac{1}{\rho} = qn\mu_n + qp\mu_p, \tag{1.55a}$$

where in lightly doped silicon at 300°K

$$\mu_n \approx 1350 \text{ cm}^2/\text{volt sec}$$

$$\mu_p \approx 480 \text{ cm}^2/\text{volt sec}.$$

Equation (1.55a) shows that the resistivity ρ, or conductivity σ, of a crystal is a strong function of the carrier concentrations and the mobilities. Figure 1.10 shows the resistivity of a ~ 60 ohm-cm (300°K) *n*-type silicon crystal and a ~ 20 ohm-cm (300°K) *n*-type germanium crystal presented as a function of reciprocal absolute temperature (°K). In the case of the silicon crystal, as the temperature rises from below 50°K to near 100°K the resistivity decreases by several orders of magnitude. This is caused by increase in charge carriers because of extrinsic ionization (ionization of donors), as temperature increases, and because mobility increases as a result of decrease in impurity scattering ($\mu \propto T^{3/2}$). At the resistivity minimum near 100°K impurity scattering becomes relatively unimportant, and also no further carriers are available from donors; hence the minimum. A further increase in temperature to near

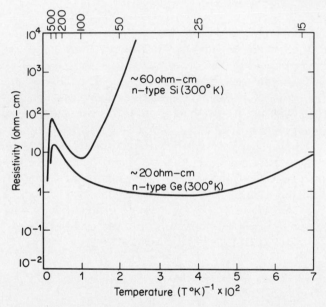

Fig. 1.10 Resistivity of ~ 60 ohm-cm Si crystal and a ~ 20 ohm-cm Ge crystal as a function of reciprocal temperature (°K)$^{-1}$.

500°K results in an increase in resistivity, because of decrease in mobility resulting from increased lattice vibration (phonon) scattering ($\mu \propto T^{-3/2}$). Beyond 500°K the resistivity drops sharply because of intrinsic carrier ionization (from valence band to conduction band) and a rapid increase in both electrons and holes. In this region the electron and hole densities are almost equal. The slope of the curve in this temperature range can be used to determine the so-called thermal band gap of the semiconductor [see equations (1.18) or (1.19)].

Frequently it is useful to have the resistivity of *n*- and *p*-type crystals as a function of net donor or acceptor concentration. Figure 1.11 shows such data (300°K) for *n*- and *p*-type silicon in a range from intrinsic to degenerate doping. The fact that the resistivity curve for p-type material lies above that for n-type material implies that $\mu_n > \mu_p$. This is true of many semiconductors.

Besides the drift that an electric field may impose on the carriers of a crystal, a net carrier motion may also arise from *diffusion*. As stated above, electrons and holes in a crystal are in a constant state of thermal agitation and motion. Consequently, if the concentration of holes (or electrons), let us say, is increased in a given region by light, on the average more holes will tend to wander *out* of the region of greater density than will tend to wander *in* from the surrounding region of lesser density. Holes in either region possess the same velocities (thermal equilibrium velocities, $\sim 10^7$ cm/sec); hence, it is

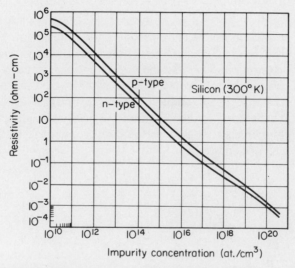

Fig. 1.11 Silicon room temperature resistivity as a function of impurity concentration.

not velocity difference but random motion and a difference in density that causes a net diffusion carrier flow from a region of high density to a region of lesser density. The spatial difference in density is expressed as the gradient (spacial derivative), and the electron and hole diffusion-current densities, which are proportional to their respective gradients, can be expressed as

$$\mathbf{J}_n = qD_n\nabla n$$
$$\mathbf{J}_p = -qD_p\nabla p,$$

(1.56)

where D_n and D_p are electron and hole diffusion constants and q is the magnitude of the carrier charge. In silicon at room temperature

$$D_n \approx 38 \text{ cm}^2 \text{ sec}^{-1}$$

$$D_p \approx 13 \text{ cm}^2 \text{ sec}^{-1}.$$

The first of equations (1.56) has a positive sign because electrons flow opposite to the direction of increasing density but, because of their negative charge, give a positive current in the direction of the gradient. The second equation requires a negative sign because holes (positive carriers) flow opposite to the direction of increasing gradient. Ordinarily we shall be concerned with one-dimensional problems and can drop our vector notation. Thus equations (1.55) and (1.56) combine to give

$$J_n = qn\mu_n\mathscr{E} + qD_n\frac{\partial n}{\partial x} \equiv \sigma_n\mathscr{E} + qD_n\frac{\partial n}{\partial x}$$

$$J_p = qp\mu_p\mathscr{E} - qD_p\frac{\partial p}{\partial x} \equiv \sigma_p\mathscr{E} - qD_p\frac{\partial p}{\partial x}$$

(1.57)

for the total electron and hole currents (drift and diffusion).

In order to determine electron and hole flow in large regions, certain partial differential equations must be solved which, as usual in physical processes, describe the carrier or particle behavior at various points in space (i.e., describe the behavior in infinitesimal volumes). These equations for the present case are the conventional continuity equations modified to fit semiconductors. Thus, holes in an *n*-type semiconductor and electrons in a *p*-type semiconductor are governed by

$$\frac{\partial p}{\partial t} = g_p - \frac{(p - p_0)}{\tau_p} - \frac{1}{q}\,\nabla\cdot\mathbf{J}_p$$

(1.58a)

$$\frac{\partial n}{\partial t} = g_n - \frac{(n - n_0)}{\tau_n} + \frac{1}{q}\,\nabla\cdot\mathbf{J}_n,$$

(1.58b)

or, in one dimension,

$$\frac{\partial p}{\partial t} = g_p - \frac{(p - p_0)}{\tau_p} - \frac{1}{q}\frac{\partial J_p}{\partial x}$$

(1.58c)

$$\frac{\partial n}{\partial t} = g_n - \frac{(n - n_0)}{\tau_n} + \frac{1}{q}\frac{\partial J_n}{\partial x}.$$

(1.58d)

Equations (1.58a) and (1.58b) state that three processes contribute to the time rate of change of holes (in a "small" volume, which has been divided out of the equation). The first process is the rate g_p at which external radiation or a similar process increases the hole density. The second is the rate at which excess holes recombine and thus decrease the density. The third is the rate at which the density decreases owing to the divergence of hole current. The third term represents the change in hole density owing to a difference in hole current that flows into and out of a "small" volume. The equation governing the behavior of electrons is interpreted similarly.

Frequently no external generating influences are present, and g_p and g_n

may be dropped from (1.58). Also, in many cases the drift currents are negligible, and (1.56) or (1.57) substituted in (1.58) give

$$\frac{\partial p}{\partial t} = -\frac{(p - p_0)}{\tau_p} + D_p \nabla^2 p \qquad (1.59a)$$

$$\frac{\partial n}{\partial t} = -\frac{(n - n_0)}{\tau_n} + D_n \nabla^2 n, \qquad (1.59b)$$

or, in one dimension,

$$\frac{\partial p}{\partial t} = -\frac{(p - p_0)}{\tau_p} + D_p \frac{\partial^2 p}{\partial x^2} \qquad (1.59c)$$

$$\frac{\partial n}{\partial t} = -\frac{(n - n_0)}{\tau_n} + D_n \frac{\partial^2 n}{\partial x^2}. \qquad (1.59d)$$

For steady-state conditions the partial derivatives with respect to time become zero. Let us consider this case for a "long" n-type rectangular bar such that by some unspecified means we are able to hold the excess hole concentration $p - p_0$ equal to P_0 at $x = 0$. Then equation (1.59c), the diffusion equation for holes in a neutral n-type semiconductor, may be rewritten as

$$\frac{d^2(p - p_0)}{dx^2} - \frac{(p - p_0)}{D_p \tau_p} = 0 \qquad (1.60)$$

and may be solved to give

$$p - p_0 = P_0 \exp\left(-\frac{x}{\sqrt{D_p \tau_p}}\right) \equiv P_0 \exp\left(-\frac{x}{L_p}\right), \quad x > 0, \quad (1.61)$$

where the boundary condition above ($p - p_0 = P_0$) has been applied at $x = 0$. The quantity $L_p = \sqrt{D_p \tau_p}$ is the diffusion length, the characteristic distance in which the excess hole concentration decreases by a fraction $1/e$. The diffusion length L_p (or L_n for electrons in p-type material) is a measure of how far a hole diffuses before it recombines with an electron.

Let us consider another example, that of a semiconductor in which the doping is nonuniform. This is a situation which gives rise to a built-in electric field in the specimen. At equilibrium no net current flow of electrons or holes occurs in the specimen in spite of the built-in field, and from (1.57)

$$\mathbf{J}_p = 0 = qp\mu_p \mathscr{E} - qD_p \nabla p. \qquad (1.62)$$

From (1.31)

$$\nabla p = \nabla\left[n_i \exp\frac{q(\varphi - \psi)}{kT}\right] = -\frac{q}{kT} p \nabla \psi = \frac{q}{kT} p \mathscr{E}$$

and when substituted in (1.62) gives

$$0 = \mu_p p \mathscr{E} - \frac{qD_p}{kT} p \mathscr{E}$$

or

$$D_p = \frac{kT}{q} \mu_p. \qquad (1.63)$$

Similarly, for electrons

$$D_n = \frac{kT}{q} \mu_n. \qquad (1.64)$$

These are the well-known Einstein relations which relate diffusion constants to mobilities. In deriving these expressions, we have made use of the fact that the Fermi potential φ does not vary with position ($\nabla\varphi = 0$) for the case of no externally applied voltage.[2,5]

In the general case, it is essentially impossible to solve equations (1.58) in closed form. For simple boundary and initial conditions, one-dimensional geometries, and relatively low-level conditions involving mainly diffusion, we can use the simpler forms of equations (1.58) to obtain solutions for minority-carrier densities under dynamic conditions and then substitute the solutions in (1.56) to determine the electron and hole currents of interest. Ordinarily, we shall be concerned with conditions in which the semiconductor can be considered to be neutral, that is, situations in which each additional minority carrier is compensated by an additional majority carrier (which is rapidly available, usually from an ohmic contact). In regions in which strong fields exist, for example, in the transition region of a *p-n* junction, charge neutrality does not always obtain. The potential in such regions can be determined by solving Poisson's equation

$$\nabla^2\psi = \frac{-q(N_d - N_a + p - n)}{K\epsilon_0}, \tag{1.65}$$

where N_d is the ionized donor density, N_a the ionized acceptor density, p the hole density, n the electron density, ϵ_0 the permittivity of free space (8.85 $\times$ 10^{-12} farad/m), and K the dielectric constant (11.8 in silicon). The solution of this equation is not simple in the general case, because p and n are both functions of potential.

1.8 *p-n* Junctions, Minority-carrier Injection and Collection

Perhaps most fundamental to the understanding of *p-n-p-n* switches is an understanding of *p-n* junctions, minority-carrier injection, and minority-carrier transport and collection. In this section we shall first develop the equations describing simple *p-n* junctions and then generalize the treatment to include transistor action. In most respects the material of this section is a straightforward application of the concepts, expressions for carrier concentrations, and equations of Secs. 1.5, 1.6, and 1.7.

Although in practice *p-n* junctions are formed by growing techniques, alloying techniques, or impurity diffusion, let us consider a hypothetical *p-n* junction formed by an ideal mechanical splice of a *p*-type rectangular bar of unit cross section to an *n*-type semiconductor bar of unit cross section. This is a rather miraculous splice, because we have assumed no difficulties with surface contaminants, surface irregularities, or oxides at the interface (junction). We have assumed further that the atoms of the *p*-type semiconductor are so aligned with those of the *n*-type semiconductor that a single-crystal *p-n* structure is obtained. Let the concentration of holes in the *p*-type section be designated as p_p and electrons (minority carriers) as $n_p(p_p \gg n_p)$. In terms of earlier notation $p_p \approx N_a$. Likewise, in the *n*-type section let the concentration of electrons be designated as $n_n(n_n \approx N_d)$ and holes (minority carriers) as $p_n(n_n \gg p_n)$. Zero used as a subscript in this notation indicates thermal-equilibrium values.

Because of the large density of electrons on the *n*-type side and the lesser electron density on the *p*-type side of the junction, electrons will tend to escape by diffusion from *n*-type side to *p*-type side. Similarly, holes will tend to diffuse in the opposite direction. The electrons which tend to depart from the *n*-type side leave behind some uncompensated positive donor ions in the junction transition region. Also, holes which diffuse from the *p*-side similarly leave some uncompensated negative acceptor ions in the junction transition region. The fixed charge in the junction transition region, which is uncompensated by electrons and holes, sets up a dipole layer, and an electric field directed from *n*-side to *p*-side. The field establishes a potential step that is sufficient to retard the free diffusion of carriers and allows as many thermally generated electrons (per unit time) from *p*-side to diffuse and be accelerated across the junction by the field as are able to climb the barrier by diffusion from *n*-side to *p*-side. For thermal equilibrium, hole current (in the same manner as electron current) is zero across the junction. The height of the potential step V_0 (built-in potential) from *p*-type side to *n*-type side (or the amount $-qV_0$ the *n*-type side is depressed in energy relative to the *p*-type side) is just such as to allow the Fermi level on the two sides of the junction to coincide. In more detailed and rigorous arguments than those presented here, it is shown that under thermal-equilibrium conditions (and no applied external voltages or excitations) the Fermi level in a semiconductor, with or without junctions or doping gradients, is at the same level throughout the material.[2,5]

1.8.1 JUNCTION BOUNDARY CONDITIONS

Figure 1.12(a) shows a diagram of the energy levels in a *p-n* junction in equilibrium (no voltage applied to the junction). For this case the net electron and hole currents are each zero, and from (1.57)

$$J_{px} = q\mu_p p \mathscr{E}_x - qD_p \frac{dp}{dx} = 0. \tag{1.66}$$

Equation (1.66) may be rearranged and integrated, from left to right across the junction, to give

$$\int_{p_{p0}}^{p_{n0}} \frac{dp}{p} = \frac{q}{kT} \int_0^{W_0} \mathscr{E}_x \, dx = \frac{q}{kT} \int_0^{V_0} -d\psi = -\frac{qV_0}{kT}$$

or

$$p_{n0} = p_{p0} \exp\left(-\frac{qV_0}{kT}\right) \tag{1.67}$$

where use has been made of the Einstein relation to eliminate μ_p/D_p. Equation (1.67) shows that a Boltzmann factor involving the barrier height relates hole density on one side of the junction to hole density on the opposite side. If the barrier is reduced by application of a forward bias V [Fig. 1.12(b)], equation (1.67) becomes

$$p_n = p_p \exp \frac{-q(V_0 - V)}{kT}$$

or, for low-level conditions ($p_p \gg n_p$ and $n_n \gg p_n$) in which $p_p \approx p_{p0}$,

$$p_n = p_{p0} \exp \frac{-q(V_0 - V)}{kT} = p_{n0} \exp \left(\frac{qV}{kT}\right). \tag{1.68}$$

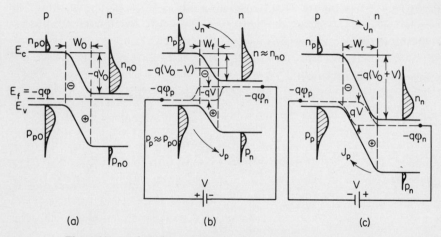

Fig. 1.12 *p-n* junction (a) in thermal equilibrium, (b) in forward bias, and (c) in reverse bias. Junction transition width, $W_f < W_0 < W_r$.

Similar arguments for electrons give

$$n_p = n_{p0} \exp \left(\frac{qV}{kT}\right). \tag{1.69}$$

Equation (1.68) states that the density of holes (minority carriers) on the *n*-type side of the junction, i.e., just to the right of the space-charge region, is the equilibrium magnitude multiplied by a Boltzmann factor of the applied bias V. Equation (1.69) has similar meaning applied to electrons (minority carriers) in the *p*-type region just to the left of the space-charge region.

Although we have not called attention to this explicitly, the voltages applied to either side of a *p-n* junction, as shown in Figs. 1.12(b) and 1.12(c), shift the Fermi level ($-q\varphi_p$) on the *p*-type side with respect to the Fermi level ($-q\varphi_n$) on the *n*-type side of a junction. This in turn causes a shift in potential across the junction, as correctly accounted for in equations (1.68) and (1.69). A more precise formulation of these concepts,[2,5] however, shows more properly that (1.68) and (1.69) arise from a change in Fermi potential φ across the junction.

The application of forward bias to a junction lowers the potential barrier and allows holes from the *p*-side to diffuse in greater numbers across the junction and thus increase the minority-carrier density p_n on the *n*-type side. Similarly, electrons on the *n*-type side diffuse in greater numbers across the barrier and increase the minority-carrier density n_p on the *p*-type side of the junction. Equations (1.68) and (1.69) show that reverse bias (negative exponents) reduces the minority-carrier densities near the junction to magnitudes less than those which pertain to thermal equilibrium. In forward bias, the increased minority carriers (injected carriers) diffuse beyond the junction and decay by recombination with majority carriers, which enter via ohmic end contacts in just sufficient numbers to compensate the charge of injected minority carriers.

1.8.2 JUNCTION CURRENT

The current across a junction in which little recombination or charge generation takes place in the junction transition region itself is caused almost completely by injection and diffusion of minority carriers, or in reverse bias by collection of minority carriers within a diffusion length of either side of the junction. For steady-state conditions we may turn to the solution (1.61) of equation (1.60) and substitute $(p_n - p_{n0})$ as given by (1.68) for P_0, i.e., for the excess hole density at $x = 0$, and obtain

$$p_n(x) - p_{n0} = p_{n0}\left[\exp\left(\frac{qV}{kT}\right) - 1\right]\exp\left(-\frac{x}{L_p}\right) \tag{1.70}$$

for the excess hole density in the *n*-type region (assumed to be "long") as a function of distance x to the right of the junction. From (1.56) and (1.70) the hole-diffusion current evaluated at the junction, i.e., at $x = 0$, becomes

$$J_p = -qD_p\frac{d(p_n - p_{n0})}{dx}\bigg|_{x=0} = \frac{qD_p p_{n0}}{L_p}\left[\exp\left(\frac{qV}{kT}\right) - 1\right]. \tag{1.71}$$

Repeating the arguments above for electrons gives

$$n_p(x) - n_{p0} = n_{p0}\left[\exp\left(\frac{qV}{kT}\right) - 1\right]\exp\left(\frac{x}{L_p}\right) \tag{1.72}$$

for the excess electron density in the *p*-type region as a function of distance x (negative) to the left of the junction. The electron-diffusion current is readily evaluated at $x = 0$ as

$$J_n = \frac{qD_n n_{p0}}{L_n}\left[\exp\left(\frac{qV}{kT}\right) - 1\right], \tag{1.73}$$

32   Semiconductor and *p-n* Junction Properties

and from (1.71) and (1.73) the total current (density) becomes

$$J = J_n + J_p = q\left(\frac{D_n n_{p0}}{L_n} + \frac{D_p p_{n0}}{L_p}\right)\left[\exp\left(\frac{qV}{kT}\right) - 1\right]. \qquad (1.74)$$

This is the familiar diode equation, which shows that the current increases exponentially in the forward direction and saturates at

$$J_{ns} + J_{ps} = q\,\frac{D_n n_{p0}}{L_n} + q\,\frac{D_p p_{n0}}{L_p} \qquad (1.75)$$

in the reverse direction [V negative, Fig. 1.12(c)]. The saturation current (1.75) is seen to be due simply to the minority carriers, within a diffusion length,

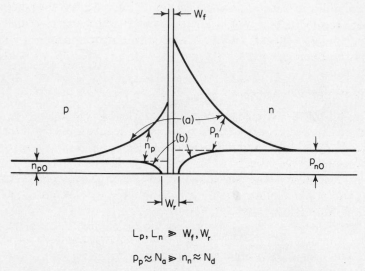

$$L_p, L_n \gg W_f, W_r$$

$$p_p \approx N_a \gg n_n \approx N_d$$

Fig. 1.13 Minority carrier densities near a *p-n* junction in (a) forward bias and (b) reverse bias.

which diffuse to the junction and are swept across by the dipole field of the junction. This is an example of minority-carrier collection which is very much akin to minority-carrier collection in a transistor or *p-n-p-n* switch.

Figure 1.13 shows a schematic representation of the minority carriers near a *p-n* junction under the conditions described above of forward bias (a) and of reverse bias (b). At the very edge of the transition region, the hole and electron densities are given by (1.68) and (1.69). For the situation depicted in Fig. 1.13, the doping on the *p*-side, N_a, is much larger than the doping on the *n*-side, N_d.

1.8.3 INJECTION EFFICIENCY

The *p-n* junction shown in Figs. 1.12 and 1.13 may be considered as an approximation to an emitter junction in a transistor or a *p-n-p-n* switch, and the question may be raised concerning how efficiently the junction acts as a hole emitter. That is, of the total current flowing across the junction what fraction γ is hole current (or electron current)? From equation (1.74)

$$\gamma \equiv \frac{J_p}{J_n + J_p} = \left(\frac{D_p p_{n0}}{L_p}\right)\left(\frac{D_n n_{p0}}{L_n} + \frac{D_p p_{n0}}{L_p}\right)^{-1}. \tag{1.76}$$

By making use of Einstein's relationship $qD = \mu kT$ and by recalling that $n_{p0}p_{p0} = n_i^2$, $p_{n0}n_{n0} = n_i^2$, $\sigma_n \approx q\mu_n n_{n0}$, and $\sigma_p \approx q\mu_p p_{p0}$ [see equations (1.18) and (1.55a)], we may reduce (1.76) to

$$\gamma = \left(1 + \frac{J_n}{J_p}\right)^{-1} = \left[1 + \frac{(1/\sigma_p L_n)}{(1/\sigma_n L_p)}\right]^{-1} = \left[1 + \frac{(\rho_p/L_n)}{(\rho_n/L_p)}\right]^{-1}. \tag{1.77}$$

The quantity ρ_p/L_n is the transverse (parallel to the junction) sheet resistivity R_p (ohms per square) of a layer on the p-type side of the junction which is one diffusion length L_n thick. Likewise, ρ_n/L_p is the transverse sheet resistivity R_n of a layer on the n-type side of the junction which is one diffusion length L_p thick. Hence, (1.77) can be written as

$$\gamma = (1 + R_p/R_n)^{-1}. \tag{1.78}$$

If the p-side of the junction is considerably more heavily doped than the n-side, $R_p \ll R_n$ and

$$\gamma \approx 1 - R_p/R_n. \tag{1.79}$$

Equation (1.79) shows that the injection efficiency γ can readily approach unity, and for the case we have selected, most of the current across the junction is carried by holes.

We have chosen to represent the injection efficiency in terms of sheet resistances (or sheet conductivities), for, as will be clear later, the formulation is sufficiently general to account for most real situations in which the transverse sheet thickness on the left might be determined by an ohmic contact rather than a diffusion length and the sheet-thickness dimension on the right (n-region) might actually be the thickness of the base of a transistor or p-n-p-n switch.

1.8.4 MINORITY-CARRIER TRANSPORT AND TRANSISTOR ACTION

In the junction (emitter) of Fig. 1.13 holes injected from left to right into the "long" n-region decay exponentially toward equilibrium relatively far to the right. The situation which leads to the transistor is that of another junction, a collector junction, introduced at a distance W less than a diffusion length L_p to the right of the emitter. The collector junction is ordinarily reverse-biased and, as stated earlier, tends to draw the minority-carrier densities near it down to zero. Hence, the minority-carrier densities in the structure appear as shown in Fig. 1.14. In Fig. 1.14 minority carriers injected into the n-type base region have been approximated by a linear function whose magnitude is zero at the collector, $x = W$. Actually, some of the minority carriers (holes) injected into the base recombine with electrons and thus lead to a true density, as shown just below the doubly cross-hatched region. We notice that the slope (proportional to current) of minority carriers is not constant across the base, as given by the approximation of a linearly decreasing density, but instead decreases in magnitude, as it must to account for injected minority carriers which recombine and which do not contribute to the current collected at $x = W$.

The minority-carrier injection efficiency for this case becomes (at $x = 0$)

$$\gamma = \left(1 + \frac{J_n}{J_p}\right)^{-1} \approx \left[1 + \frac{(qD_n n_{p0}/L_n)\exp(qV_e/kT)}{(qD_p p_{n0}/W)\exp(qV_e/kT)}\right]^{-1}$$

$$\approx \left[1 + \frac{(1/\sigma_{pe}L_n)}{(1/\sigma_{nb}W)}\right]^{-1} \equiv \left(1 + \frac{R_{pe}}{R_{nb}}\right)^{-1}, \tag{1.80}$$

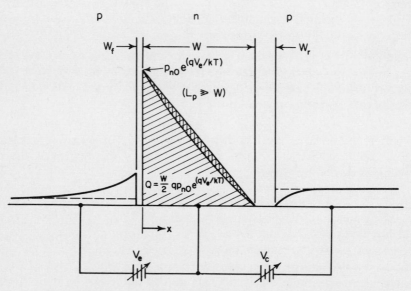

Fig. 1.14 Minority carrier densities in a *p-n-p* transistor with the emitter in forward bias and the collector in reverse bias.

where the result is as given by (1.78), except that now the sheet resistance R_{nb} is that of the base region (i.e., has thickness W instead of L_p). As before, if the emitter is doped much more heavily than the base (i.e., $R_{nb} \gg R_{pe}$), the injection efficiency is near unity.

If the injection efficiency γ is high and the transport efficiency β of minority carriers across the base is high (near unity), the ratio of collector current to emitter current, defined as *alpha* (α), approaches unity. The result is an efficient transistor, i.e., a device in which a current is injected at low impedance (forward-biased junction) and is collected at high impedance (reverse-biased junction)—hence power gain. The transport efficiency β is defined as the ratio of the minority current arriving at the collector to the minority current injected into the base by the emitter. The reader can readily calculate β by first solving equation (1.60) with the proper boundary conditions (1.68) applied at $x = 0$ and $x = W$ and by then evaluating the currents at the boundaries by means of (1.56). This procedure gives

$$\beta = \frac{J_{pc}}{J_{pe}} = \frac{1}{\cosh W/L_p} \approx 1 - \frac{W^2}{2L_p^2}, \qquad (1.81)$$

and shows that β approaches unity for $W \ll L_p$.

The approximate form of (1.81) may be obtained by rather simple physical arguments. From the simple linear approximation of the hole distribution in the transistor base region, the hole-current density injected into the base region (slope multiplied by $-qD_p$) is

$$J_{pe} \approx \frac{qD_p p_{n0} \exp{(qV_e/kT)}}{W}. \qquad (1.82)$$

Not all of this current traverses the base. An amount J_{rec} is carried out of the base by electrons which enter the base region and recombine with some holes. The recombination current is simply the time rate of recombination of excess holes in the entire base region, or

$$J_{\text{rec}} \approx \frac{W}{2} qp_{n0} \exp{\left(\frac{qV_e}{kT}\right)} \times \frac{1}{\tau_p}. \qquad (1.83)$$

Thus, from (1.82) and (1.83)

$$\beta \approx \frac{J_{pe} - J_{\text{rec}}}{J_{pe}} = 1 - \frac{J_{\text{rec}}}{J_{pe}} = 1 - \frac{W^2}{2D_p\tau_p} \equiv 1 - \frac{W^2}{2L_p^2}, \qquad (1.84)$$

which is seen to be the same as the approximate form of (1.81).

In addition to the contributions of injection efficiency γ and transport efficiency β to the alpha of a transistor (or *p-n-p-n* switch), alpha (over-all minority-carrier transfer efficiency) may also be influenced by the collection efficiency. For example, in Fig. 1.14 holes which diffuse across the base and are collected as majority carriers in the *p*-region at the right (collector) create a field in the collector which tends to draw electrons from the collector body to the collector junction. These electrons constitute additional collected minority carriers which add to the collector efficiency and to alpha. If an emitter junction or metal contact exists relatively far to the right in or on the *p*-collector body, this source of electrons, plus the aid of the ohmic field we have described, can lead to a distinguishable electron alpha, from right to left. The electron alpha when added to the hole alpha can give potentially an over-all alpha equal to unity. This leads to a device which can exhibit switching in the sense of *p-n-p-n* devices, as described in detail later.

Another important means by which collection efficiency (and alpha) can be increased is by avalanche effects. At sufficiently high reverse biases, the field in the collector-junction transition region becomes large enough and spread over enough distance to allow carrier avalanche multiplication. Carriers arriving at the collector junction are accelerated by the field in the junction transition region and receive enough energy so that in collisions with the lattice they ionize electrons and holes which can repeat the process and lead to avalanche. This mechanism is one of the important means of increasing alpha (at high enough collector voltages) and also is extremely important in determining the voltage breakdown limitations of junctions, a subject of considerable importance which will be treated in greater detail later (Sec. 1.9).

The situation shown in Fig. 1.14 is that of the usual transistor with emitter in forward bias, collector in reverse bias, and normal alpha from left to right. The role of emitter and collector can be interchanged, and then the alpha of concern is the inverse alpha and applies to holes injected and transported from right to left. Corresponding to the slope (linear approximation) of minority carriers in the base of the transistor of Fig. 1.14, a given current flows from emitter to collector. The same current can be carried from left to right if the slope is maintained even when the collector is in *forward* bias (saturated transistor) and the minority-carrier density in the base near the collector is not zero. For this case, more minority carriers must be stored in the base region; i.e., more voltage must be applied on the emitter to increase the base minority-carrier concentration near the emitter ($x = 0$). In other words, the entire cross-hatched region of Fig. 1.14 is translated upward with the slope maintained constant and the minority-carrier charge in the base increased. At this point conceptually we can break into two parts the total minority-carrier charge stored in the base. The first part is a linear decreasing density which drops from the proper magnitude at the emitter to zero at the collector. The second is a similarly linear decreasing magnitude which drops from $qp_{n0} \exp(qV_c/kT)$ at the forward-biased collector to zero at the emitter. The sum of these two distributions gives a net distribution (linear from emitter to collector) with slope downward from the emitter to the collector in the proper magnitude to give the net current from left to right which we have assumed. The charge, when so broken into two parts, shows the role of forward or normal alpha and the role of reverse or inverse alpha. We shall use these concepts later in analyzing *p-n-p-n* switches.

The concepts presented above make it possible to present the equations describing a transistor in the following very general form:[1,10]

$$I_e = I_{e0}\left[\exp\left(\frac{qV_e}{kT}\right) - 1\right] - \alpha_i I_{c0}\left[\exp\left(\frac{qV_c}{kT}\right) - 1\right]$$

$$I_c = -\alpha_n I_{e0}\left[\exp\left(\frac{qV_e}{kT}\right) - 1\right] + I_{c0}\left[\exp\left(\frac{qV_c}{kT}\right) - 1\right],$$

(1.85)

where I_e is the total emitter current (current density × area), I_c the total collector current, I_{e0} the emitter saturation current measured with collector-base voltage equal to zero, I_{c0} the collector saturation current measured with emitter-base voltage equal to zero, α_n the normal or forward alpha, and α_i the inverse or reverse alpha. The coefficients multiplying the exponential quantities in brackets in (1.85) may be readily calculated by solving the continuity equations with appropriate boundary conditions, and then are expressed in the usual semiconductor parameters and geometrical factors. In practice this is unnecessary, since the coefficients in (1.85) can also be measured. Equations (1.85) have the virtue of being almost intuitively obvious, are convenient for description and analysis of transistor operation, and, as shown by Moll, can be extended to describe the operation of *p-n-p-n* devices, as is shown in Chap. 2.

1.8.5 SPEED PROPERTIES

A problem of major concern in *p-n* junctions, and all junction devices in general, is that of speed of response to time-varying signals. In general, this is a complex problem which, except for simple cases, is never solved with any real generality. We will not attempt an exhaustive description of this problem, but will, instead, treat several simple cases, by simple or lazy methods, which will demonstrate some of the major ideas and problems of concern.

Some of the major speed problems of junction devices are associated with minority-carrier diffusion (or drift) transit times, minority-carrier storage, and *RC* time-constant limitations. Transit times are of concern in determining how fast injected minority carriers can traverse base regions. Stored minority carriers hold a junction in forward bias or a region in a high-conductance state for a period of time beyond the instant a signal is applied to drive these regions into a higher-impedance condition; hence the delay in turn-off. The finite parasitic resistances of various regions and contacts in a junction device, along with the capacitance owing to stored charge (minority carriers), and/or junction barrier capacitances, lead to *RC* circuit limitations on response time. Capacitance owing to stored charge (injected minority carriers compensated by additional majority carriers) may be calculated by taking the ratio of incremental charge stored in a region to an incremental voltage applied to a junction (or region) to effect the charge change. Junction-transition or barrier capacitance is readily seen to be caused by the incremental charge (mainly fixed charge) uncovered at the outer edges of the junction transition or barrier region by an incremental change in the voltage across the junction (see Fig. 1.12). [2,3,5] If the incremental charge owing to free holes and electrons can be ignored, the barrier capacitance as a function of voltage and impurity concentration and profile may be calculated from Poisson's equation (1.65). [2,3,5] This calculation is given in almost every book written on semiconductors and will not be repeated here (exercise for the reader).

In order to obtain some idea of the problem of charge storage and removal in junction devices, let us consider the relatively simple case of a p^+-n junction (high, uniform acceptor doping on the p-side and lesser, uniform donor doping on the n-side) which initially is carrying a steady forward current I_f. This leads to an exponential spacial distribution of excess (injected) stored holes in the n-region, as shown in Fig. 1.15. At time $t = 0$ suppose the junction is switched to reverse bias. For the sake of analysis, we shall let the external circuitry withdraw (collect) a reverse current of magnitude I_r and ask how long, t_r, this current persists until the diode impedance begins to increase and the external circuit no longer can maintain a fixed current I_r.

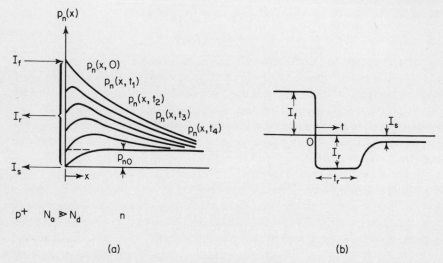

Fig. 1.15 (a) Stored charge (holes in n-region) in a p^+-n junction; (b) current in a p^+-n junction.

In an ideal diode (if one existed) when switching occurs from forward to reverse bias, conduction would cease immediately. In the case of the diode of Fig. 1.15, holes stored on the n-side contribute a reverse current until all of the excess holes are either withdrawn (diffuse to the junction and are collected) or recombine. A steady current I_r exists for a time t_r until the excess hole concentration p' ($p' \equiv p_n - p_{n0}$) becomes zero at the junction. Thus, t_r can be determined by calculating how long it takes for the excess hole population p' (and voltage) at the junction edge (n-side) to become zero when the initial spacial hole concentration [see equation (1.70)] is

$$p'(x, 0) = p_{n0}\left[\exp\left(\frac{qV_0}{kT}\right) - 1\right]\exp\left(-\frac{x}{L_p}\right) \qquad (1.86)\dagger$$

† Here V_0 applies to the external applied voltage at time $t = 0$ and should not be confused with the built-in potential, which we have also labeled V_0.

and the boundary condition at $x = 0$, because of fixed I_r and equation (1.56), is

$$-I_r = -AqD_p \frac{\partial p'(0, t)}{\partial x} \quad \text{or} \quad \frac{\partial p'(0, t)}{\partial x} = \frac{I_r}{AqD_p}. \quad (1.87)$$

In order to determine the recovery time t_r, we must first solve the continuity equation (1.59a):

$$\frac{\partial p'}{\partial t} = \frac{-p'}{\tau_p} + D_p \frac{\partial^2 p'}{\partial x^2} \quad (1.88)$$

or

$$\frac{\partial p'}{\partial t'} = -p' + \frac{\partial^2 p'}{\partial z^2}, \quad (1.89)$$

where $t' \equiv t/\tau_p$ and $z \equiv x/L_p$. If $p'(z, t')$ is defined as

$$p'(z, t') \equiv P(z, t') \exp(-t') \quad (1.90)$$

and is substituted in (1.89), equation (1.89) reduces to

$$\frac{\partial P(z, t')}{\partial t'} = \frac{\partial^2 P(z, t')}{\partial z^2}. \quad (1.91)$$

Since the initial steady forward current $I_f(t < 0)$ is given as

$$I_f = -AqD_p \frac{\partial p'(0, 0)}{\partial x} = \frac{AqD_p p_{n0}}{L_p} \left[\exp\left(\frac{qV_0}{kT}\right) - 1\right],$$

the initial condition (1.86) can be written as

$$p'(x, 0) = \frac{L_p}{AqD_p} I_f \exp\left(-\frac{x}{L_p}\right)$$

or

$$P(z, 0) = \frac{L_p}{AqD_p} I_f \exp(-z). \quad (1.92)$$

Similarly, (1.87) can be rewritten as

$$\frac{\partial p'(0, t)}{\partial x} = \frac{\partial p'}{\partial z} \frac{\partial z}{\partial x} = \frac{\partial P(0, t) \exp(-t/\tau_p)}{\partial z} \frac{}{L_p} = \frac{I_r}{AqD_p}$$

or

$$\frac{\partial P(0, t')}{\partial z} = \frac{L_p}{AqD_p} I_r \exp(t') \equiv P_z(0, t'). \quad (1.93)$$

The system of equations (1.91), (1.92), and (1.93) is in the form of a standard classical boundary-value problem with the known solution[11]

$$P(z, t') = \frac{1}{2\sqrt{\pi t'}} \int_0^\infty P(\xi, 0)\left\{\exp\left[\frac{-(z - \xi)^2}{4t'}\right] + \exp\left[\frac{-(z + \xi)^2}{4t'}\right]\right\} d\xi$$

$$- \frac{1}{\sqrt{\pi}} \int_0^{t'} \frac{P_z(0, T)}{\sqrt{t' - T}} \exp\left[\frac{-z^2}{4(t' - T)}\right] dT. \quad (1.94)$$

Since ultimately we shall want to know how the excess hole concentration at the junction ($x = 0$ or $z = 0$) varies as a function of time, we shall first set $z = 0$ before evaluating the integrals in (1.94). Thus, (1.94) becomes

$$P(0, t') = \frac{1}{\sqrt{\pi t'}} \frac{L_p}{AqD_p} I_f \int_0^\infty \exp(-\xi) \exp\left(\frac{-\xi^2}{4t'}\right) d\xi$$

$$- \frac{1}{\sqrt{\pi}} \frac{L_p}{AqD_p} I_r \int_0^{t'} \frac{\exp(T)}{\sqrt{t' - T}} dT. \quad (1.95)$$

With a little labor and a few substitutions, (1.95) can be reduced by elementary means to

$$p'\left(0, \frac{t}{\tau_p}\right) = \frac{L_p}{AqD_p} I_f \frac{2}{\sqrt{\pi}} \int_{t/\tau_p}^\infty \exp(-\xi^2) d\xi - \frac{L_p}{AqD_p} I_r \frac{1}{\sqrt{\pi}} \int_0^{t/\tau_p} \frac{\exp(-\xi)}{\sqrt{\xi}} d\xi,$$

and finally to

$$p'\left(0, \frac{t}{\tau_p}\right) = \frac{L_p}{AqD_p} [I_f(1 - \operatorname{erf} \sqrt{t/\tau_p}) - I_r \operatorname{erf} \sqrt{t/\tau_p}], \quad (1.96)$$

where

$$\operatorname{erf} x = \frac{2}{\sqrt{\pi}} \int_0^x \exp(-\xi^2) d\xi$$

is a well-known, tabulated function. This solution applies until the excess hole population p' at the junction becomes zero[12,13] and gives the expression

$$\operatorname{erf} \sqrt{t_r/\tau_p} = (1 + I_r/I_f)^{-1} \quad (1.97)$$

for the recovery time t_r. If I_f and I_r are adjusted to be equal, from (1.97) $t_r = 0.228\tau_p$. The junction can obviously be made to switch from low forward impedance to high reverse impedance in a lesser time if the stored charge is decreased (lesser I_f), if the reverse current I_r is increased (lesser circuit impedance), or if the lifetime τ_p is decreased (greater density of recombination centers).

Although the example considered here is quite simple, the calculation of the junction recovery time is relatively complicated. In more complex cases such calculations become hopelessly involved. For transistors and *p-n-p-n* switches, in which excess minority carriers can be stored in a number of regions, the analysis of recovery from the ON to the OFF state (or vice versa) is carried out frequently by approximate "charge analysis" procedures[14,15] which consider the excess charge in a given region as an average charge; i.e., the detailed initial spacial charge distribution is not considered.

As a further example of charge storage and the part it plays in determining diffusion-capacitance limitations, let us consider the *p-n-p* transistor shown in Fig. 1.14, in which the minority-carrier density in the base is approximated by a linear distribution

$$p(x) = p_{n0} \exp\left(\frac{qV_e}{kT}\right)\left(1 - \frac{x}{W}\right), \quad (1.98)$$

and the total stored charge Q_b is given as

$$Q_b = \frac{AW}{2} qp_{n0} \exp\left(\frac{qV_e}{kT}\right). \tag{1.99}$$

(Here A represents area and is not assumed to be equal to unity.) The emitter current (and collector current, if we assume no recombination in the base) is

$$I_e = -AqD_p \frac{dp}{dx} = \frac{AqD_p}{W} p_{n0} \exp\left(\frac{qV_e}{kT}\right) = \frac{2D_p}{W^2} Q_b. \tag{1.100}$$

If the voltage on the emitter is increased by an incremental amount, the minority-carrier stored charge in the base is increased also by an incremental amount (the charge distribution is tilted a "little" higher) and from (1.100) leads to a diffusion capacitance

$$C_d = \frac{dQ_b}{dV_e} = \frac{W^2}{2D_p} \frac{dI_e}{dV_e} = \frac{q}{kT} \frac{W^2}{2D_p} I_e, \tag{1.101}$$

which indicates that the capacitance increases as the square of the base width and directly with increasing emitter current (or stored charge Q_b).

If the emitter resistance is defined as $dV_e/dI_e = R_e$, from (1.101)

$$R_e C_d = \frac{W^2}{2D_p}, \tag{1.102}$$

and the angular cutoff frequency (from $\omega_\alpha R_e C_d \sim 1$) becomes

$$\omega_\alpha = \frac{1}{R_e C_d} = \frac{2D_p}{W^2}. \tag{1.103}$$

This is within a small numerical factor of the cutoff frequency determined on the basis of a small-signal sinusoidal analysis of transistor frequency response.[16] We should repeat that "stored charge" analysis of the frequency-response and switching times of junction devices is much more sophisticated and intricate, and plays a much wider role than we have indicated here with these simple examples. Our purpose has been to show that stored charge can be a major factor in establishing the speed of junction devices, i.e., those junction devices depending upon minority-carrier injection and transport.

We may intuitively expect that an excitation applied at the emitter of the transistor of Fig. 1.14 will be carried to the collector by the transport of minority carriers across the base region. Accordingly, the properties and width of the base region and the transit time of minority carriers across it would be expected to have considerable influence on frequency response or speed. If the base transit time is defined as

$$t_t = \int_0^W \frac{dx}{v} \tag{1.104}$$

and the velocity v is related to the current I_e traversing the base by

$$Aqp(x)v = I_e \quad \text{or} \quad \frac{1}{v} = \frac{Aqp(x)}{I_e},$$

then from (1.100)

$$t_t = \int_0^W \frac{Aqp(x)\,dx}{I_e} = \frac{W^2}{2D_p}\frac{1}{Q_b}\int_0^W Aqp(x)\,dx. \tag{1.105}$$

Since the last integral in (1.105) is nothing but Q_b,

$$t_t = \frac{W^2}{2D_p}, \tag{1.106}$$

and as above (from $\omega_t t_t \sim 1$)

$$\omega_t = \frac{1}{t_t} = \frac{2D_p}{W^2}. \tag{1.107}$$

Again, this is equivalent to the result obtained for frequency cutoff from a small-signal sinusoidal analysis. In present-day diffused-impurity devices, often a considerable impurity (doping) gradient exists from emitter to collector, in which case the expression (1.106) for transit time does not apply.[17] No matter what form of analysis is adopted, generally speaking, all lead to more or less similar conclusions and, depending upon the device, state that, for high speeds, narrow base widths, high mobilities (or high diffusion constants D_p or D_n), and short lifetimes are required.

1.9 Avalanche Breakdown in *p-n* Junctions

A problem of major concern and design importance in most junction devices (except tunnel diodes) is that of reverse-bias junction breakdown, i.e., that region where slight increase in reverse voltage across a *p-n* junction causes a sharp increase in current. In a *p-n-p-n* switch the voltage at which breakdown of the center collector junction occurs establishes the maximum range over which the device can be used in the forward direction. Likewise, the reverse breakdown of one or both emitter junctions establishes the range in which the device is capable of blocking in the reverse direction. Premature breakdown can occur because of uncontrolled surface conditions or gross flaws in a junction, but neither will be of interest here. Further discussion will be concerned with the important topic of avalanche breakdown, a subject which, because of its considerable importance to *p-n-p-n* devices, will be discussed below in considerable detail.

Early explanations[18] of the breakdown phenomena observed in *p-n* junctions were based on a theory first described by Zener for breakdown in insulators. Hence, this phenomenon was and still is sometimes referred to (mistakenly) as Zener breakdown. The mechanism of Zener breakdown (also, tunneling or field emission) appears to describe adequately the reverse break-down of very low-voltage junctions, i.e., junctions with extremely narrow transition regions. For reverse breakdowns above approximately six volts for silicon or three volts for germanium, the experimental data deviate significantly from those which would be expected on the basis of internal field emission. Instead, breakdown above the voltages mentioned occurs by an avalanche mechanism[19,20] similar to that occurring in gases; it is shown schematically in Fig. 1.16.

Under the influence of the field, a hole which diffuses from the *n*-region and enters the space-charge layer (transition region) at x_1 will gain energy as it accelerates and travels toward the *p*-region. During its journey from x_1 to x_2, the hole undergoes repeated collisions with the crystal lattice. If the electric field (reverse voltage) is sufficiently strong, the hole can gain enough energy between collisions so that most of the collisions will result in impacts able to break lattice bonds and, consequently, create an additional hole-electron pair with each collision. The holes created by collisions (impact ionization) will repeat the process and create even more hole-electron pairs. As is evident in Fig. 1.16, free electrons created by the collisions are accelerated toward the *n*-region (opposite to the direction of motion of holes) and, like holes, may have collisions with the lattice, resulting in creation of still more hole-electron pairs. Thus, the cumulative effect of

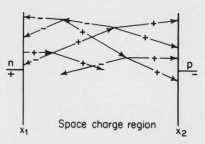

Fig. 1.16 Avalanche multiplication process in reverse-biased junction.

one hole entering the space-charge region at x_1 is such that many holes reach x_2; similarly, for one electron that enters the junction space-charge region at x_2, many arrive at x_1. This process is the well-known avalanche or impact ionization process which, if uniformly distributed over the area of the device, results in the breakdown observed in good, "clean," "hard" *p-n* junctions. The degree or amount of carrier multiplication occurring in avalanche is dependent upon the magnitude of the electric field, the width of the space charge layer, and the ionizing capability of a carrier.[20,21,22,23,24]

1.9.1 Analysis of Avalanche Breakdown

Let us consider the reverse-biased junction shown in Fig. 1.17. Hole current (density) $J_p(x)$ flows and increases to the right, as shown at the incremental layer Δx. Electrons (particles) flow and increase in number to the left; hence, the term $[dJ_n(x)/dx] \Delta x$ to the right of Δx is a negative quantity. The term $J_n(x)$ is used here as a positive quantity, and, even though it is caused by a particle flow to the left, it gives a positive current (decreasing) to the right because of the negative charge of an electron. A steady-state hole-electron pair-generation rate G per unit area and distance (i.e., per unit volume) produces a generation component of electron current (density) $qG\Delta x$, and, similarly, a component of hole current (density) $qG\Delta x$. In order to account for the current change across Δx, we define a set of ionization coefficients

$\alpha(x)$ = number of hole-electron pairs produced (per unit area) per centimeter of travel of an electron.

$\beta(x)$ = number of hole-electron pairs produced per centimeter of travel of a hole.

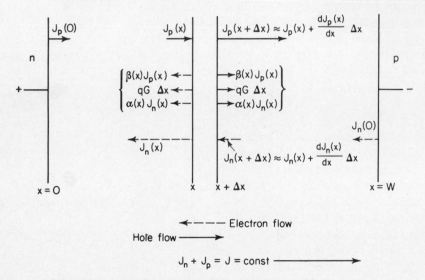

Fig. 1.17 Avalanche multiplication of electron and hole currents in the transition region of a reverse-biased *p-n* junction.

The symbols $\alpha(x)$ and $\beta(x)$ are assumed to be functions of the local electric field, and the effects of past collision history of electrons and holes are neglected.[21,22,23,24]

From the definitions above and Fig. 1.17, the change in hole current across the incremental layer Δx is

$$J_p(x + \Delta x) - J_p(x) = \alpha(x)J_n(x)\,\Delta x + \beta(x)J_p(x)\,\Delta x + qG\,\Delta x$$

or

$$\frac{dJ_p(x)}{dx} = \alpha(x)J_n(x) + \beta(x)J_p(x) + qG. \tag{1.108}$$

Similarly, for electrons

$$J_n(x + \Delta x) - J_n(x) = -\alpha(x)J_n(x)\,\Delta x - \beta(x)J_p(x)\,\Delta x - qG\,\Delta x$$

or

$$\frac{dJ_n(x)}{dx} = -\alpha(x)J_n(x) - \beta(x)J_p(x) - qG. \tag{1.109}$$

The negative signs on the right-hand side of (1.109) are in accord with the fact that electron current decreases as x increases (i.e., ionization phenomena cause electron current to increase to the left).

The total current J across the junction is independent of position, and is given by

$$J = J_n(x) + J_p(x) = \text{const.} \tag{1.110}$$

Equations (1.108), (1.109), and (1.110) may be combined to give

$$\frac{dJ_p(x)}{dx} + [\alpha(x) - \beta(x)]J_p(x) = \alpha(x)J + qG \tag{1.111}$$

and

$$\frac{dJ_n(x)}{dx} + [\alpha(x) - \beta(x)]J_n(x) = -\beta(x)J - qG. \tag{1.112}$$

These equations may be easily integrated if they are first multiplied by the integrating factor

$$\exp\left[\psi(x)\right] \equiv \exp\left\{\int^x [\alpha(\xi) - \beta(\xi)]\, d\xi\right\}$$

and are rewritten as

$$\frac{d}{dx}\{J_p(x)\exp\left[\psi(x)\right]\} = \exp\left[\psi(x)\right][\alpha(x)J + qG] \tag{1.113}$$

and

$$\frac{d}{dx}\{J_n(x)\exp\left[\psi(x)\right]\} = \exp\left[\psi(x)\right][-\beta(x)J - qG]. \tag{1.114}$$

If (1.113) is integrated from 0 to x, the hole current $J_p(x)$ at x is given as

$$J_p(x) = \exp\left[-\psi(x)\right]\left\{J_{p0} + \int_0^x [\alpha(\xi)J + qG]\exp\left[\psi(\xi)\right] d\xi\right\}, \tag{1.115}$$

where J_{p0} is the diffusion current of holes entering the left side of the junction transition region, and ξ is a dummy variable of integration substituted for x. Electron current $J_n(x)$ at x is given by integrating (1.114) from W to x, and is given as

$$J_n(x) = \exp\left[-\psi(x)\right]\left\{J_{n0}\exp\left[\psi(w)\right] + \int_x^W [\beta(\xi)J + qG]\exp\left[\psi(\xi)\right]d\xi\right\}, \tag{1.116}$$

where J_{n0} is the diffusion current of electrons entering the right-hand side of the junction transition region. Finally, from (1.110), (1.115), and (1.116) the total junction current J is

$$J = \frac{\exp\left[-\psi(w)\right]\left\{J_{p0} + J_{n0}\exp\left[\psi(w)\right] + \int_0^w qG\exp\left[\psi(\xi)\right]d\xi\right\}}{1 - \exp\left[-\psi(w)\right]\left\{\int_0^w \alpha(\xi)\exp\left[\psi(\xi)\right]d\xi\right\}} \tag{1.117}$$

When the denominator of equation (1.117) approaches zero, J tends to increase without limit and, by definition, breakdown occurs.

If we make the assumption that the electron and hole ionization coefficients are nearly equal; i.e., $\alpha(x) \approx \beta(x)$, then equation (1.117) becomes

$$J = \frac{J_{n0} + J_{p0} + \int_0^W qG\,dx}{1 - \int_0^W \alpha(x)\,dx}. \tag{1.118}$$

Equation (1.118) can be written in the form

$$J = M\left(J_{n0} + J_{p0} + \int_0^W qG\,dx\right), \tag{1.119}$$

where M is defined as the multiplication factor

$$M = \frac{1}{1 - \int_0^W \alpha(x)\,dx}, \tag{1.120}$$

and the numerator of (1.118) obviously consists of the electron-diffusion, hole-diffusion, and generation components of current which are multiplied by the avalanche process. To determine under what conditions avalanche breakdown occurs, it is necessary to determine under what circumstances

$$\int_0^W \alpha(x)\,dx \to 1.$$

It should be noted that since $\alpha(x)$ is a function of electric field $\mathscr{E}$, moderate values of field which do not result in breakdown will result in a finite value of current multiplication M. The multiplied current can be expected to increase with applied voltage until a value of field is reached which results in $M \to \infty$, and the junction goes into breakdown.

In real cases multiplication and breakdown do not necessarily or often occur uniformly across the junction. Instead, breakdown frequently occurs at surface sites, at regions of high field concentration caused by geometrical irregularities (such as uneven planar windows), at metal precipitates or other junction flaws, and at various other gross imperfections which lead to local microplasmas. Means to obtain uniform rather than localized breakdown are constantly under study. For example, the recent introduction of surface contouring[25] has removed many of the past difficulties with surface breakdown and has made possible reliable, high-voltage, high-power (volume) breakdown devices. In the material that follows, we shall be concerned with uniform-bulk junction breakdown and refer the reader to the journal literature for detailed studies of localized breakdown.

1.9.2 Avalanche Breakdown in Planar p^+-n (n^+-p) Junctions

Above it was shown that avalanche breakdown occurs when

$$\int_0^W \alpha(x)\,dx = 1, \tag{1.121}$$

where W is the width of the junction space-charge layer and $\alpha(x)$ is the previously defined ionization coefficient. The problem which now confronts us is to find an expression for $\alpha(x)$ (known to be a function of field) which will allow us to calculate (1.121) and relate the breakdown voltage to the geometrical and doping properties of the junction.

The ionization coefficient $\alpha(\mathscr{E})$ is extremely difficult to calculate from first principles. However, from various experimental studies[23] it is known that the effective ionization rate for holes and electrons in silicon can be represented by

$$\alpha(\mathscr{E}) = A \exp\left(\frac{-B}{|\mathscr{E}|}\right) \qquad (1.122)$$

where (in silicon) $A = 9 \times 10^5$ cm^{-1} and $B = 1.8 \times 10^6$ v/cm. Although in silicon (and germanium) the ionization rate for holes is substantially different from that for electrons, they contribute essentially equally at breakdown.[21,22,23] Thus an effective $\alpha(\mathscr{E})$ can be used in breakdown analyses.

Before (1.121) can be evaluated in its present form, the dependence of (1.122) on field $\mathscr{E}$ must be converted to dependence on position x. This is accomplished by solving Poisson's equation (ignoring mobile charge)

$$\frac{d\mathscr{E}}{dx} = \frac{q(N_d - N_a)}{K\epsilon_0}, \qquad (1.123)$$

where

$K = 11.8$ for silicon (dielectric constant).

$\epsilon_0 = 8.85 \times 10^{-14}$ farad/cm (free-space permittivity).

$q = 1.6 \times 10^{-19}$ coulomb (charge of electron).

N_d = donor at./cm^3.

N_a = acceptor at./cm^3.

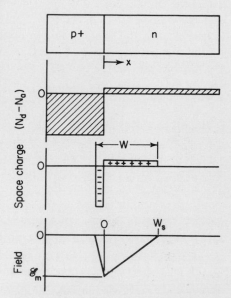

Fig. 1.18 Impurity, space charge, and field distributions in an abrupt p^+-n junction in reverse bias.

Consider now the model in Fig. 1.18 of a reverse-biased p^+-n junction. Integration of (1.123) from the center of the junction (point of maximum field $\mathscr{E}_m$) to an arbitrary point x in the n region yields

$$\int_{\mathscr{E}_m}^{\mathscr{E}(x)} d\mathscr{E} = \frac{q(N_d - N_a)}{K\epsilon_0} \int_0^x dx \qquad (1.124)$$

or

$$\mathscr{E}(x) = \mathscr{E}_m + \frac{q(N_d - N_a)}{K\epsilon_0}\, x. \qquad (1.125)$$

If we define

$$W_S \equiv - \frac{\mathscr{E}_m K \epsilon_0}{q(N_d - N_a)}, \tag{1.126}$$

then the field in the junction transition region as a function of position becomes

$$\mathscr{E}(x) = \mathscr{E}_m \left(1 - \frac{x}{W_s} \right) \tag{1.127}$$

and is obviously zero at $x = W_s$. At this point (1.127) could be substituted into (1.122) to give the ionization coefficient as a function of position. This will be more convenient later, after $\mathscr{E}_m$ and W_s are related to the total voltage V across the junction.

The total voltage V (built-in voltage plus applied voltage, $V_0 + V_a$) supported by the depletion layer (space-charge layer) is

$$V = - \int_0^{W_s} \mathscr{E}(x) \, dx \tag{1.128}$$

or with the aid of (1.127)

$$V = - \frac{\mathscr{E}_m W_s}{2}. \tag{1.129}$$

Since $\mathscr{E}_m$ is a negative quantity (Fig. 1.18), equation (1.129) shows that the voltage at W_s is a large positive quantity (as it must be for reverse bias). It should be noted that (1.128) and (1.129) ignore the voltage across the left-hand p^+ portion ($x < 0$) of the depletion region. The reader can show (by remembering that the amounts of negative and positive space charges are equal) that this is true only if the p^+ region is much more heavily doped than the n-region. From (1.126) and (1.129) the upper limit in the integral of (1.121) becomes

$$W \approx W_s = \sqrt{\frac{2VK\epsilon_0}{q(N_d - N_a)}}, \tag{1.130}$$

and the maximum field $\mathscr{E}_m$ becomes

$$\mathscr{E}_m = - \sqrt{\frac{2Vq(N_d - N_a)}{K\epsilon_0}}. \tag{1.131}$$

If equation (1.127) for the electric field is substituted into (1.122), then (1.122) becomes

$$\alpha(\mathscr{E}) = \alpha(x) = A \exp - \left[\frac{B}{|\mathscr{E}_m|(1 - x/W_s)} \right]. \tag{1.132}$$

By means of the binomial expansion the exponent of (1.132) can be written

$$\frac{B}{|\mathscr{E}_m|} \frac{1}{(1 - x/W_s)} = \frac{B}{|\mathscr{E}_m|} \left[1 + \frac{x}{W_s} + \left(\frac{x}{W_s} \right)^2 + \cdots \right]. \tag{1.133}$$

Since avalanche is a high-field phenomenon, there is not much of a contribution to the process near $x = W_s$. In other words, the main contribution to the integral of (1.121) is near the center of the junction, where $\mathscr{E}$ and $\alpha(\mathscr{E})$ are large. Hence, only the first two terms of (1.133) must be retained and

$$1 \approx \int_0^{W_s} A \exp\left[\frac{-B}{|\mathscr{E}_m|}\left(1 + \frac{x}{W_s}\right)\right] dx. \qquad (1.134)$$

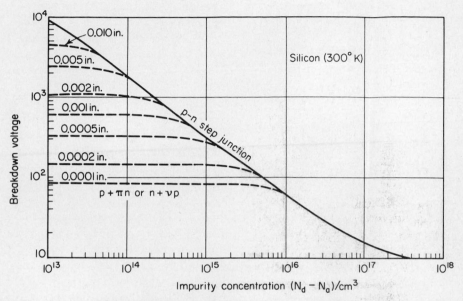

Fig. 1.19 Avalanche breakdown in silicon *p-n*; p^+-π-n^+, and p^+-v-n^+ junctions.

A straightforward integration of (1.134) yields

$$1 \approx \frac{AW_s|\mathscr{E}_m|}{B} \exp\left(\frac{-B}{|\mathscr{E}_m|}\right)\left[1 - \exp\left(\frac{-B}{|\mathscr{E}_m|}\right)\right]. \qquad (1.135)$$

If equations (1.130) and (1.131) for W_s and $|\mathscr{E}_m|$ are substituted into (1.135), the breakdown voltage V is given as a function of the net impurity concentration $(N_d - N_a)$ and is shown as the solid line in Fig. 1.19. The breakdown voltage can be related to resistivity by means of

$$\rho = \frac{1}{q\mu(N_d - N_a)} \qquad (1.136)$$

or by means of the data presented in Figs. 1.19 and 1.11.

50   Semiconductor and *p-n* Junction Properties

1.9.3 AVALANCHE BREAKDOWN IN PLANAR p^+-ν-n^+ AND p^+-π-n^+ JUNCTIONS

The final example of interest to us is the p^+-i-n^+ diode, or, more realistically, the p^+-ν-n^+ or p^+-π-n^+ diode, where ν refers to weakly n-type material and π to weakly p-type material. For purposes of analysis, consider the p^+-ν-n^+ diode shown in Fig. 1.20. When reverse bias is applied to this structure, avalanche breakdown can occur in either of two manners. As voltage is applied, positive space charge spreads rapidly from $x = 0$ to the right into the ν-region. If the net donor concentration $(N_d - N_a)$ in the ν-region is sufficiently large and the ν-region is of large enough extent W_i, breakdown can occur in the manner described above for the p^+-n junction. In this case the space charge in the ν-region spreads to the right a distance, given by equation (1.130), which is less than W_i. The second case, the one of interest here, occurs when the space charge spreads through the ν-region and into the n^+-region at breakdown. This case, the one shown in Fig. 1.20, is the one to be considered in the analysis below.

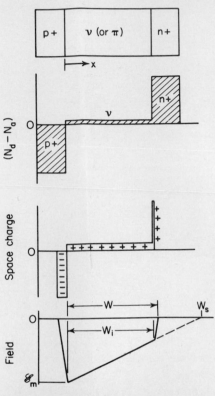

Fig. 1.20 Impurity, space charge, and field distributions in p^+-ν-n^+ junction.

Beginning again with equation (1.123) and integrating from $x = 0$ to the right, we have

$$\mathscr{E}(x) = \mathscr{E}_m + \frac{q(N_d - N_a)_\nu}{K\epsilon_0}\, x, \quad x < W_i$$

$$= \mathscr{E}_m + \frac{q(N_d - N_a)_\nu}{K\epsilon_0}\, W_i + \frac{q(N_d - N_a)_{n+}}{K\epsilon_0}\, (x - W_i), \quad x > W_i. \quad (1.137)$$

Equation (1.137) shows that the electric field decreases linearly, as shown in the lower figure of Fig. 1.20 and can be represented from $x = 0$ to $x = W_i$ by

$$\mathscr{E}(x) = \mathscr{E}_m\left(1 - \frac{x}{W_s}\right), \quad (1.138)$$

where, as shown in the figure, W_s is far to the right of W_i and is simply a computational aid. Since $-dV/dx = \mathscr{E}(x)$, integration of (1.137) gives

$$V(W) = -\mathscr{E}_m W + \frac{q(N_d - N_a)_v}{2K\epsilon_0}(W - W_i)^2 - \frac{q(N_d - N_a)_v}{2K\epsilon_0} W^2$$
$$- \frac{q(N_d - N_a)_{n+}}{2K\epsilon_0}(W - W_i)^2, \quad (1.139)$$

and integration of (1.138) gives

$$V \approx V(W_i) = -\mathscr{E}_m\left(W_i - \frac{W_i^2}{2W_s}\right). \quad (1.140)$$

Both of these expressions are based upon the assumption that the p^+-region is very heavily doped and supports little or none of the voltage. Equation (1.140) also makes use of the assumption that the n^+-region is similarly heavily doped and supports little or none of the voltage. The same assumption in (1.139) gives

$$V \approx V(W_i) = -\mathscr{E}_m W_i - \frac{q(N_d - N_a)_v}{2K\epsilon_0} W_i^2$$

or

$$\mathscr{E}_m = -\frac{1}{W_i}\left[V + \frac{q(N_d - N_a)_v}{2K\epsilon_0} W_i^2\right], \quad (1.141)$$

and from (1.141) and (1.140)

$$W_s = \left[\frac{VK\epsilon_0}{W_i q(N_d - N_a)_v} + \frac{W_i}{2}\right]. \quad (1.142)$$

Equation (1.141) shows that the maximum field becomes directly proportional to the applied voltage when the depletion layer punches through to the n^+-region or, in other words, when (1.130) equals W_i.

As before, the conditions under which breakdown occurs are determined by evaluating the integral of (1.121). Thus, from (1.121), (1.122), (1.138), and the same binomial expansion used previously,

$$1 \approx \int_0^{W_i}\left\{A \exp\left[-\frac{B}{|\mathscr{E}_m|}\left(1 + \frac{x}{W_s}\right)\right]\right\} dx. \quad (1.143)$$

Integration of (1.143) leads to

$$1 \approx \frac{AW_s|\mathscr{E}_m|}{B}\exp\left(-\frac{B}{|\mathscr{E}_m|}\right)\left\{1 - \exp\left[-\left(\frac{B}{|\mathscr{E}_m|}\right)\left(\frac{W_i}{W_s}\right)\right]\right\}. \quad (1.144)$$

Since

$$W_s = -\frac{\mathscr{E}_m K\epsilon_0}{q(N_d - N_a)_v}, \quad (1.145)$$

equation (1.144) can be rewritten

$$1 \approx -\frac{A\mathscr{E}_m^2 K\epsilon_0}{Bq(N_d - N_a)_v}\exp\left(-\frac{B}{|\mathscr{E}_m|}\right)\left\{1 - \exp\left[\frac{Bq(N_d - N_a)_v W_i}{\mathscr{E}_m^2 K\epsilon_0}\right]\right\}. \quad (1.146)$$

For given impurity concentration $(N_d - N_a)$ and given W_i, equation (1.146) can be used to determine $\mathscr{E}_m$, and in turn $\mathscr{E}_m$, W_i, and $(N_d - N_a)$ can be substituted into (1.141) to determine the avalanche-breakdown voltage V. These results are shown graphically in Fig. 1.19. Finally, the reader can easily show from (1.121) and (1.122) that the avalanche-breakdown voltage in a p^+-i-n^+-structure $[\mathscr{E}(x) = V/W_i = \text{const}]$ is

$$V = \frac{BW_i}{\ln (AW_i)}. \tag{1.147}$$

In concluding this section, we should mention that increasing the temperature of a *p-n* (or *p-i-n*) junction increases the voltage at which avalanche breakdown occurs. As temperature increases, the increase in thermal scattering which follows causes a decrease in the ionization probability, and thus leads to an increase in voltage required for breakdown. Ordinarily, manufacturers supply experimentally determined values of the temperature coefficient of avalanche breakdown for devices in which such data are important.

In the discussions above many of the more subtle and detailed features of avalanche breakdown, e.g., hot electron effects and microplasma and localized breakdown phenomena, have been ignored. The interested reader is referred to the journal literature cited earlier for detailed discussions of such topics.

1.10 Control and Variation of Alpha

Fundamental to the operation of the *p-n-p-n* class of devices is the mechanism of variable alpha, i.e., variation in efficiency of minority-carrier injection (γ), transport (β), and collection as a function of a parameter such as collector current (or base-region charge). Furthermore, in order to design *p-n-p-n* devices for turn-off gain (in addition to turn-on gain), it is desirable to control and restrict one alpha (by controlling γ or β) to rather low values (0.1 or less). Hence, in this section we shall consider some of the more representative mechanisms which can govern the magnitude and variation in alpha. The avalanche process described in the previous section is an obvious means of multiplying minority carriers arriving at the collector (at higher voltages) and will not be discussed further in this section as a means of increasing alpha.[1]

1.10.1 TRANSPORT EFFICIENCY β

Turning to the exact form of equation (1.81), we see that the transport efficiency

$$\beta = \frac{1}{\cosh W/L_p} \tag{1.81}$$

across a uniformly doped base region (and hence one of the alphas) may be restricted to rather low values by employing a wide base region W or by "killing" the lifetime (high density of recombination centers) and reducing the diffusion length L_p (or L_n). At higher injection levels, as the recombination centers tend toward saturation, the minority-carrier lifetime in the base region can increase and cause an increase in alpha. This effect may be desirable, if it is sought as a means of switching on a p-n-p-n switch; it may be undesirable if deep-level doping is sought as a means of restricting alpha to low values, or if it is also sought as a means of keeping the base minority-carrier charge level low for purposes of rapid turn-off.

Another means by which minority-carrier transport may be enhanced (and varied) across a base region is by an applied electric field which can be made to increase with current.[26] Let us consider the structure shown in Fig. 1.21, which is essentially a long (W_n) n-type bar that is driven at the bottom by a high-alpha (α_n) n-p-n transistor (with long collector region W_n). Since α_n is near unity, most of the current $I \left(I \sim I_b \dfrac{\alpha_n}{1 - \alpha_n} \right)$ collected at J_c is electron current which establishes an ohmic field $\mathscr{E} \sim \rho_n I/A$ in W_n. The field $\mathscr{E}$ (directed from top to bottom) causes a downward hole-drift rate $v_d = \mu_p \mathscr{E}$ and yields a transit time $t = W_n/v_d$. The hole-transport efficiency β_p from top to bottom of the bar can be approximated, if the usual exponential recombination is assumed, as

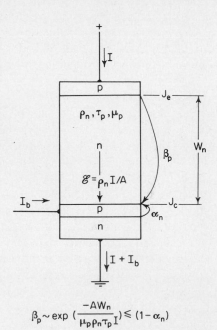

$$\beta_p \sim \exp \left(\frac{-AW_n}{\mu_p \rho_n \tau_p I} \right) \lessgtr (1 - \alpha_n)$$

Fig. 1.21 Field $\mathscr{E} \sim \rho_n I/A$ enhanced minority carrier (holes) transport β_p across a long base region W_n.

$$\beta_p \sim \exp \left(-\frac{t}{\tau_p} \right) = \exp \left(\frac{-AW_n}{\mu_p \rho_n \tau_p I} \right) \leq (1 - \alpha_n), \qquad (1.148)$$

where τ_p is the hole lifetime in the long n-type bar W_n (or second base in a p-n-p-n switch). [The inequality on the right of (1.148) is the p-n-p-n switch condition.]

Holes may be injected at the top end of the long bar from a p-type region as shown in Fig. 1.21, or from a metal contact or almost any type of imperfect "ohmic" contact. The approximate equation (1.148) shows that the transport efficiency (and alpha, provided the top region or contact is assumed to have unit injection efficiency) increases as the base drive I_b and thus collector current I is increased, and may obviously be made greater by increasing ρ_n or

τ_p and by decreasing W_n. The minority-carrier transport and decay in the long base region W_n not only affects the transport efficiency β_p but also places an obvious limitation on device response time. If a step input signal I_b is applied to the device, a delay time and a rise time are associated with the response of the high-alpha *n-p-n* transistor section of the device and a further delay (before the device turns on) associated with the minority-carrier transit time t in the long base region W_n. The broad extent and heavy conductivity modulation that occurs in the wide base region W_n of practical devices which are commonly made in the configuration of Fig. 1.21 result in considerable charge storage and long turn-off time, both of which are undesirable for high operating speed.

1.10.2 INJECTION EFFICIENCY γ

Of the mechanisms for achieving alphas which vary with current (or charge), perhaps the most useful and flexible for design purposes are those based upon variation in minority-carrier injection efficiency γ. Not only can the injection efficiency be made to vary (with current) owing to the internal structure (e.g., recombination centers) of an emitter junction, but also it can be made variable by shorting an external resistor across the junction, by shorting the underlying base region directly to emitter[27] (shorted-emitter, geometrical means), or by introducing gross shorting flaws or metal precipitates throughout the junction (nonideal junction). The absolute magnitude of the injection efficiency may be restricted to low values (e.g., for turn-off gain devices[28]) by utilizing extremely thin but heavily doped (for low ohmic losses) emitter junctions. From the discussion concerning equation (1.80) and from equation (1.80) itself, it is obvious that an *extremely* thin emitter region leads to an emitter layer of relatively high transverse sheet resistivity and hence leads to low injection efficiency, as is desired in many practical-device designs.

Inherent in the theory of *p-n* junctions is the fact that in forward bias the current (and minority-carrier injection) does not rise sharply until a voltage of the order of the built-in voltage V_0 is applied to the junction. That is, the junction exhibits slight minority-carrier injection and high impedance until the voltage across the junction approaches $\sim V_0$. It follows immediately that an external resistor, when connected across an emitter junction, shunts and carries most of the current at low voltages. As the current through the combination of emitter junction and resistive shunt is increased and the voltage approaches V_0, the junction becomes highly conductive, more so than the resistive shunt, and a larger fraction of the current is carried by minority-carrier injection. Thus, the emitter-injection efficiency increases as the total current increases through *p-n* junction and external resistive shunt.†

† This mechanism for achieving variable γ and alpha was considered and abandoned as unnecessary in the early phase of the work at Bell Telephone Laboratories (1954–55) which led to the first practical silicon *p-n-p-n* switches.

A refinement of the idea of using an external resistive shunt across a *p-n* junction to achieve variable injection efficiency is the shorted emitter.[27] In the shorted emitter, the emitter region is shorted along its periphery to the underlying base region by a common metal contact. As current is driven through the device, current in the base region (under the emitter) flows transversely toward the shorted region at the periphery of the emitter and flows in or out of the device via the common shorting ohmic contact that overlaps emitter and base. The transverse base current under the emitter develops a transverse voltage which eventually is sufficient to bias the center of the emitter junction into heavy forward conduction (and injection). At this stage of operation, the transverse bias current (flowing around the emitter) represents a smaller percentage of the total current than does the injected current supplied by the center of the emitter. In addition to the fact that a shorted emitter exhibits current-variable minority-carrier injection, it also allows fabrication of several unique forms of symmetrical and asymmetrical *p-n-p-n* devices and permits design of *p-n-p-n* devices with reduced temperature and transient turn-on sensitivity.[27]

The ideal *p-n* junction theory presented earlier made use of the assumption that little or no generation or recombination charge occurred in the junction transition region. This assumption implies that all current across the junction is diffusion current. In real junctions, e.g., silicon junctions, this assumption is not accurate. Deep-level recombination-generation centers within the junction transition region (near the surface or within the bulk semiconductor) contribute what may be regarded as a shunt or parallel component of current that may, under certain circumstances, predominate over normal diffusion currents (reverse-saturation or forward-injection). This mechanism may be viewed roughly as a nonlinear resistive shunt which, in the forward direction, carries the current until minority-carrier injection processes become significantly operative (i.e., until the recombination centers are overwhelmed and diffusion currents predominate—hence variable injection efficiency).

At low current levels, before significant injection, a *p-n* junction operating under the influence of recombination-generation centers is somewhat comparable to the *p-i-n* diode.[29] In the case of the *p-i-n* diode, current in the forward direction is carried by recombination (at recombination-generation centers) of electrons and holes which are injected from either side into the center *i*-region. Carriers injected into the *i*-region do not arrive as minority carriers at the end regions, as would be required for the *p-i-n* to function as an emitter junction. Similar behavior obtains at low-current levels in a junction with appreciable recombination centers, as is shown quantitatively below.

Consider the diagram of the forward-biased junction shown in Fig. 1.22. Holes from the *p*-side and electrons from the *n*-side are injected into the space-charge region (transition region). Those carriers which diffuse through the space-charge layer give rise to the normal diffusion current. Once they have traversed the space-charge region, they become excess minority carriers (compensated by excess majority carriers drawn in to preserve neutrality) and diffuse in relatively field-free regions until they recombine or are collected. Those injected carriers which recombine in the space-charge region constitute a recombination current given as

$$J_{rg} = q \int R \, dx, \qquad (1.149)$$

where the integration is taken over the space-charge layer, and, from (1.45) and the definitions in Sec. 1.6, the recombination rate is

$$R = \frac{np - n_i^2}{\tau_{p0}(n + n_1) + \tau_{n0}(p + p_1)}. \qquad (1.150)$$

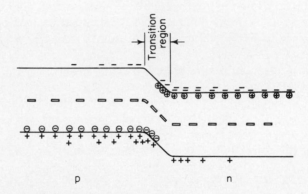

Fig. 1.22 Forward-biased *p-n* junction.

In expression (1.150), as has been mentioned earlier,

n = density of electrons in the conduction band.

p = density of holes in the valence band.

n_i = density of electrons or holes in intrinsic material.

τ_{p0} = lifetime of holes in strongly *n*-type material.

τ_{n0} = lifetime of electrons in strongly *p*-type material.

p_1 = density of holes in the valence band if the Fermi level were located at the energy level of the recombination centers.

n_1 = density of electrons in the conduction band if the Fermi level were located at the energy level of the recombination centers.

The problem now at hand is to substitute (1.150) into (1.149) and evaluate the resulting integral for the recombination current J_{rg}.

In order to integrate (1.149), we must have some idea of how the various electron- and hole-density quantities in (1.150) vary as a function of position.

From equations (1.30) and (1.31) and Sec. 1.6 [also equations (1.27) and (1.29)] the electron and hole densities of interest in (1.150) may be expressed as

$$n = n_i \exp\left\{\frac{q}{kT}\left[\psi(x) - \varphi_n\right]\right\}, \qquad (1.151)$$

$$p = n_i \exp\left\{\frac{q}{kT}\left[\varphi_p - \psi(x)\right]\right\}, \qquad (1.152)$$

$$n_1 = n_i \exp\left[\frac{1}{kT}(E_t - E_i)\right], \qquad (1.153)$$

and

$$p_1 = n_i \exp\left[\frac{1}{kT}(E_i - E_t)\right], \qquad (1.154)$$

where φ_p is the quasi-Fermi potential[2,5] (see Sec. 1.8) for holes, φ_n is the quasi-Fermi potential for electrons, $\psi(x)$ is the electrostatic potential as a function of position, E_i is the energy level corresponding to the Fermi level in an intrinsic crystal, and E_t is the energy level at which the recombination-generation centers are located. These expressions may be substituted in equation (1.150) to give

$$R = \frac{n_i^2\left\{\exp\left[\frac{q}{kT}(\varphi_p - \varphi_n)\right] - 1\right\}}{\tau_{n0}n_i\left(\exp\left\{\frac{q}{kT}\left[\varphi_p - \psi(x)\right]\right\} + \exp\left[\frac{1}{kT}(E_i - E_t)\right]\right)}$$
$$+ \tau_{p0}n_i\left(\exp\left\{\frac{q}{kT}\left[\psi(x) - \varphi_n\right]\right\} + \exp\left\{\frac{1}{kT}(E_t - E_i)\right\}\right). \qquad (1.155)$$

By making use of the identities

$$\varphi_p \equiv \frac{\varphi_p + \varphi_n}{2} + \frac{\varphi_p - \varphi_n}{2}$$

and

$$\varphi_n \equiv \frac{\varphi_p + \varphi_n}{2} - \frac{\varphi_p - \varphi_n}{2}$$

and, by considerable rearranging of (1.155), we obtain

$$R = \frac{n_i}{\sqrt{\tau_{p0}\tau_{n0}}} \frac{\sinh\left[\frac{q}{2kT}(\varphi_p - \varphi_n)\right]}{\cosh\left\{\frac{q}{kT}\left[\psi(x) - \frac{\varphi_p + \varphi_n}{2}\right] + \ln\sqrt{\frac{\tau_{p0}}{\tau_{n0}}}\right\}}$$
$$+ \exp\left[\frac{-q}{2kT}(\varphi_p - \varphi_n)\right]\cosh\left(\frac{E_t - E_i}{kT} + \ln\sqrt{\frac{\tau_{p0}}{\tau_{n0}}}\right). \qquad (1.156)$$

An exact solution for the recombination-generation current J_{rg} requires that equation (1.156) be integrated over the junction transition region (space-charge layer). Such a solution requires that φ_p, φ_n, and $\psi(x)$ be known over the whole region of interest. Exact determination of these functions is extremely difficult and will not be considered here. As indicated in Fig. 1.23, φ_p and φ_n are very nearly constant through the junction transition region,[2,5] and the difference in Fermi potentials $(\varphi_p - \varphi_n)$ throughout the transition region is very nearly equal to the applied voltage V_a. As we mentioned in Sec. 1.6, recombination-generation centers are most effective when near the middle of the forbidden gap. Hence, to simplify our present problem, let us assume that $E_t = E_i$ or $n_1 = p_1 = n_i$. For convenience and simplicity, let us also assume that $\tau_{p0} = \tau_{n0} \equiv \tau$. Thus, equation (1.156) reduces to

$$R = \frac{n_i}{\tau} \frac{\sinh \dfrac{qV_a}{2kT}}{\cosh \left\{ \dfrac{q}{kT} \left[\psi(x) - \dfrac{\varphi_p + \varphi_n}{2} \right] \right\} + \exp \left(\dfrac{-qV_a}{2kT} \right)}. \qquad (1.157)$$

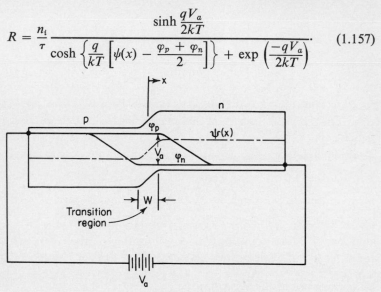

Fig. 1.23 Potential diagram of forward-biased *p-n* junction.

From the potential diagram sketched in Fig. 1.23, it is evident that as a first approximation (linear) the electrostatic potential $\psi(x)$ can be expressed as

$$\psi(x) = \frac{\varphi_p + \varphi_n}{2} + \left(\frac{V_0 - V_a}{W} \right) x, \quad -\frac{W}{2} < x < \frac{W}{2}, \qquad (1.158)$$

where W is the width of the space-charge layer and V_0 is the built-in voltage (the difference in the electrostatic potential on *p*-side and *n*-side at zero bias). The second term on the right of (1.158) accounts for the lowering of the junction potential barrier by the applied bias V_a. Over most of the space-charge region

$$\cosh \left\{ \frac{q}{kT} \left[\psi(x) - \frac{\varphi_p + \varphi_n}{2} \right] \right\} \gg 1,$$

and for any value of forward bias V_a

$$\exp \left(\frac{-qV_a}{2kT} \right) < 1$$

and is much less than unity for forward biases greater than kT/q. Under these conditions and with the aid of (1.158), equation (1.157) becomes

$$R \approx \frac{n_i}{\tau} \frac{\sinh \left(\frac{qV_a}{2kT} \right)}{\cosh \left[\frac{q}{kT} \left(\frac{V_0 - V_a}{W} \right) x \right]}. \tag{1.159}$$

From (1.149) and (1.159), the space-charge recombination current is given as

$$J_{rg} \approx \frac{qn_i}{\tau} \sinh \left(\frac{qV_a}{2kT} \right) \int_{-W/2}^{W/2} \frac{dx}{\cosh \left[\frac{q}{kT} \left(\frac{V_0 - V_a}{W} \right) x \right]} \tag{1.160}$$

or

$$J_{rg} \approx \frac{qn_i}{\tau} \sinh \left(\frac{qV_a}{2kT} \right) \frac{2kT}{q} \left(\frac{W}{V_0 - V_a} \right) \tan^{-1} \left[\exp \frac{q}{kT} \left(\frac{V_0 - V_a}{W} \right) x \right] \Big|_{-W/2}^{W/2}. \tag{1.161}$$

By making use of equation (1.67) for the built-in potential, we obtain

$$V_0 = \frac{kT}{q} \ln \frac{p_p}{p_n} \approx \frac{kT}{q} \ln \frac{N_a N_d}{n_i^2}, \tag{1.162}$$

where, as before, N_a is the acceptor doping concentration on the p-side of the junction, N_d is the donor doping concentration on the n-side of the junction, and n_i is the intrinsic carrier concentration. Typical values of V_0 in silicon junctions range from about 0.5 to 0.8 v. Since at room temperature $q/kT \approx 40$, we see that, for values of V_a up to about 0.5 v,

$$\tan^{-1} \left\{ \exp \left[\frac{q}{kT} \left(\frac{V_0 - V_a}{W} \right) x \right] \right\} \Big|_{-W/2}^{W/2} \approx \frac{\pi}{2}$$

so that (1.161) becomes

$$J_{rg} \approx \pi \left(\frac{qn_i W}{\tau} \right) \left(\frac{kT/q}{V_0 - V_a} \right) \sinh \left(\frac{qV_a}{2kT} \right). \tag{1.163}$$

A more careful derivation[30] of the recombination-generation current J_{rg} yields essentially an expression like (1.163) with, however, numerical correction factors which differ from the factor π in (1.163).

From equation (1.163) it is evident that the space-charge recombination-generation current varies essentially as $\exp (qV_a/2kT)$, compared to diffusion currents, which vary as $\exp (qV_a/kT)$. Data are presented in the journal literature[31,32] which show that at relatively low voltages the recombination-generation current, as we have stated earlier, may predominate. As more voltage is applied and more current flows through a forward-biased junction, diffusion current begins to take over. This leads to an increase in injection efficiency (and hence alpha) and is, of course, a variable alpha mechanism which is controlled by the kind and number of deep levels (flaws, traps, recombination centers, etc.) in the emitter junction transition region.

Besides the fact that current increase leads to variable alpha as diffusion current takes over from recombination-generation current, temperature increase leads to similar behavior. This is evident from the fact that diffusion current increases as $n_i^2(T)$ [see equation (1.74) and remember that $n_p \approx n_i^2/N_a$ and $p_n \approx n_i^2/N_d$], and from (1.163) recombination-generation current increases as $n_i(T)$.

Although we have considered some of the more representative, more common mechanisms serving to give alphas which vary with current (or other parameters), our discussion has not been exhaustive. Two mechanisms which are presently rather unimportant but which may assume greater importance in the future are tunnel-junction emitters[33] and double-injection emitters.[34,35] The former provides variable injection efficiency by virtue of the fact that up to a certain magnitude all current flow is caused by majority-carrier tunneling, whereupon switching occurs to the usual minority-carrier injection mechanism. The double-injection emitter consists of a *p-i-n* structure in which, at higher current levels, lifetime increase makes possible hole transport across the *i*-region and injection into the *n*-region. This behavior to some extent resembles the behavior of the conventional *p-n* junction when it is operating under the influence of deep-level recombination-generation centers.

REFERENCES

1. J. L. Moll, M. Tanenbaum, J. M. Goldey, and N. Holonyak, Jr., "*p-n-p-n* Transistor Switches," *Proc. I.R.E.*, Vol. **44** (September, 1956), pp. 1174–82.

2. W. Shockley, *Electrons and Holes in Semiconductors*. Princeton, N.J.: D. Van Nostrand Co., Inc., 1950.

3. R. A. Smith, *Semiconductors*. London: Cambridge University Press, 1959.

4. N. B. Hannay, *Semiconductors*. New York: Reinhold Publishing Corp., 1959.

5. A. Nussbaum, *Semiconductor Device Physics*. Englewood Cliffs, N.J.: Prentice-Hall, Inc., 1962.

6. F. Herman, "The Electronic Energy Band Structure of Silicon and Germanium," *Proc. I.R.E.*, Vol. **43** (December, 1955), pp. 1703–32.

7. R. A. Smith, *Wave Mechanics of Crystalline Solids*. London: Chapman and Hall, Ltd., 1961.

8. R. N. Hall, "Electron-Hole Recombination in Germanium," *Phys. Rev.*, Vol. **87** (July 15, 1952), p. 387.

9. W. Shockley and W. T. Read, Jr., "Statistics of the Recombination of Holes and Electrons," *Phys. Rev.*, Vol. **87** (September 1, 1952), pp. 835–42.

10. J. J. Ebers and J. L. Moll, "Large-Signal Behavior of Junction Transistors," *Proc. I.R.E.*, Vol. **42** (December, 1954), pp. 1761–72.

11. B. M. Boodak, A. A. Samarskii, and A. N. Tichonov, *Collection of Problems on Mathematical Physics*, in Russian. Moscow: State Publishing House of Technical and Theoretical Literature, 1956, p. 59 and p. 319.

12. R. H. Kingston, "Switching Time in Junction Diodes and Junction Transistors," *Proc. I.R.E.*, Vol. **42** (May, 1954), pp. 829–34.

13. B. Lax and S. F. Neustadter, "Transient Response of a *p-n* Junction," *Jour. Appl. Physics*, Vol. **25** (September, 1954), pp. 1148–54.

14. R. Beaufoy and J. J. Sparks, "The Junction Transistor as a Charge Controlled Device," *A.T.E. Journal*, Vol. **B** (October, 1957), pp. 310–27.

15. S. S. Hakim, *Junction Transistor Circuit Analysis*. New York: John Wiley and Sons, Inc., 1962.

16. A. van der Ziel, *Solid State Physical Electronics*. Englewood Cliffs, N.J.: Prentice-Hall, Inc., 1957.

17. J. L. Moll and I. M. Ross, "The Dependence of Transistor Parameters on the Distribution of Base Layer Resistivity," *Proc. I.R.E.*, Vol. **44** (January, 1956), pp. 72–78.

18. K. B. McAfee, E. J. Ryder, W. Shockley, and M. Sparks, "Observation of Zener Current in Germanium *p-n* Junctions," *Phys. Rev.*, Vol. **83** (August 1, 1951), pp. 650–51.

19. K. G. McKay and K. B. McAfee, "Electron Multiplication in Silicon and Germanium," *Phys. Rev.*, Vol. **91** (September, 1953), pp. 1079–84.

20. K. G. McKay, "Avalanche Breakdown in Silicon," *Phys. Rev.*, Vol. **94** (May, 1954), pp. 877–84.

21. S. L. Miller, "Avalanche Breakdown in Germanium," *Phys. Rev.*, Vol. **99** (August 15, 1955), pp. 1234–41.

22. S. L. Miller, "Ionization Rates for Holes and Electrons in Silicon," *Phys. Rev.*, Vol. **105** (February, 1957), pp. 1246–49.

23. A. G. Chynoweth, "Ionization Rates for Electrons and Holes in Silicon," *Phys. Rev.*, Vol. **109** (March, 1958), pp. 1537–40.

24. P. A. Wolff, "Theory of Electron Multiplication in Silicon and Germanium," *Phys. Rev.*, Vol. **95** (September 15, 1954), pp. 1415–20.

25. R. L. Davies and F. E. Gentry, "Control of Electric Fields at the Surface of *p-n* Junctions," Electron Device Conference (PGED), October 26, 1962, Washington, D.C.

26. R. W. Aldrich and N. Holonyak, Jr., "Multi-terminal *p-n-p-n* Switches," *Proc. I.R.E.*, Vol. **46** (June, 1958), pp. 1236–39.

27. R. W. Aldrich and N. Holonyak, Jr., "Two-terminal Asymmetrical and Symmetrical Silicon Negative Resistance Switches," *Jour. Appl. Phys.*, Vol. **30** (November, 1959), pp. 1819–24.

28. J. M. Goldey, I. M. Mackintosh, and I. M. Ross, "Turn-Off Gain in *p-n-p-n* Triodes," *Solid-State Electronics*, Vol. 3 (March, 1961), pp. 119–22.

29. R. N. Hall, "Power Rectifiers and Transistors," *Proc. I.R.E.*, Vol. **40** (November, 1952), pp. 1512–18.

30. C. T. Sah, R. N. Noyce, and W. Shockley, "Carrier Generation and Recombination in *p-n* Junctions and *p-n* Junction Characteristics," *Proc. I.R.E.*, Vol. **45** (September, 1957), pp. 1228–43.

31. H. S. Veloric and M. B. Prince, "High-Voltage Conductivity-Modulated Silicon Rectifier," *Bell System Tech. Jour.*, Vol. **36** (July, 1957), pp. 975–1004.

32. A. E. Bakanowski and J. H. Forster, "Electrical Properties of Gold-Doped Diffused Silicon Computer Diodes," *Bell System Tech. Jour.*, Vol. **39** (January, 1960), pp. 87–105.

33. I. A. Lesk and H. A. Jensen, "Germanium *p-n* Junction-Tunnel Junction Combination Devices," *Solid-State Electronics*, Vol. **1** (July, 1960), pp. 183–87.

34. M. A. Lampert, "Injection Currents in Insulators," *Proc. I.R.E.*, Vol. **50** (August, 1962), pp. 1781–96.

35. N. Holonyak, Jr., "Double Injection Diodes and Related DI Phenomena in Semiconductors," *Proc. I.R.E.*, Vol. **50** (December, 1962), pp. 2421–28.

CHAPTER 2

THEORY OF *p-n-p-n* OPERATION

2.1 Introduction

p-n-p-n switches are bistable devices whose operation depends on an internal feedback mechanism. In many respects the electrical characteristics are similar to the gas thyratron or ignitron, having both high- and low-impedance states which are governed by the applied voltage, current, temperature, etc. However, in a *p-n-p-n* device, current is carried by holes and electrons instead of by electrons and ions. A description of the mechanism of operation and of the flow of holes and electrons through *p-n-p-n* devices is presented in this chapter. Extensive use and application is made of the concepts and equations developed in Chap. 1.

2.2 *p-n-p-n* Operation

Basically, a *p-n-p-n* device consists of at least four *p*- and *n*-layers, and three junctions designed so that the interaction between layers results in an electrical characteristic of the type shown in Fig. 2.1. Power switches with only four layers, three junctions, and three terminals are commonly called semiconductor controlled rectifiers (SCR). Diagrammatically, the simple *p-n-p-n* device, or SCR, can be represented as shown in Fig. 2.2.

At first glance, it would appear that with the anode terminal biased positively, $J1$ and $J3$ would be forward-biased, whereas $J2$ would be reverse-biased so that current flow would be blocked, resulting in a forward blocking state. However, transistor action will cause the device to behave like two transistors with current gains of α_{pnp} and α_{npn}, respectively, sharing a common

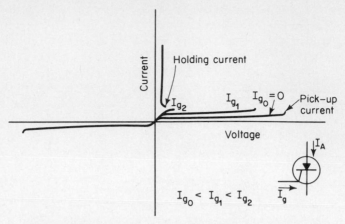

Fig. 2.1 Electrical characteristic of a simple *p-n-p-n* structure.

collector. The result is that each transistor section is supplied with base driving current by the collector current of its counterpart. As a consequence, positive feedback results, provided that the current gains of the two transistors are of sufficient magnitude. This positive-feedback loop causes both transistors to be driven into a saturated state so that the collector junction will no longer support the applied voltage; thus, the device switches to a low-voltage state. If the current gains of the two transistors do not rise sufficiently to cause saturation, then *J*2 will block the flow of current.

With a negative voltage applied to the anode, junctions *J*1 and *J*3 are reverse-biased and will block current, whereas *J*2 is forward-biased. Since

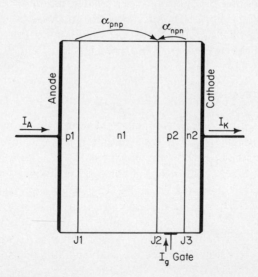

Fig. 2.2 Simple *p-n-p-n* structure.

there is no common collector, the two transistor sections cannot provide base current for each other, and the device will not switch.

The magnitudes of the current-gain parameters α_{pnp} and α_{npn} of the two transistor sections are dependent primarily on the current through it and secondarily on the voltage across it. In fact, bistable operation of the device is dependent on these alpha variations. Typically, alpha varies with emitter-current density, as shown in Fig. 2.3. The mechanisms which account for these changes in alpha with current, temperature, and voltage are described in Sec. 1.10. With the knowledge that alpha is a function of current through the device, we can develop a criterion for switching.

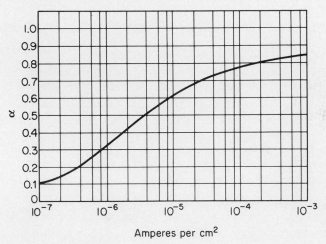

Fig. 2.3 Typical alpha variation with current density.

2.2.1 TRANSISTOR ANALOGUE

A primitive but easily understood analysis, which demonstrates the positive feedback action that results when a *p-n-p-n* device switches, can be carried out with the aid of a two-transistor analogue. By studying Fig. 2.2 we see that the device can be considered as an *n-p-n* and a *p-n-p* transistor connected with the collector of one transistor attached to the base of the other and vice versa, as shown in Figs. 2.4(a) and 2.4(b).

The relationship between emitter, collector, and base currents (I_E, I_C, and I_B, respectively) and the current-transfer factor α for a *p-n-p* transistor is shown in Fig. 2.5(a). The relationships for an *n-p-n* transistor are the same, except that the currents are reversed. From Fig. 2.4(b) it is evident that the collector of the *n-p-n* transistor provides base drive for the *p-n-p* transistor. Also, the collector of the *p-n-p* transistor along with gate current I_g supplies the base drive for the *n-p-n* transistor. Thus, a regeneration situation results when the total loop gain exceeds one.

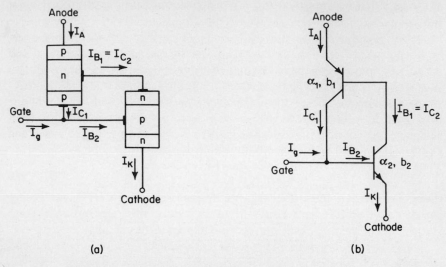

(a)   (b)

Fig. 2.4 Two-transistor analogue of *p-n-p-n* switch.

The base current of the *p-n-p* transistor is

$$I_{B_1} = (1 - \alpha_1)I_A - I_{CBO_1}, \tag{2.1}$$

which is supplied by the collector of the *n-p-n* transistor. However, the collector current of the *n-p-n* transistor is

$$I_{C_2} = \alpha_2 I_K + I_{CBO_2}. \tag{2.2}$$

By equating I_{B_1} and I_{C_2}, we obtain

$$(I - \alpha_1)I_A - I_{CBO_1} = \alpha_2 I_K + I_{CBO_2}. \tag{2.3}$$

Since $I_K = I_A + I_g$, equation (2.3) can be solved for

$$I_A = \frac{\alpha_2 I_g + I_{CBO_1} + I_{CBO_2}}{1 - \alpha_1 - \alpha_2}. \tag{2.4}$$

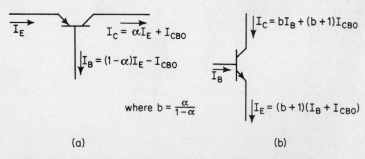

(a)   (b)

Fig. 2.5 Current versus alpha relationship for transistors.

If the base drive current $I_g + I_{C_1}$ is equated to the base current of the *n-p-n* transistor, exactly the same solution results. Thus, we see that a regenerative effect will occur when $\alpha_1 + \alpha_2 = 1$, i.e., that the denominator of equation (2.4) approaches zero. With increasing emitter current, the alphas of the device will increase (owing to internal mechanisms) and switching will occur, provided the gate drive raises the emitter-current densities to the point where the sum of the alphas is unity. Moreover, this condition can occur without gate drive by other means, such as exposure to a beam of light, or by a sufficient rise in either the device temperature or the anode voltage. The effect of these stimuli in causing the alphas to increase will be evident later when we consider the internal mechanisms of the device.

For those individuals more familiar with common-emitter operation of transistors, the derivation above may be made clearer by repeating it and using the common-emitter gain factor *b*. In this case, the relationship among emitter, collector, and base currents is as shown in Fig. 2.5(b).

Again, from Fig. 2.4(b), the base-current-to-collector-current relationship for the *p-n-p* transistor is

$$I_{C_1} = b_1 I_{B_1} + (b_1 + 1)I_{CBO_1} \tag{2.5}$$

and for the *n-p-n* transistor is

$$I_{C_2} = b_2 I_{B_2} + (b_2 + 1)I_{CBO_2}. \tag{2.6}$$

Since $I_{B_2} = I_g + I_{C_1}$,

$$I_{C_2} = b_2 I_g + b_2 I_{C_1} + (b_2 + 1)I_{CBO_2}. \tag{2.7}$$

Substituting equation (2.5) into equation (2.7) and noting that $I_{C_2} = I_{B_1}$ gives

$$I_{B_1} = b_2 I_g + b_2 b_1 I_{B_1} + b_2(b_1 + 1)I_{CBO_1} + (b_2 + 1)I_{CBO_2}. \tag{2.8}$$

Solving equation (2.8) for I_{B_1} gives

$$I_{B_1} = \frac{b_2 I_g + b_2(b_1 + 1)I_{CBO_1} + (b_2 + 1)I_{CBO_2}}{1 - b_1 b_2}. \tag{2.9}$$

Thus, we see that the base drive tends to increase without bound when $b_1 b_2 \to 1$. By using the relationship between base current and emitter current, we obtain

$$I_A = (b_1 + 1)(I_{B_1} + I_{CBO_1}). \tag{2.10}$$

A solution for the anode current can be found by substituting equation (2.9) into (2.10) and rearranging so that

$$I_A = \frac{(b_1 + 1)(b_2 + 1)(I_{CBO_1} + I_{CBO_2}) + b_2(b_1 + 1)I_g}{1 - b_1 b_2}. \tag{2.11}$$

These equations can be further simplified by observing that the terms $(b_1 + 1)I_{CBO_1}$ and $(b_2 + 1)I_{CBO_2}$ are the collector-to-emitter currents with the base leads open, and are defined as I_{CEO_1} and I_{CEO_2}, respectively. Then equation (2.9) becomes

$$I_{B_1} = \frac{b_2 I_g + b_2 I_{CEO_1} + I_{CEO_2}}{1 - b_1 b_2}, \tag{2.12}$$

and equation (2.11) reduces to

$$I_A = \frac{(1 + b_2)I_{CEO_1} + (1 + b_1)(I_{CEO_2} + b_2 I_g)}{1 - b_1 b_2}. \tag{2.13}$$

2.2.2 PHYSICAL THEORY

To obtain a physical insight into *p-n-p-n* operation, let us first consider the device to be in a nonbiased state. At each junction a space-charge layer develops which results in a "built-in potential," as described in Sec. 1.8. The hole and electron concentrations throughout the device are determined by the impurity doping levels, dimensions, and temperature. This distribution is pictorially represented in Fig. 2.6. By applying voltage to the device or by irradiating it with light, we cause the equilibrium situation shown in Fig. 2.6 to be upset and the space-charge layers modified to counteract the disturbance.

Now, if we slowly apply a positive voltage to the anode of the device, junction *J*2 will tend to become reverse-biased, whereas *J*1 and *J*3 will become lightly forward-biased. Electrons on the *n*-type side of *J*2 move toward the positively biased anode, leaving behind donor impurities that are stripped of electrons; in like manner, holes move toward the cathode, leaving uncompensated acceptor impurities on the *p*-type side of *J*2.† The donor impurities in the vicinity of *J*2, having been deprived of their compensating electrons, become positively charged, whereas the acceptors stripped of holes are negatively charged. The result is that a space-charge layer composed of donors and acceptors that are uncompensated by mobile charge carriers develops in the neighborhood of *J*2 and creates a high electric field which

† In a homogeneous semiconductor material under equilibrium conditions, Poisson's equation reduces to zero:

$$\nabla^2 V = - \frac{q}{K\epsilon_0} (N_d - N_a + p - n) = 0,$$

since the net charge, composed of donors, acceptors, holes, and electrons, is zero (the material is said to be charge-balanced). If a region is stripped of majority and minority carriers (as is the case of a depletion region), the equation becomes

$$\nabla^2 V = - \frac{q}{K\epsilon_0} (N_d - N_a) = 0,$$

and the charge is not in balance. Thus, a space-charge layer is formed which supports voltage.

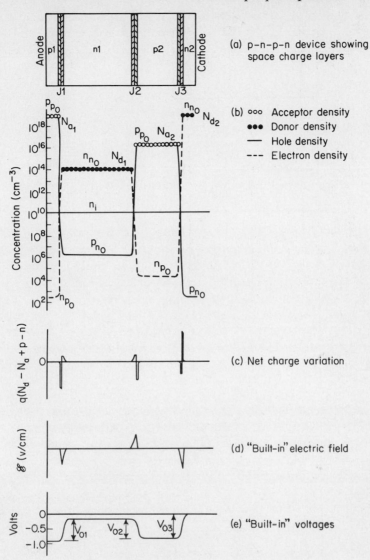

(a) p-n-p-n device showing space charge layers

(b)
- ∘∘∘ Acceptor density
- ••• Donor density
- —   Hole density
- - - Electron density

(c) Net charge variation

(d) "Built-in" electric field

(e) "Built-in" voltages

Fig. 2.6 *p-n-p-n* device at equilibrium.

sustains the applied voltage, as shown in Fig. 2.7. The space-charge, or depletion, region required to support the applied voltage can be determined by solving Poisson's equation, as explained in Sec. 2.4. Voltage will be supported so long as the donor and acceptor impurities within the depletion region of $J2$ are deprived of compensating electrons and holes.

As the anode voltage rises, the electrons removed from the vicinity of $J2$ move toward $J1$. Since electrons are majority carriers in the $n1$ base layer,

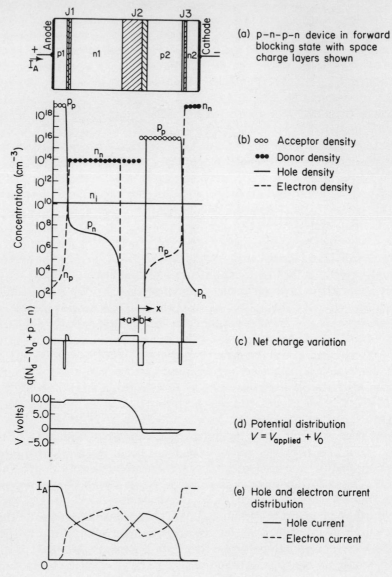

(a) p–n–p–n device in forward blocking state with space charge layers shown

(b) ∘∘∘ Acceptor density
    ••• Donor density
    —— Hole density
    - - - Electron density

(c) Net charge variation

(d) Potential distribution
    $V = V_{applied} + V_0$

(e) Hole and electron current distribution
    —— Hole current
    - - - Electron current

Fig. 2.7 *p-n-p-n* device in forward blocking state.

they will rearrange themselves during a period approximately equal to the relaxation time ($< 10^{-10}$ sec) in such a way that there is negligible field in the base region. Uncompensated charges can exist only at the edges of the base region, that is, on the space-charge-layer capacitances. Consequently, some of these electrons which move from $J2$ serve to compensate a few of the donor impurities which had been stripped by the diffusion action which created the "built-in potential" at $J1$. Thus, the potential of $n1$ is lowered with respect to $p1$, the space-charge layer becomes narrower, $J1$ becomes forward-biased, and holes are injected from $p1$ into $n1$. In an analogous manner, the holes removed from $J2$ move toward the cathode and cause $J3$ to become forward-biased so that electrons are injected from $n2$ into $p2$. As a consequence, the space-charge layers at the three junctions are modified from those shown in Fig. 2.6 to those in Fig. 2.7.

Now with $J1$ and $J3$ forward-biased, and $J2$ reverse-biased by a fixed applied voltage, let us examine the steady-state current-carrier flow. Throughout the semiconductor, hole-electron pairs are generated by thermal agitation. Those generated within the space-charge layer of $J2$ are immediately swept into the adjoining base regions by the high electric field, with the holes going into $p2$ and the electrons into $n1$. In addition, the high electric field in the space-charge layer of $J2$ causes the minority-carrier concentration at its edges to be essentially negligible so that a gradient of minority carriers is formed in the base regions. Thus, holes injected into, or generated in, base region $n1$ diffuse toward $J2$ and are swept by its field into region $p2$. In the same manner, electrons in region $p2$ diffuse to $J2$ and are swept into $n1$.

The base regions adjacent to the space-charge layer of $J2$ are essentially space-charge neutral.† Thus, the carriers which diffuse to the edge of the space-charge layer and are swept out (i.e., collected) leave a charge unbalance which, in turn, further forward-biases the emitter junction. Carriers of the same sign are injected into the base, or carriers of opposite sign are injected out of the base into the emitter region, until balance is restored. Thus, if a hole diffused from the base region of $n1$ is collected at $J2$, a hole must be injected from $p1$ to $n1$ or an electron from $n1$ to $p1$ to preserve charge neutrality.

If the current flowing into the anode of the device is defined as I_A (see Figs. 2.7 and 2.8), then the fraction γ of this current which is due to holes injected through $J1$ into $n1$ is defined as the injection efficiency of $J1$. Thus, the hole current flowing into the base region of $n1$ is $\gamma_1 I_A$. This means that the remaining fraction of current, $(1 - \gamma_1)I_A$, is composed of electrons which flow from the base region of $n1$ into the space-charge layer of $J1$; part of these electrons recombine with holes in the space-charge layer of $J1$, and the remainder are injected into $p1$, where they diffuse across to the anode contact and recombine, or they recombine in transit. The holes which are injected into base region $n1$ will diffuse toward junction $J2$, with some of them recombining with electrons as they cross the base layer. The fraction of the injected hole

---

† In our model we have assumed that there are no acceptor impurities in region $n1$ and no donor impurities in $p2$. For neutrality,

$$\nabla \cdot \mathscr{E} = \frac{q}{K\epsilon_0}(N_d - N_a + p - n) = 0.$$

Then, in the base region of $n1$, $n - p = N_d$; and, in the base region of $p2$, $p - n = N_a$.

current which reaches $J2$ is defined as the transport factor β_1. Thus, $\gamma_1\beta_1 = \alpha_1$ is the fraction of the anode current which is transported as holes from region $p1$ across $n1$ and collected at $J2$, as discussed in Chap. 1.

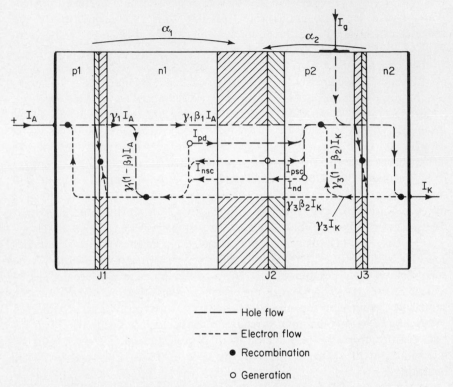

— — — Hole flow

- - - - - Electron flow

● Recombination

○ Generation

Fig. 2.8 Hole and electron flow in a *p-n-p-n* structure while in the forward blocking state.

We can now determine the hole current which is swept into region $p2$ by the space-charge layer of $J2$. The current consists of the following components:

$$\begin{Bmatrix} \text{holes swept} \\ \text{into } p2 \text{ by} \\ J2\text{'s space-} \\ \text{charge} \\ \text{layer} \end{Bmatrix} = \begin{Bmatrix} \text{holes injected} \\ \text{through } J1 \text{ into} \\ n1 \text{ which diffuse} \\ \text{across } n1 \text{ and are} \\ \text{collected at } J2 \end{Bmatrix} + \begin{Bmatrix} \text{holes thermally} \\ \text{generated within} \\ \text{base region of } n1 \\ \text{which diffuse to } J2 \end{Bmatrix} + \begin{Bmatrix} \text{holes thermally} \\ \text{generated with-} \\ \text{in space-charge} \\ \text{layer of } J2 \end{Bmatrix}.$$

In equation form, this hole current at the $p2$ side of $J2$'s space-charge layer can be written as

$$I_p = \alpha_1 I_A + I_{pd} + I_{psc}. \tag{2.14}$$

Since $J3$ is also forward-biased, electrons are injected from $n2$ across $J3$ into $p2$. These electrons, plus those thermally generated in the base region of

$p2$, diffuse toward the space-charge layer of $J2$. The electrons which do not recombine in transit are swept by the space-charge field of $J2$ into region $n1$. Thus, the electron current at the $p2$ side of $J2$'s space-charge layer becomes

$$I_n = \alpha_2 I_K + I_{nd}. \tag{2.15}$$

The total current flowing across the reference plane at the $p2$ side of junction $J2$ is

$$I_A = I_n + I_p. \tag{2.16}$$

Thus, from (2.14) and (2.15),

$$I_A = \alpha_1 I_A + \alpha_2 I_K + I_{pd} + I_{psc} + I_{nd}. \tag{2.17}$$

But with gate drive

$$I_K = I_A + I_g, \tag{2.18}$$

so

$$I_A = (\alpha_1 + \alpha_2)I_A + \alpha_2 I_g + I_{pd} + I_{nd} + I_{psc}. \tag{2.19}$$

The total thermally generated diffusion current is $I_d = I_{pd} + I_{nd}$. Since the space-charge generated term of current is evaluated on the $p2$ side of $J2$'s space-charge layer, $I_{psc} = I_{sc}$. Using these equations and solving for I_A, we may reduce equation (2.19) to

$$I_A = \frac{\alpha_2 I_g + I_d + I_{sc}}{1 - \alpha_1 - \alpha_2}, \tag{2.20}$$

where α_1 varies with I_A and α_2 varies with $I_A + I_g$.[1] As long as $\alpha_1 + \alpha_2 < 1$, $J2$ remains in reverse bias, and the device has the capability of supporting forward blocking voltage.

Since both α_1 and α_2 vary with blocking current I_A, it is necessary only to increase I_g or to raise the device temperature (which causes $I_d + I_{sc}$ to rise) in order to cause the denominator of equation (2.20) to approach zero. When $\alpha_1 + \alpha_2 \rightarrow 1$, $I_A \rightarrow \infty$. However, switching is initiated even before $\alpha_1 + \alpha_2 \rightarrow 1$. By considering the small-signal behavior of a *p-n-p-n* device, we can show that switching will begin when the sum of the small-signal alphas reach unity.[2] Because the alphas of a *p-n-p-n* may be quite nonlinear (as a function of emitter current), the small-signal α_{1s} and α_{2s} may be appreciably greater than the d-c values. Let us consider the situation which results when the gate current I_g is increased by a small amount ΔI_g. As a consequence of this increase, the anode current will increase by an amount ΔI_A, and by Kirchhoff's law we can write the cathode current as

$$\Delta I_K = \Delta I_A + \Delta I_g. \tag{2.21}$$

Since we are interested in a small increase in gate current, we shall use the small-signal alphas, which, by definition, are

$$\alpha_{1s} = \lim_{\Delta I_A \to 0} \frac{\Delta I_C}{\Delta I_A} \qquad (2.22)$$

and

$$\alpha_{2s} = \lim_{\Delta I_K \to 0} \frac{\Delta I_C}{\Delta I_K}. \qquad (2.23)$$

Thus the hole current collected by $J2$ will be $\alpha_{1s} \Delta I_A$, and the electron current will be $\alpha_{2s} \Delta I_K$. Equating the change in anode current to the change in current across $J2$, we see that

$$\Delta I_A = \alpha_{1s} \Delta I_A + \alpha_{2s} \Delta I_K. \qquad (2.24)$$

Substituting equation (2.21) into (2.24), we find that

$$\frac{\Delta I_A}{\Delta I_g} = \frac{1}{1 - \alpha_{1s} - \alpha_{2s}}. \qquad (2.25)$$

Thus, when $\alpha_{1s} + \alpha_{2s}$ becomes unity, any small increase in gate current will cause the device to become unstable, because $\Delta I_A / \Delta I_g$ would be infinite under this condition. This condition implies that a small increase in gate current will cause an infinite increase in anode current. Although gate current was used in this analysis, a slight increase in temperature or voltage could have the same effect. A more general and rigorous analysis is presented in Appendix A.

Actually, upon switching, the current through the device must be limited to a reasonable value by the external load resistance; otherwise, the device would destroy itself if the supply voltage were a few volts. Note that if $\alpha_1 + \alpha_2 = 1$, equation (2.19) implies that the sum of electron and hole current collected at $J2$ exceeds the current flowing into the terminals of the device. Such a condition would violate continuity of current. Of course, this cannot happen and is the result of using steady state equations to examine transient operation. Actually, a buildup of electrons and holes occurs in the vicinity of $J2$ during switching. As a consequence, a large amount of the uncompensated donor and acceptor impurities which make up the space-charge layer of $J2$ become compensated with electrons and holes, so $J2$ will no longer support blocking voltage and the device switches to the conducting state. In this condition $J2$ is in forward bias; hence, in a low-impedance condition. Note that the criterion for conduction was that $\alpha_1 + \alpha_2 = 1$, and in addition the tacit assumption was made that a mechanism existed that would cause the alphas to increase appropriately when or as desired so that switching would occur.

Stated another way, holes which diffuse from $J1$ to $J2$ are swept by the field in the space-charge layer into $p2$ where, as majority carriers, they raise the forward-bias voltage across *J*3, causing it to inject more electrons. Under efficient transport conditions (which are a function of current or injection level), most of these electrons diffuse across the base region of *p*2 to *J*2, are swept into *n*1, and, as majority carriers in that region, cause an increase in forward bias across *J*1, so more holes are injected through *J*1 into *n*1. Thus

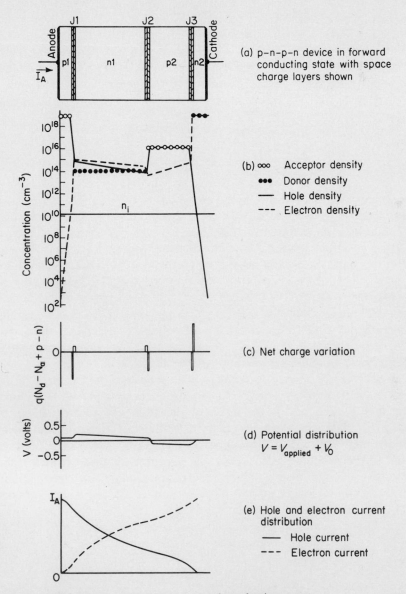

(a) p–n–p–n device in forward conducting state with space charge layers shown

(b) ∞∞   Acceptor density
    ●●●   Donor density
    —   Hole density
    ‑‑‑   Electron density

(c) Net charge variation

(d) Potential distribution
    $V = V_{applied} + V_0$

(e) Hole and electron current distribution
    —   Hole current
    ‑‑‑   Electron current

Fig. 2.9 *p-n-p-n* device in forward conducting state.

the process is basically a regenerative one, initiated by an alpha increase with current. This process continues until the voltage across the *p-n-p-n* structure drops to the order of one volt. This low value of voltage results because the space-charge layer of $J2$ continues to sweep holes from $n1$ into $p2$ and electrons from $p2$ into $n1$, until a sufficient number of the uncompensated acceptors and donors in $J2$'s space-charge layer become compensated so that $J2$ becomes forward-biased. With $J2$ forward-biased, its potential barrier is sufficiently low for holes to diffuse from $p2$ into $n1$ and electrons from $n1$ into $p2$. The minority-carrier concentrations in the base regions are thereby raised in the neighborhood of $J2$ until the recombination current in the base is equal to the collected current of $J2$ and further buildup of carriers in the bases ceases. Thus $J2$ is just sufficiently forward biased to

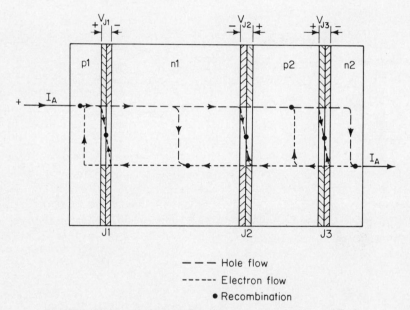

Fig. 2.10 Hole and electron flow in a *p-n-p-n* structure while in the forward conducting state.

permit collection of enough electrons and holes to replace the majority carriers that are injected from the bases into $J1$ and $J3$ (emitter efficiency losses) and those lost by recombination with minority carriers in the bases. The current and carrier distributions of a *p-n-p-n* device in the forward conducting mode of operation are shown in Figs. 2.9 and 2.10. This mode of operation is considered in detail in Secs. 2.5 and 2.6.3.

When the device is in its conducting mode the total voltage drop from anode to cathode is equal to the voltage across each junction plus the resistive drops across the various regions of the device. At low levels of load current, the potential field drops across the base regions are negligible, because most of the current flows by minority-carrier diffusion. Thus, the anode-to-cathode voltage drop is approximately equal to the algebraic sum of junction drops.

$$V_{AK} = V_{J1} - V_{J2} + V_{J3}.$$

Since all three junctions are forward-biased, the voltage drop across the device is less than the voltage drop across two p-n junctions but greater than that of one junction.† As an example, typical silicon rectifiers and SCR's will have forward drops of 0.9 and 1.1 v, respectively, when operated at the same current density.

2.3 Triggering Mechanisms

Most p-n-p-n devices are designed to have a bistable characteristic. The two modes of operation are referred to as the OFF state (condition of high impedance) and the ON state (condition of low impedance). In most p-n-p-n devices these two modes of operation require that the current amplification factors, or alphas, of the device vary with current density. Figure 2.3 shows the effect of current on one of the alphas of a typical small-area p-n-p-n device. In Sec. 2.2 it was noted that the criterion for conduction was that $\alpha_1 + \alpha_2 = 1$. Thus, switching from the OFF to the ON state requires that the emitter-current density be raised to a level high enough to satisfy this criterion. In addition, the increase of current must also be applied for a finite duration of time, since the alphas are time-dependent, owing to the time required for the minority carriers to cross the base regions. In the following sections are listed a number of methods whereby p-n-p-n devices can be triggered from the OFF to the ON state by means of externally applied stimulus.

2.3.1 THERMAL TURN-ON

In Sec. 2.2 the equation for anode current in a p-n-p-n device in the forward blocking state was given as

$$I_A = \frac{\alpha_2 I_g + I_d + I_{sc}}{1 - \alpha_1 - \alpha_2}. \tag{2.20}$$

Now I_d and I_{sc} increase exponentially with temperature, as we shall show in Sec. 2.4.4. Thus, as temperature increases, more hole-electron pairs are created

---

† This condition results because collector junction J2 does not "back-inject" as heavily as the normal emitters J1 and J2; thus, the voltage rise across J2 is not as great as the drop across J1.

and collected by the blocking junctions. With the alphas being strongly dependent on current density, both $\alpha_1 + \alpha_2$ and $\alpha_{1s} + \alpha_{2s}$ rapidly approach unity with increasing temperature. In addition, minority-carrier lifetime increases with temperature, thus contributing to the increase of the alphas; however, this effect is generally a minor one. Figure 2.11 shows the rise of

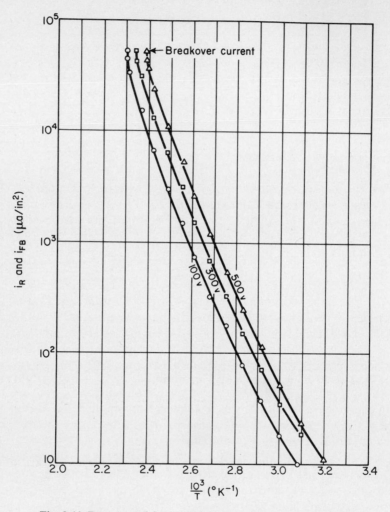

Fig. 2.11 Reverse and forward blocking current of a typical SCR versus temperature.

forward blocking current with temperature and the trigger point. Figure 2.12 shows the forward blocking voltage which can be withstood versus temperature. This characteristic, which can be altered considerably, is discussed more thoroughly in Chap. 3.

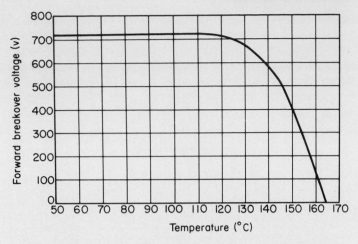

Fig. 2.12 Typical forward breakover voltage versus temperature for an SCR.

2.3.2 LIGHT OR RADIATION TRIGGERING

When light impinges on a semiconductor, electron-hole pairs may be produced. Figure 2.13 shows the absorption coefficient for silicon as a function of wavelength. Silicon has a band gap of 1.08 ev. Since wavelength λ of radiation (photons) is related to energy E by the deBroglie relation,[3]

$$\lambda = \frac{hc}{E},\tag{2.26}$$

where

$c = 3 \times 10^{10}$ cm/sec, the velocity of light.

$h = 6.62 \times 10^{-27}$ erg sec, Planck's constant.

We can determine approximately the maximum wavelength at which electron-hole pairs can be created by photon absorption by substituting the band gap for silicon into the expression. Using the conversion 1 ev $= 1.6 \times 10^{-12}$ erg and $1\text{Å} = 10^{-8}$ cm, we find that $\lambda = 11{,}500$ Å, which is in agreement with Fig. 2.13. Thus, radiation of wavelength longer than 11,500 Å does not contain photons sufficiently energetic to create hole-electron pairs by transition across the band gap.

When light is directed into a silicon device, the hole-electron pairs that are created diminish exponentially with penetration distance. Using Lambert's law of absorption, we can write the number of electron-hole pairs created per unit time in a unit area of a layer of thickness dx at a distance x below the surface as[4]

$$g(x)\,dx = N(\lambda)\alpha(\lambda)\exp\left[-\alpha(\lambda)x\right]dx,\tag{2.27}$$

where $N(\lambda)$ is the number of photons impinging on the surface and $\alpha(\lambda)$ is the intrinsic absorption constant.† Note that as $\alpha(\lambda)$ increases, more of the electron-hole pairs are created near the surface. The practical result is that as λ decreases, more of the minority carriers which are generated recombine at the surface of the device instead of being collected at a junction. Thus, the number of photons required to trigger a *p-n-p-n* device increases with decreasing wavelength and is dependent on the depths of the junctions below the surface as well as the surface recombination velocity.

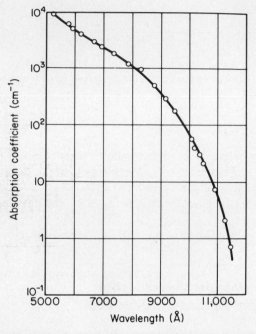

Fig. 2.13 Intrinsic absorption coefficient for silicon [from R. Braunstein, *et al.*, *Physical Review*, **109** (1958), 695.]

A first-order approximation of the spectral response of a *p-n-p-n* device can be derived by using equation (2.27) and Fig. 2.13. If it is assumed that all the hole-electron pairs which are created within the device are equally effective in causing the current to increase, and if it is assumed that those pairs created very near the surface are ineffective owing to recombination, then by using the

† The tacit assumption is made that all the photons which strike the surface are absorbed. Actually,

$$g(x) \, dx = N(\lambda)[1 - r(\lambda, \, \theta)]\alpha(\lambda) \exp\left[-\alpha(\lambda)x\right] dx,$$

where $r(\lambda, \, \theta)$ is the percentage of incident photons reflected from the surface.

model pictured in Fig. 2.14, we can find a simple expression for the spectral response. Using these assumptions, we may determine the total quantity of hole-electron pairs created within the device as a function of wavelength by integrating equation (2.27) from x_1 to $2x_2$. Thus,

$$G = \int_{x_1}^{2x_2} N(\lambda)\alpha(\lambda) \exp\left[-\alpha(\lambda)x\right] dx, \tag{2.28}$$

$$G = N(\lambda)\{\exp\left[-\alpha(\lambda)x_1\right] - \exp\left[-2\alpha(\lambda)x_2\right]\}. \tag{2.29}$$

The value $2x_2$ is used because, as a simple approximation, it is assumed that

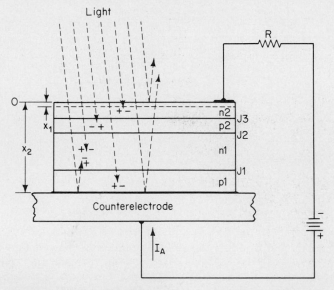

Fig. 2.14 Model used for deriving the spectral response of a light-activated p-n-p-n switch.

the longer wavelengths of light pass through the silicon pellet and are reflected back up through it again. From the absorption constant chosen from Fig. 2.13 and used in equation (2.29), the spectral response curve shown in Fig. 2.15 was obtained. The experimental points shown were obtained by using a small silicon p-n-p-n switch specifically designed for light triggering.

Other forms of radiation, such as gamma rays, neutrons, protons, electrons, and X rays, can be used to trigger a p-n-p-n device. However, great care must be exercised in their use, or the radiation lattice collisions will cause permanent damage. A more complete description of radiation-damage effects is presented in Chap. 4.

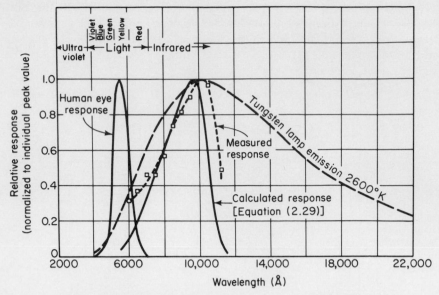

Fig. 2.15 Spectral response of typical silicon light-activated *p-n-p-n* device as compared to the human eye and tungsten lamp emission.

2.3.3 GATE TRIGGERING

To trigger a *p-n-p-n* device into its conducting state, the blocking junction *J*2, as shown in Fig. 2.7, must be discharged. Discharge is accomplished by increasing the concentration of majority carriers adjacent to *J*2. If majority carriers are supplied to the base regions of *n*1 and *p*2 at a rate in excess of emitter efficiency and minority-carrier recombination requirements, then a buildup of carriers will occur in the base regions causing the sum of the electron and hole current collected at junction *J*2 to increase. This results in an increase in emitter current and thus an increase in alphas. Since the minority-carrier current collected by *J*2 is determined by emitter bias, the control which can be exercised by the addition of a third lead becomes rather apparent.

If the sum of the alphas of the device are less than unity in the blocking state, then gate current must be forced into it to cause switching. Figure 2.8 shows gate current passing into the base region of a *p-n-p-n* structure so that the cathode current is equal to $I_g + I_A$. Using equation (2.20),

$$I_A = \frac{\alpha_2 I_g + I_{sc} + I_d}{1 - \alpha_1 - \alpha_2}, \tag{2.20}$$

we note that α_1 is a function of I_A, whereas α_2 varies with the current $I_g + I_A$. As I_g increases, α_2 rises, causing I_A to rise, thus raising α_1, etc. Conduction occurs when the alpha sum becomes unity, and in most cases further control by means of the gate lead is lost in a manner reminiscent of a gas thyratron.

Using Fig. 2.8 and equations (2.20) and (1.85), we can obtain the gate current-voltage relationship by noting that $I_A = I_K - I_g$. Then†

$$I_g = \frac{I_K(1 - \alpha_1 - \alpha_2) - (I_{sc} + I_d)}{1 - \alpha_1}, \tag{2.30}$$

and

$$I_g = \frac{I_{EO}[\exp(qV_g/nkT) - 1](1 - \alpha_1 - \alpha_2)}{1 - \alpha_1}$$
$$- \frac{(I_{sc} + I_d)\{1 - \alpha_{2I}[\exp(-qV_{J2}/nkT) - 1]\}(1 - \alpha_1 - \alpha_2)}{1 - \alpha_1}, \tag{2.31}$$

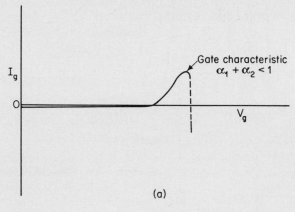

(a)

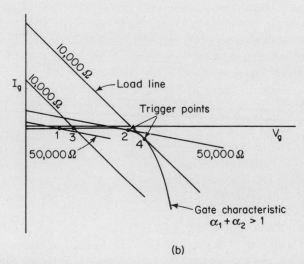

(b)

Fig. 2.16 Gate current versus gate voltage for *p-n-p-n* structures in the forward blocking mode.

† The *n* in the exponent qV/nkT is included to allow for deviation from simple theory. The value of *n* varies from 1 to 2 and depends on current level, the density of trapping sites, and their energy levels.[3,17,18,22]

where α_{2I} is the inverse alpha for the *n-p-n* transistor portion and I_{EO} is the saturation current for junction $J3$. Both α_1 and α_2 are functions of current; consequently, it is difficult to make calculations using equation (2.31). However, it can be seen that when $V_g = 0$, the thermally generated current which crosses $J2$ flows from base region $p2$ into the gate circuit, and then I_g is negative. As gate voltage is applied, this current reverses and flows into the base region, rises to a maximum, then decreases rapidly as $1 - \alpha_1 - \alpha_2 \to 0$ as shown in Fig. 2.16(a). When $\alpha_{1s} + \alpha_{2s} = 1$, the load current through the device begins increasing and continues until limited by the external load resistance. This rise in current is the result of the drive provided to the base of each transistor section by the other adjacent transistor section. The gate voltage is then determined by the emitter-current density, and the gate current becomes

$$I_g = \frac{E_{gs} - V_g}{R_g},$$

where E_{gs} is the gate supply voltage and R_g is the gate circuit resistance, as shown in Fig. 2.17. For the idealized model just discussed, turn-off could be achieved by shorting the gate lead to the cathode, causing V_g to drop to zero. In actual practice, this cannot be accomplished with most *p-n-p-n* devices because of internal voltage drop resulting from the lateral base resistance, which prevents the voltage across $J3$ from dropping to zero over its entire area. The gate turn-off problem is discussed in detail in Sec. 2.7.

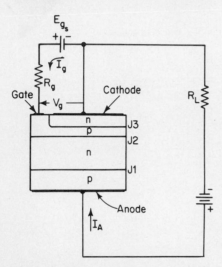

Fig. 2.17 Circuit used for analysis of gate triggering.

It is not absolutely necessary that the sum of the alphas of a *p-n-p-n* device be less than unity to be in the blocking state. If the gate circuit of a *p-n-p-n* structure whose alpha sum exceeds unity is open-circuited, the device will not block the flow of current. However, by providing a low-resistance path from gate to cathode, such as would be the case in Fig. 2.17, and with E_{gs} and R_g zero or quite small, junction $J2$ will build up a space-charge layer and support the applied voltage. In this case the current through the *p-n-p* portion of the device bypasses the emitter of the *n-p-n* transistor. Although equation (2.20) is still valid, it is difficult to ascertain the switching criterion, since $\alpha_1 + \alpha_2 > 1$ and I_g is negative. As a consequence, better insight into the problem can be gleaned by a slightly different analysis.

The base current required to drive the *p-n-p* section of the device is

$$I_{B_1} = (1 - \alpha_1)I_A - I_{pd}, \tag{2.32}$$

and the drive provided to it by the *n-p-n* section is

$$I_n = I_{nd} + \alpha_2 I_K + I_{sc}. \tag{2.33}$$

Now, by considering the emitter efficiency of the *n-p-n* section to be effectively lowered by the current which bypasses the cathode emitter via the gate circuit, we can define an effective emitter efficiency

$$\gamma^* = \frac{I_K}{I_A} \tag{2.34}$$

The electron current collected by *J*2 is then obtained from equation (2.33).

$$I_n = \gamma^* \alpha_2 I_A + I_{nd} + I_{sc}. \tag{2.35}$$

Equating the base current required to drive the *p-n-p* [equation (2.32)] and the drive current provided by the collection of electrons at *J*2 [equation (2.35)], we get

$$\gamma^* \alpha_2 I_A + I_{nd} + I_{sc} = (1 - \alpha_1)I_A - I_{pd}. \tag{2.36}$$

Solving for I_A, we obtain

$$I_A = \frac{I_{sc} + I_d}{1 - \alpha_1 - \gamma^* \alpha_2}. \tag{2.37}$$

Thus, the criterion for conduction is the relation

$$\alpha_1 + \gamma^* \alpha_2 = 1, \tag{2.38}$$

or

$$\frac{I_K}{I_A} = \frac{1 - \alpha_1}{\alpha_2}. \tag{2.39}$$

If the cathode-to-anode current ratio reaches the value $(1 - \alpha_1)/\alpha_2$, then switching will occur.

The gate current-voltage characteristic for a *p-n-p-n* device in which $\alpha_1 + \alpha_2 > 1$ can be expressed by equation (2.31). In this case I_g is negative, since gate current must flow into the gate circuit for the device to remain in the blocking state. As V_g increases, the current flowing out of the base into the gate lead increases, so the gate input impedance behaves like a negative resistance, as shown in Fig. 2.16(b). As a consequence, the trigger point becomes a function of the gate circuit resistance. The load lines for two different values of gate supply voltage E_{gs} with gate circuit resistance R_g are shown in Fig. 2.16(b). Points 1 and 3 are stable points at which the device will not switch, and points 2 and 4 are trigger points. It is apparent that the trigger point occurs at a higher gate voltage with lower gate circuit resistance.

In many *p-n-p-n* devices, lateral base biasing plays a significant role in determining their gate characteristics. Larger-area structures are particularly affected. This effect is probably most easily visualized by considering a large-area structure to be essentially many small ones in parallel, as shown in

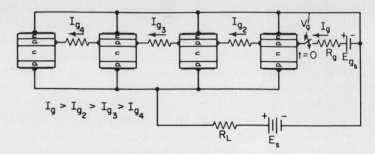

Fig. 2.18 Equivalent circuit for a large area *p-n-p-n* immediately after gate circuit is closed.

Fig. 2.18. Note that the device nearest the gate lead has full gate voltage between gate and cathode, whereas the voltage on the remainder of the structures is reduced by an amount equal to the voltage drop across the connecting resistors. Since the current through each device varies exponentially with its base-to-emitter voltage, the structures nearest the gate connections will carry the bulk of the current resulting from a gate voltage pulse. This situation is shown in Fig. 2.19 for a large-area device. With the application of gate voltage, electrons are not injected uniformly across *J*3, but conform to the expression[5]

$$J(x) = K \exp\left\{\left(\frac{q}{nkT}\right)[V_g - i_g(x)r_b(x)]\right\},\qquad(2.40)$$

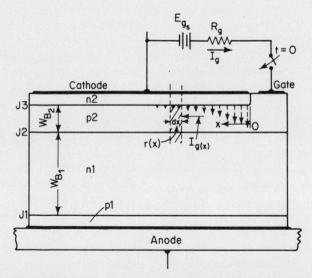

Fig. 2.19 Electron current distribution in the cathode emitter immediately after the gate circuit is closed.

where $i_g(x)$ and $r_b(x)$ are the lateral gate current and base resistance, respectively, and V_g the externally applied gate-to-emitter voltage. Thus, the higher the sheet resistance of the base region, the more nonuniform will be the density of injected carriers across the area of the device. The injected-current density will be greatest near the gate connection, and, since alpha is a function of carrier density, turn-on will occur in the vicinity of the gate connections when the alpha sum in that neighborhood becomes unity. In a few microseconds the whole device becomes turned on, as a result of the positive feedback effect which supplies base drive to the rest of the device. As a consequence, the gate current required to trigger an SCR is not a strong function of emitter area. However, if the load current rises too rapidly, not all of the device may have sufficient time to become turned on, and damage may occur because of excessively large current flow in the turned-on region. The subject is discussed further in Sec. 2.6. In addition, the gate current required to trigger the device is a function of pulse width. This type of operation is also discussed in Sec. 2.6.

2.3.4 Voltage Triggering

p-n-p-n devices can be switched from the forward blocking state to the conducting mode by the application of a rapidly rising anode voltage wavefront (referred to as *dv/dt* triggering) or by exceeding the breakover voltage of the device. Section 2.6.2 treats *dv/dt* effects in detail; the calculation of breakover voltages is described in Sec. 2.4. Two possible mechanisms for body breakdown are generally responsible for nonthermally generated breakovers.[6] They are avalanche breakdown and collector space-charge breakdown; i.e., the space-charge layer spreads through the base to the emitter punchthrough. A third type, localized zener breakdown, results in "soft" characteristics and is generally believed to be caused by metallic impurity precipitates in the blocking junction.[7] The characteristics resulting from these impurities are very difficult to predict, and are beyond the scope of this book. However, their effect is to allow increase of current through the device as a function of voltage, which, in turn, causes the alphas to increase.

When a blocking junction approaches its avalanche breakdown voltage point, carrier multiplication will occur; that is, as minority carriers reach the space-charge layer, they are swept through at sufficient velocity so that collisions with the lattice result in the creation of the hole-electron pairs. In Fig. 2.20 the multiplication factor for holes passing through the space-charge region of $J2$ will be defined as

$$M_p = \frac{I_p(p2)}{I_p(n1)}, \tag{2.41}$$

where $I_n(p2) = 0$. It is the fraction of the hole current (majority carriers) which emerges from the space-charge layer on the $p2$ side relative to the hole current (minority carriers) entering the space-charge layer on the $n2$ side. Similarly, the multiplication of electron current in the space-charge layer is defined as

$$M_n = \frac{I_n(n1)}{I_n(p2)},$$ (2.42)

where $I_p(n1) = 0$.

The action can be visualized by considering Fig. 2.20. Holes are injected through $J1$ with an emitter efficiency γ_1 and diffuse across the base region of

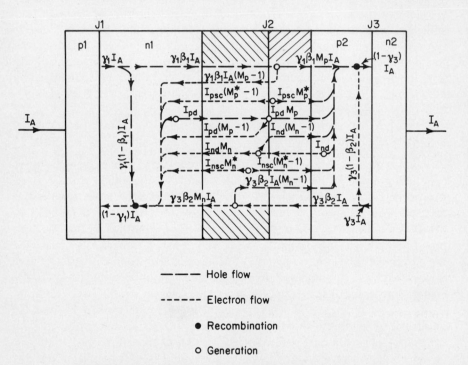

- - - - Hole flow

------ Electron flow

● Recombination

○ Generation

Fig. 2.20 Hole and electron flow (including avalanche multiplication) in a *p-n-p-n* device with the collector reverse-biased.

$n1$ with a transport efficiency β_1; they are accelerated by the space-charge field of $J2$ and collide with the lattice, causing avalanche multiplication, provided the blocking voltage is sufficiently great. Since these collisions create hole-electron pairs, these pairs also are accelerated and, in turn, may create more pairs. This process also occurs when holes, which are thermally generated in the base region of $n1$, are swept into the space-charge layer. Those carriers which are thermally generated within the space-charge layer of $J2$ are multiplied also, but by a different factor, since those generated within it are not accelerated over the total space-charge layer. Thus, the hole current swept into the base region of $p2$ by $J2$'s space-charge layer is

$$I_p = (\gamma_1\beta_1 I_A + I_{pd})M_p + M_p^* I_{psc} + (M_n^* - 1)I_{nsc} + (\gamma_3\beta_2 I_A + I_{nd})(M_n - 1),$$
(2.43)

where the last two terms represent the holes resulting from hole-electron pairs created by the lattice collision of electrons collected at the $p2$ side of $J2$. The electron current entering $J2$'s space-charge layer at the n-p-n side of $J2$ is

$$I_n = \gamma_3\beta_2 I_A + I_{nd}.$$
(2.44)

The total current on the $p2$ edge of $J2$'s space-charge layer is $I_A = I_n + I_p$, so

$$I_A = \frac{M_p I_{pd} + M_n I_{nd} + M_p^* I_{psc} + (M_n^* - 1)I_{nsc}}{1 - \gamma_1\beta_1 M_p - \gamma_3\beta_2 M_n}.$$
(2.45)

The breakover voltage is reached and triggering must result as $I_A \to \infty$. Therefore, equation (2.45) shows that switching will result if

$$\gamma_1\beta_1 M_p + \gamma_3\beta_2 M_n = 1,\dagger$$
(2.46)

or

$$\alpha_1 M_p + \alpha_2 M_n = 1.$$
(2.47)

M_n and M_p are different; however, we can see the effect on breakover voltage if we assume that they are equal and can be characterized by an expression of the form[1]

$$M = \frac{1}{1 - (V/V_{BD})^n},$$
(2.48)

where n is a parameter which is a function of breakdown voltage (between 3 to 6 for silicon), and V_{BD} is the breakdown voltage of the junction without transistor effects. Using equations (2.47) and (2.48), we get

$$V_{BO} = V_{BD}(1 - \alpha_1 - \alpha_2)^{1/n}.$$
(2.49)

The calculation of V_{BD} is discussed in the next section (as well as in Chap. 1).

From equation (2.49) it is apparent that triggering is determined by both V_{BD} and the alphas α_1 and α_2, which both increase as the blocking voltage is increased, because as $J2$'s barrier spreads, the base regions become narrower. Thus, if the alphas increase significantly with voltage, breakover will occur at a voltage much less than V_{BD}. This mode of operation is the result for punch-through limited devices. If the alphas are small and do not increase significantly with voltage, then the breakover voltage will result from avalanche and be near the value of V_{BD}.

† More accurately, we should take the derivative of anode current with respect to voltage and equate the sum of the small-signal alphas to unity, as described in Appendix A, to determine when switching is initiated.

2.4 Reverse and Forward Blocking Characteristics

Typical reverse and forward voltage-current characteristics of a simple *p-n-p-n* device in the blocking state are shown in Figs. 2.11 and 4.4. For voltages up to the reverse breakdown or the forward breakover regions, a relatively small saturation or leakage current flows. At higher voltages, avalanche, surface breakdown, thermal runaway, punchthrough, or turn-on will cause rapidly increasing currents. Although these effects may occur simultaneously, it is instructive to consider them individually.

2.4.1 SPACE-CHARGE LAYER SPREADING AND PUNCHTHROUGH

As with other *p-n* junction devices, current is effectively blocked in the *p-n-p-n* structure by the buildup of a space-charge layer surrounding the common collector junction. The space-charge layer consists of donor atoms on the *n*-side and acceptor atoms on the *p*-side which have been stripped of the usual compensating electrons and holes in their neighborhood. The distribution of charge and thus the space-charge width obey Poisson's equation

$$\nabla \cdot \mathscr{E} = \frac{q}{K\epsilon_0} (N_d - N_a + p - n).$$
(2.50)

If the structure shown in Fig. 2.2 has a positive voltage applied to the cathode junction, $J1$ and $J3$ become reverse-biased and $J2$ forward-biased, as shown in Fig. 2.21. If a negative voltage is applied to the cathode, $J2$ will become reverse-biased (provided the structure is in the blocking state; see Fig. 2.7). To calculate the width of the space-charge layers and the electric fields within them, Poisson's equation must be solved for each junction in a manner similar to that described in Sec. 1.9.

If uniform impurity concentrations and asymmetrical step junctions such as those shown in Fig. 2.7 are assumed, then by reverse-biasing a junction, electrons and holes in its vicinity move toward the positive and negative

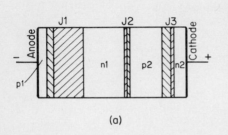

(a)

(b)

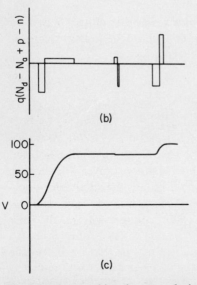

(c)

Fig. 2.21 Reverse-biased *p-n-p-n* device.

electrodes, respectively, leaving a space-charge region. A sufficient number of fixed donor and acceptor impurities become uncompensated and sustain the applied voltage. Because the region in the neighborhood of the junction is depleted of electrons and holes, a space-charge layer is formed, and equation (2.50) reduces to

$$\nabla \cdot \mathscr{E} = \frac{q}{K\epsilon_0}(N_d - N_a).\tag{2.51}$$

Outside the space-charge layers the semiconductor material is essentially in charge balance; that is, the charges of the donor and acceptor ions are neutralized by the presence of free holes and electrons. The result is that outside the space-charge regions the device acts as a conductor rather than as an insulator, so the electric field in that region is negligible.

To determine the electric field and the width of the space-charge layer, equation (2.51) must be integrated. If the junction is chosen as a plane of reference, then the ionized donor and acceptor impurities which have been depleted of electrons and holes contribute a charge-density distribution as shown in Fig. 2.7. Poisson's equation becomes

$$\frac{d\mathscr{E}}{dx} = \frac{qN_d}{K\epsilon_0}, \quad -a < x < 0;\tag{2.52}$$

$$\frac{d\mathscr{E}}{dx} = \frac{-qN_a}{K\epsilon_0}, \quad 0 < x < b.\tag{2.53}$$

Integrating these equations, we find that the field is

$$\mathscr{E} = \frac{qN_d}{K\epsilon_0}x + A_2 \quad \text{on the } n\text{-side } (-a < x < 0),\tag{2.54}$$

$$\mathscr{E} = -\frac{qN_a}{K\epsilon_0}x + A_1 \quad \text{on the } p\text{-side } (0 < x < b),\tag{2.55}$$

where A_1 and A_2 are constants of integration.

Since the field at the junction must be continuous, equations (2.54) and (2.55) can be equated at $x = 0$, giving $A_1 = A_2$. Moreover, the field at $x = -a$ and at $x = b$ is negligible. Thus

$$A_1 = A_2 = +\frac{qN_d a}{K\epsilon_0} = \frac{qN_a b}{K\epsilon_0},$$

or

$$(N_d a = N_a b),\tag{2.56}$$

showing that the total charge on the n-side is equal to that on the p-side.[†]

† Actually, the fact that the negative charge compensates the positive charge (over-all charge neutrality) implies that beyond $-a$ and beyond b the field is essentially zero.

The voltage being blocked is found by integrating the field across the space-charge region.

$$V = - \int_{-a}^{b} \mathscr{E} \, dx, \tag{2.57}$$

$$V = - \frac{q}{K\epsilon_0} \left[\int_{-a}^{0} -(N_d)(x + a) \, dx + \int_{0}^{b} (N_a)(x - b) \, dx \right], \tag{2.58}$$

$$V = \frac{q}{K\epsilon_0} \left(\frac{N_d a^2}{2} + \frac{N_a b^2}{2} \right), \tag{2.59}$$

or, since $N_a b = N_d a$ and $W_{sc} = a + b$ (the total space-charge width),

$$V = \frac{qN_d W_{sc}^2}{2K\epsilon_0} \left(1 + \frac{N_d}{N_a} \right)^{-1}. \tag{2.60}$$

If the doping of the *p*-region is much greater than that of the *n*-region, i.e., $\frac{N_d}{N_a} \ll 1$, then the voltage supported by the depletion region is

$$V \cong \frac{qN_d W_{sc}^2}{2K\epsilon_0}. \tag{2.61}$$

The voltage $V = V_0 + V_A$, where V_0 is the built-in potential and V_A is the applied voltage. Thus the barrier or space-charge-layer width is

$$W_{sc} = \sqrt{\frac{2K\epsilon_0}{q} \frac{(V_A + V_0)}{N_d} \left(1 + \frac{N_d}{N_a} \right)}, \tag{2.62}$$

where N_d is the net impurity concentration on the high-resistivity *n*-type side of the junction and N_a is the net impurity concentration on the *p*-type side.

The maximum electric field occurs at the junction (see Fig. 2.7) and is found by substituting equations (2.56) and (2.59) into (2.54).

$$\mathscr{E}_{max} = \sqrt{\frac{2qN_d(V_A + V_0)}{K\epsilon_0(1 + N_d/N_a)}}. \tag{2.63}$$

For a linear graded junction the barrier width is

$$W_{sc} = \left(\frac{12K\epsilon_0}{qs} \right)^{1/3} (V_A + V_0)^{1/3}, \tag{2.64}$$

where s is the gradient of the impurity concentration. The maximum electric field in a linear graded junction is

$$\mathscr{E}_{max} = \left(\frac{9qs}{32K\epsilon_0} \right)^{1/3} (V_A + V_0)^{2/3}. \tag{2.65}$$

Reverse-biased junctions will effectively block current until punchthrough, avalanche, thermal runaway, or surface breakdown occurs. Punchthrough results when the edge of the space-charge layer spreads through the base region to the opposite junction. When this occurs, a space-charge limited current flows, resulting in breakdown of the blocking characteristic.[9] The shape of the punchthrough breakdown characteristic is similar in appearance to that of avalanche breakdown. No damage results, provided the device current is held to reasonable limits. From equation (2.61), it is apparent that for a transistor structure with a fixed base width and uniform base resistivity, the voltage that can be supported is directly proportional to the impurity concentration in the base (if it is assumed that emitter and collector regions are heavily doped compared to the base layer, and that avalanche breakdown

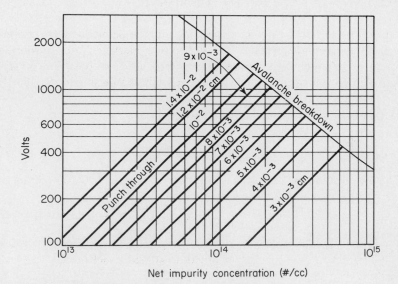

Fig. 2.22 Punchthrough and avalanche voltage as a function of net impurity concentration and base width.

does not occur). Using the relation between resistivity and impurity concentration,

$$\rho_n = \frac{1}{q(\mu_n n + \mu_p p)} \cong \frac{1}{q\mu_n N_d},$$
(2.66)

we determine punchthrough voltage breakdown as a function of base resistivity as

$$V_{PT} = \frac{qN_d a^2}{2K\epsilon_0} = \frac{qa^2}{2K\epsilon_0 \mu_n \rho_n},$$
(2.67)

where μ is the mobility of the majority carrier in the base region and ρ is the resistivity. Punchthrough and avalanche breakdown are both plotted in Fig. 2.22 to show the maximum blocking voltage achievable as a function of base width for an *abrupt-junction, uniform-base resistivity p-n-p* structure.[10]

2.4.2 AVALANCHE BREAKDOWN

Avalanche breakdown occurs in silicon when the electric field reaches a critical value, which depends but slightly on the distance over which that field is spread. Thus, a junction avalanches when free carriers in the space-charge layer are accelerated to a sufficient speed, such that their collisions with the lattice result in the creation of hole-electron pairs which, in turn, accelerate, collide, and create more hole-electron pairs. This ionization rate for holes and electrons in silicon can be represented by the equation

$$\alpha(\mathscr{E}) = A \exp\left(\frac{-B}{|\mathscr{E}|}\right), \tag{2.68}$$

where A and B are constants depending on the semiconductor material. Although the ionization rates for holes and electrons are substantially different, essentially equal numbers are produced at breakdown, so an effective alpha can be used for breakdown analysis (for silicon $A = 9 \times 10^5$ cm^{-1}, $B = 1.8 \times 10^6$ v/cm).[11]

It can be shown (see Sec. 1.9) that when

$$A \int_{-a}^{b} \exp\left(\frac{-B}{|\mathscr{E}|}\right) dx = 1, \tag{2.69}$$

avalanche breakdown will occur. Solution of equation (2.69) results in a curve which can be fitted closely by the expression[5,10]

$$V_{BD} \cong mN_I^{-3/4}. \tag{2.70}$$

For silicon m is equal to 5.6×10^{13}, and N_I is the number of impurities in the high-resistivity base region. The breakdown and punchthrough curves for typical *p-n-p* structures are shown in Fig. 2.22.

2.4.3 SURFACE BREAKDOWN

Surface breakdown is generally believed to be an avalanche phenomenon similar in many respects to the body breakdown just described.[13] Intuitively, one would expect that less electric field would be required to produce surface avalanche. Carriers are not as tightly bound to the lattice near the surface, owing to gross imperfections and disturbances at the semiconductor surface. Therefore, with a uniform electric field across the junction, surface breakdown would be expected to occur before the voltage across the device reaches a sufficiently high value to cause bulk breakdown. Because of the nonuniform nature of the lattice at the surface, or because of contaminants, breakdown in that region is usually of highly localized nature, resulting in high-power density and intense heating. As a consequence, very little reverse power is generally required to cause severe damage during surface breakdown.

To eliminate the possibility of surface breakdown, the device should be designed so that breakdown occurs in the bulk with a lower voltage than is required for surface breakdown. A solution is to make the field in the interior of the device significantly greater than around its periphery. Several methods can be used to realize this criterion. A guard ring of higher-resistivity semi-conductor around the periphery of the blocking junction can be used to lower the field at the surface.[14] Proper contouring of the surface in the neighbor-hood of the junction is a very practical method for reducing the surface field.[12] Such a structure is shown in Fig. 2.23. Another technique which aids somewhat is the use of high-dielectric-constant materials in contact with the surface to spread the field over a wider distance.[12] All these methods are used to lower the electric field at the surface as compared to the body of the device. The magnitude of the field can be calculated by a two- or three-dimensional solution of Poisson's equation.

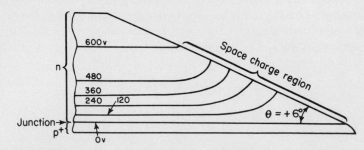

Fig. 2.23 Equipotential lines in a reverse-biased p^+-n junction with a contoured surface (the relative scale is four vertical to one horizontal).

2.4.4 Reverse and Forward Blocking Currents

To determine the forward and reverse blocking currents of a p-n-p-n device, a detailed knowledge of the interaction between the three junctions is required. In Sec. 2.2 it was shown that the forward blocking current can be expressed in the form

$$I = \frac{I_d + I_{sc}}{1 - \alpha_1 - \alpha_2}.$$ (2.71)

However, to determine the order of magnitude of the current and the device parameters which contribute to it, a more fundamental analysis is required. Such an analysis is complicated by the nonlinear current gains which are inherent in the device. Consequently, a number of assumptions must be made to make the problem tractable. A first-order simplification is the use of a planar one-dimensional model. As shown in Fig. 2.6, four regions are denoted as $p1$, $n1$, $p2$, and $n2$, with the three junctions as $J1$, $J2$, and $J3$.

With no voltage applied (i.e., equilibrium conditions) the hole and electron concentrations within the device are determined by the impurity doping levels and the temperature (note Fig. 2.6). If a positive voltage is applied to the anode of the device, $J2$ becomes reverse-biased, and the leakage current through it causes $J1$ and $J3$ to be slightly forward-biased so that the carrier distribution is altered as shown in Fig. 2.7. At each of the forward-biased junctions minority carriers are injected into their adjacent base layers to begin diffusion toward $J2$. Thus, to determine the blocking current, the leakage current across $J2$ and the current resulting from injection and transport across the base layer must be calculated.

In the case of reverse blocking (cathode positive with respect to anode), junctions $J1$ and $J3$ block the flow of current, whereas $J2$ is forward-biased (note Fig. 2.21). For most SCR's the junction adjacent to the gate has very limited voltage-blocking capability and will go into avalanche breakdown with the application of a few volts. As a consequence, the principal blocking junction is the one adjacent to the high-resistivity base region. Viewed from the equivalent-circuit point of view, the leakage becomes that of an avalanche diode in series with a transistor having no base connection. Thus, the problem becomes one of determining the current flow across a transistor having an open-base connection and an alpha which varies with current. It can be shown that the blocking current should be of the form

$$I = \frac{I_d + I_{sc}}{1 - \alpha_{pnp}}. \tag{2.72}$$

Now let us examine the actual blocking current characteristics of an SCR as a function of temperature.[15] Note in Fig. 2.11 that the reverse and forward blocking currents are essentially identical up to a temperature near that required to trigger the device. These data suggest that, as a first approximation, α_{npn} is not significant until the current through its emitter approaches that required to trigger the SCR. As a consequence, we shall use for our analysis a *p-n-p* transistor having no base connection, as shown in Fig. 2.24. A more complete analysis for a *p-n-p-n* structure is developed in Appendix B.

To determine the collector current, we examine the current flow at $x = W_B$. This current consists of holes which have diffused from within the $n1$ base layer to the edge of the collector space-charge region and electrons which have diffused from within the $p2$ collector region into the space-charge layer where they, along with the electrons generated in the depletion region, are swept into the base region by the high electric field of the space-charge layer.

To find the diffusion current of holes it is assumed that the electric field in the base region is negligible and that equation (1.60) can be used. Therefore,

$$\frac{d^2p}{dx^2} - \frac{p - p_{n0}}{D_p \tau_p} = 0. \tag{2.73}$$

Its general solution is

$$p - p_{n0} = A_1 \exp\left(\frac{x}{L_p}\right) + A_2 \exp\left(\frac{-x}{L_p}\right), \tag{2.74}$$

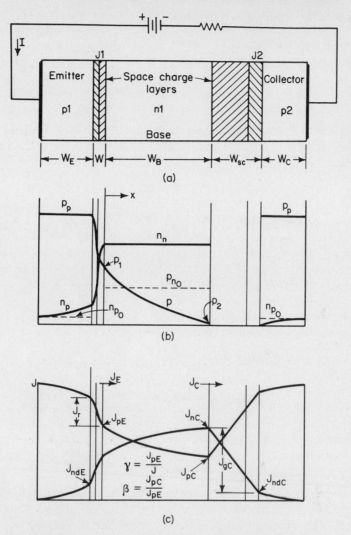

Fig. 2.24 Carrier and current densities in a biased *p-n-p* transistor with zero external base drive: (a) *p-n-p* transistor; (b) mobile carrier density; (c) current density.

where $L_p = \sqrt{D_p \tau_p}$. At the emitter edge, holes are injected into the base region and raise the concentration of minority carriers above the equilibrium value. On the collector side, the high electric field in the space-charge layer of the reverse-biased junction $J2$ reduces the concentration of carriers much below the equilibrium concentration. With the boundary conditions

$$p = p_1 \quad \text{at } x = 0, \tag{2.75}$$

$$p = p_2 \quad \text{at } x = W_B, \tag{2.76}$$

equation (2.74) can be solved to give

$$\frac{p - p_{n0}}{p_{n0}} = - \left[\frac{\left(\frac{p_1 - p_{n0}}{p_{n0}}\right) \sinh \left(\frac{x - W_B}{L_p}\right) - \left(\frac{p_2 - p_{n0}}{p_{n0}}\right) \sinh \left(\frac{x}{L_p}\right)}{\sinh \left(\frac{W_B}{L_p}\right)} \right].$$

(2.77)

The hole-current density at the emitter and collector can be determined by substituting equation (2.77) into (1.57). Thus, the hole-current density at $x = 0$ is

$$J_{pE} = -qD_p \frac{dp}{dx}\bigg|_{x=0},$$

(2.78)

so

$$J_{pE} = \frac{qD_p p_{n0}}{L_p} \left[\left(\frac{p_1 - p_{n0}}{p_{n0}}\right) \coth \frac{W_B}{L_p} - \left(\frac{p_2 - p_{n0}}{p_{n0}}\right) \operatorname{csch} \frac{W_B}{L_p} \right].$$

(2.79)

Similarly,

$$J_{pC} = \frac{qD_p p_{n0}}{L_p} \left[\left(\frac{p_1 - p_{n0}}{p_{n0}}\right) \operatorname{csch} \frac{W_B}{L_p} - \left(\frac{p_2 - p_{n0}}{p_{n0}}\right) \coth \frac{W_B}{L_p} \right].$$

(2.80)

Since we have assumed junction $J2$ to be reverse-biased, $p_2 \ll p_{n0}$, so $-(p_2 - p_{n0})/p_{n0} \rightarrow 1$, and equations (2.79) and (2.80) become

$$J_{pE} = \frac{qD_p p_{n0}}{L_p} \left(\frac{p_1 - p_{n0}}{p_{n0}} \coth \frac{W_B}{L_p} + \operatorname{csch} \frac{W_B}{L_p} \right)$$

(2.81)

and

$$J_{pC} = \frac{qD_p p_{n0}}{L_p} \left(\frac{p_1 - p_{n0}}{p_{n0}} \operatorname{csch} \frac{W_B}{L_p} + \coth \frac{W_B}{L_p} \right).$$

(2.82)

The current at $x = W_B$ consists of both holes and electrons, so the collector current density is

$$J_C = J_{pC} + J_{nC}.$$

(2.83)

Electrons which diffuse from the collector region into the space-charge layer of $J2$ are swept into the base region by the high electric field. This diffusion component of electron current can be determined by solving the diffusion equation for the collector region. For the nontransient case, equation (1.59b) is

$$\frac{d^2n}{dx^2} - \frac{n - n_{p0}}{D_n \tau_n} = 0.$$

(2.84)

Because of the high electric field in the space-charge layer, it is assumed that $n = 0$ at $x = W_B + W_{sc}$. At $x = W_B + W_{sc} + W_C$, $n = n_{p0}$ is assumed. Solving equation (2.84) and inserting these boundary conditions, we get

$$\frac{n - n_{p0}}{n_{p0}} = \frac{\left[\sinh \left(\frac{x - W_B - W_s - W_C}{L_n}\right) \right]}{\sinh \left(\frac{W_C}{L_n}\right)},$$

(2.85)

where $L_n = \sqrt{D_n \tau_n}$. The diffusion component of electron-current density entering the space-charge layer is

$$J_{ndC} = qD_n \frac{dn}{dx}\bigg|_{x=W_B+W_{sc}} \tag{2.86}$$

Then, using equation (2.85), we obtain the expression

$$J_{ndC} = \frac{qD_n n_{p0}}{L_n} \coth \frac{W_C}{L_n}. \tag{2.87}$$

Within the reverse-biased space-charge layer another component of electron current, referred to as space-charge-generated current, results from the thermal generation of electron-hole pairs.[16,17,18] These electron-hole pairs are generated in accordance with the expression derived in Sec. 1.6. That is,

$$G = \frac{n_i^2}{n_1 \tau_{p0} + p_1 \tau_{n0}}, \tag{1.50}$$

where

n_i = density of electrons or holes in intrinsic material [see equation (1.19)].

τ_{p0} = lifetime of holes in strongly n-type material.

τ_{n0} = lifetime of electrons in strongly p-type material.

n_1 = density of electrons if the Fermi level were at the energy of the recombination center = $n_i \exp q(V_t - V_i)/kT$.

p_1 = density of holes if the Fermi level were at the energy of the recombination center = $n_i \exp q(V_i - V_t)/kT$.

V_t = recombination level above the valence band.

V_i = mid-band intrinsic level.

Equation (1.50) can be rearranged in the form

$$G = \frac{n_i}{2\sqrt{\tau_{p0}\tau_{n0}} \cosh \left[q(V_t - V_i)/kT + \frac{1}{2}\ln (\tau_{p0}/\tau_{n0})\right]}, \tag{2.88}$$

which is more amenable to calculation. The reverse current density resulting from generation in the space-charge layer will be

$$J_{gC} = q \int_{W_B}^{W_B + W_{sc}} G \, dx. \tag{2.89}$$

The width of the space-charge layer W_{sc} is found by using equations (2.62) or (2.64). Substituting (2.88) into (2.89) and integrating over the space-charge layer, we obtain the generation current

$$J_{gC} = \frac{qn_i W_{sc}}{2\sqrt{\tau_{p0}\tau_{n0}} \cosh \left[q(V_t - V_i)/kT + \frac{1}{2}\ln (\tau_{p0}/\tau_{n0})\right]}. \tag{2.90}$$

The electrons which diffuse from the collector region into the space-charge region and those electrons which are generated within the space-charge layer of reverse-biased junction $J2$ are swept into the n-type base region. Using equations (2.82), (2.83), (2.87), and (2.90), we see that the collector current at $x = W_B$ is

$$J_C = \frac{qD_p p_{n0}}{L_p} \left(\frac{p_1 - p_{n0}}{p_{n0}} \operatorname{csch} \frac{W_B}{L_p} + \coth \frac{W_B}{L_p} \right) + \frac{qD_n n_{p0}}{L_n} \coth \frac{W_C}{L_n}$$

$$+ \frac{qn_i W_{sc}}{2\sqrt{\tau_{p0}\tau_{n0}} \cosh \left[q(V_t - V_i)/kT + \frac{1}{2} \ln (\tau_{p0}/\tau_{n0}) \right]}. \tag{2.91}$$

At the emitter side of the base region the current consists of holes which are injected across the emitter space-charge layer and electrons which leave the base region and recombine in the space-charge region or diffuse into the emitter layer. Thus

$$J_E = J_{pE} + (1 - \gamma)J_E, \tag{2.92}$$

or, using equation (2.81) and noting that because there is no base lead on the structure, we may set $J_E = J_C$, so that (2.92) becomes

$$\gamma J_C = \frac{qD_p p_{n0}}{L_p} \left(\frac{p_1 - p_{n0}}{p_{n0}} \coth \frac{W_B}{L_p} + \operatorname{csch} \frac{W_B}{L_p} \right). \tag{2.93}$$

If equations (2.91) and (2.93) are combined to eliminate $(p_1 - p_{n0})/p_{n0}$, we obtain the *blocking current* density through the device as a function of the design constants and the emitter efficiency. That is,

$$J_C = \frac{\dfrac{qD_p p_{n0}}{L_p} \tanh \dfrac{W_B}{L_p}}{1 - \gamma \operatorname{sech} \dfrac{W_B}{L_p}}$$

$$+ \frac{\dfrac{qn_i W_{sc}}{2\sqrt{\tau_{n0}\tau_{p0}} \cosh \left[q(V_t - V_i)/kT + \frac{1}{2}\ln (\tau_{p0}/\tau_{n0}) \right]} + \dfrac{qD_n n_{p0}}{L_n} \coth \dfrac{W_C}{L_n}}{1 - \gamma \operatorname{sech} \dfrac{W_B}{L_p}}.$$

$$\tag{2.94}$$

If we examine equation (2.94) and refer back to equations (1.80) and (1.81), we see that it is of the form

$$J_C = \frac{J_d + J_{sc}}{1 - \gamma\beta} = \frac{J_d + J_{sc}}{1 - \alpha_{pnp}}, \tag{2.95}$$

as was predicted at the beginning of this section by equation (2.72).

In order to evaluate equation (2.94), the emitter efficiency γ must be determined. By definition the emitter efficiency is

$$\gamma = \left(1 + \frac{J_n}{J_p} \right)^{-1}. \tag{1.80}$$

To determine the ratio of the electron-to-hole current across the forward-biased emitter junction, it is necessary to calculate the hole and electron currents resulting from diffusion in the base and emitter regions and that from recombination in the space-charge layer. If we consider the current flow at $x = 0$, we know from our previous calculations that the hole-current density entering the base region is

$$J_{pE} = \frac{qD_p p_{no}}{L_p} \left[\left(\frac{p_1 - p_{no}}{p_{no}} \right) \coth \frac{W_B}{L_p} - \left(\frac{p_2 - p_{no}}{p_{no}} \right) \operatorname{csch} \frac{W_B}{L_p} \right]. \qquad (2.79)$$

If it is assumed that the quasi-Fermi levels are constant across the emitter space-charge layer, then the boundary condition at $x = 0$ may be described by equation (1.68):

$$p_1 = p_{no} \exp \left(\frac{qV_E}{kT} \right). \qquad (1.68)$$

Similarly, at $x = W_B$,

$$p_2 = p_{no} \exp \left(-\frac{qV_C}{kT} \right).$$

Using equation (1.68), we find that (2.79) becomes

$$J_{pE} = \frac{qD_p p_{no}}{L_p} \left\{ \left[\exp \left(\frac{qV_E}{kT} \right) - 1 \right] \coth \frac{W_B}{L_p} - \left[\exp \left(-\frac{qV_C}{kT} \right) - 1 \right] \operatorname{csch} \frac{W_B}{L_p} \right\}. \qquad (2.96)$$

Thus we have an expression for the holes which are injected into the base region of the device.

To find the electron current across $x = 0$, note that the electrons leaving the base region and entering the emitter space-charge layer either recombine therein or diffuse into the emitter region. Thus, the electron current can be considered to consist of two components—space-charge recombination current and diffusion current. Thus,

$$J_{nE} = J_{rE} + J_{ndE}. \qquad (2.97)$$

Solving the diffusion equation for electron-current density on the emitter side of the space-charge layer, we get

$$J_{ndE} = \frac{qD_n n_{po}}{L_n} \left[\exp \left(\frac{qV_E}{kT} \right) - 1 \right] \coth \frac{W_E}{L_n}. \qquad (2.98)$$

The space-charge recombination current is given approximately by equation (1.163).

$$J_{rE} = \frac{2kTWn_i \sinh (qV_E/2kT)}{\sqrt{\tau_{no}\tau_{po}} \, (V_0 - V_E)} f(b), \qquad (2.99)$$

where $2f(b) \cong \pi$.

τ_{po} = lifetime of holes in strongly n-type material.

τ_{no} = lifetime of electrons in strongly p-type material.

V_0 = built-in potential of emitter junction.

$f(b) \cong 1.5$ for recombination centers near mid-band.[3,17,18]

V_E = the forward bias voltage applied to the emitter.

For a linear graded junction the space-charge layer becomes narrower with increasing forward bias, and for low-bias voltages its width is given by equation (2.64).

$$W = \left[\frac{12K\epsilon_0}{qs} (V_0 - V_E) \right]^{1/3}. \tag{2.100}$$

By substituting equation (2.100) into (2.99) we can express the space-charge recombination-current density in the emitter junction as

$$J_{rE} = \frac{\pi k T n_i \sinh (qV_E/2kT)}{\sqrt{\tau_{n0}\tau_{p0}} \left(\frac{12K\epsilon_0}{qs} \right)^{-1/3} (V_0 - V_E)^{2/3}}. \tag{2.101}$$

From equations (1.80), (2.96), (2.97), (2.98), and (2.101), the emitter efficiency of junction $J1$ can be expressed as

$$
\gamma^{-1} = 1 + \frac{\dfrac{qD_n n_{p0}}{L_n} \coth \dfrac{W_E}{L_n} \left[\exp \left(\dfrac{qV_E}{kT} \right) - 1 \right]}{\dfrac{qD_p p_{n0}}{L_p} \left\{ \left[\exp \left(\dfrac{qV_E}{kT} \right) - 1 \right] \coth \dfrac{W_B}{L_p} + \operatorname{csch} \dfrac{W_B}{L_p} \right\}}
$$

$$
+ \frac{\dfrac{\pi k T n_i \sinh \left(\dfrac{qV_E}{2kT} \right)}{\sqrt{\tau_{n0}\tau_{p0}} \left(\dfrac{qs}{12K\epsilon_0} \right)^{1/3} (V_0 - V_E)^{2/3}}}{\dfrac{qD_p p_{n0}}{L_p} \left\{ \left[\exp \left(\dfrac{qV_E}{kT} \right) - 1 \right] \coth \dfrac{W_B}{L_p} + \operatorname{csch} \dfrac{W_B}{L_p} \right\}}, \tag{2.102}
$$

if the collector bias is more than a volt. This equation represents γ as a function of emitter voltage. In order to determine blocking current, γ should be expressed in terms of emitter current. Emitter current versus emitter voltage can be determined by adding up the components of current across the emitter junction. Thus by using equations (2.96), (2.98), and (2.101) and observing that

$$J_E = J_{rE} + J_{ndE} + J_{pE}, \tag{2.103}$$

we finally obtain

$$J_E = \frac{\pi k T n_i \sinh \left(\dfrac{qV_E}{2kT} \right)}{\sqrt{\tau_{n0}\tau_{p0}} \left(\dfrac{qs}{12K\epsilon_0} \right)^{1/3} (V_0 - V_E)^{2/3}} + \frac{qD_n n_{p0}}{L_n} \left[\exp \left(\frac{qV_E}{kT} \right) - 1 \right] \coth \frac{W_E}{L_n}$$

$$+ \frac{qD_p p_{n0}}{L_p} \left\{ \left[\exp \left(\frac{qV_E}{kT} \right) - 1 \right] \coth \frac{W_B}{L_p} - \operatorname{csch} \frac{W_B}{L_p} \right\}. \tag{2.104}$$

Since $J_E = J_C$, the blocking-current density can be calculated by using numerical methods simultaneously to solve equations (2.94), (2.102), and (2.104).

If one of the transistor portions of a *p-n-p-n* device cannot be neglected as assumed for this derivation, then the more complete expression for the blocking current developed in Appendix B should be used.

2.5 Forward Conducting Characteristics

A typical forward voltage-current characteristic of a silicon *p-n-p-n* device is shown in Fig. 2.25. The lowest current point in the conducting mode is called the holding current and is the minimum current which the device will

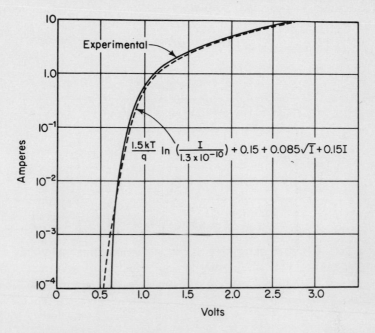

$$\frac{1.5kT}{q} \ln\left(\frac{I}{1.3 \times 10^{-10}}\right) + 0.15 + 0.085\sqrt{I} + 0.15I$$

Fig. 2.25 Typical forward conducting characteristic of a small area (approximately 15×10^{-3} cm²) *p-n-p-n* device.

carry with no gate drive and yet still will remain in the ON state. The forward conducting drop of a *p-n-p-n* device is defined simply as the voltage drop from anode to cathode in the ON state, which, of course, includes lead and contact drops. Inside the device there is a voltage rise across the center junction and voltage drops across the two outside junctions and all four regions. It must be remembered that a field current has a voltage drop associated with it, whereas a diffusion current does not. Since diffusion current is strongly dependent on minority-carrier lifetime, it is highly advantageous to maintain the lifetimes at a high level to achieve low forward drops. Unfortunately, the turn-off time characteristics grow poorer with increasing lifetime (see Sec. 2.6.1).

In Sec. 2.2.2 it was stated that the criterion for conduction was that $\alpha_1 + \alpha_2$ does exceed unity until the center junction becomes forward-biased. The result is that a buildup of charge occurs in the base regions adjacent to the center junction so that both bases become "conductivity modulated" and the transistor sections are driven into the saturation-voltage region.†[19] With the collector junction forward-biased, minority carriers are injected back into the base regions, and the net current collected decreases. Thus, the effective alpha of each transistor section drops below that of the normal alphas. When the device is in the conducting state, the center junction acts in a manner to just maintain the sum of the alphas equal to unity. With the bases heavily conductivity-modulated, both transistor sections driven into their saturation-voltage region, and virtually no lateral base drops, the voltage drop across a *p-n-p-n* device is only slightly greater than that of a *p-n* junction rectifier.

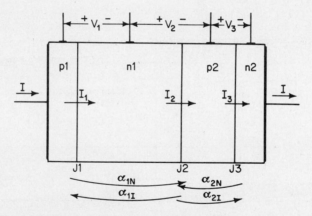

Fig. 2.26 Model used for superposition analysis.

To analyze the flow of holes and electrons in a *p-n-p-n* device in the conducting state is a rather complex process. However, by using the super-position principle, an analysis can be carried out which helps to visualize the process in a reasonably quantitative manner.[1,8]

Figure 2.26 is a schematic diagram of the structure that will be analyzed. For this particular analysis the voltage drops across the bulk portions of the various regions are assumed to be negligible, and only the junction drops are

† A transistor is in its saturation-voltage region when the base is driven with sufficient current to cause its collector junction to become forward-biased. The conductivity of a semiconductor can be expressed by equation (1.55a), $\sigma = q\mu_n n + q\mu_p p$. With large injected carrier densities both n and p, the charge carriers, may increase by orders of magnitude over that with no injection. As a result, the base resistance will drop markedly and is said to be "conductivity-modulated."

considered. These voltages V_1, V_2, and V_3 are taken to be positive from left to right across junctions $J1$, $J2$, and $J3$. The saturation current of each junction with the other junctions *short-circuited* is I_{S_1}, I_{S_2}, and I_{S_3}, respectively; and the currents through the junctions are I_1, I_2, and I_3. The emitter efficiencies of junctions $J1$, $J2$, and $J3$ are γ_1, γ_2, and γ_3, respectively; and the transport factors across $n1$ and $p2$ are β_1 and β_2, respectively. Thus, with V_1 and V_3 positive, the normal current-gain factors,

$$\alpha_{1N} = \gamma_1\beta_1 \tag{2.105}$$

and

$$\alpha_{2N} = \gamma_3\beta_2, \tag{2.106}$$

describe the flow of minority-carrier current from region $p1$ to $p2$ and from $n2$ to $n1$, respectively.

If the voltage across junction $J2$ is of the sign opposite to that indicated in Fig. 2.26, then $J2$ will be forward-biased and emit minority carriers in both directions. If γ_2 is defined as the efficiency with which $J2$ emits holes into the $n1$-region, then the remainder of the current across $J2$ will consist of electrons, so the efficiency with which electrons are emitted into region $p2$ will be $1 - \gamma_2$. The emitted holes will diffuse toward $J1$ and the electrons toward $J3$. The ratio of the minority-carrier current reaching an outer junction $J1$ or $J3$ to the total current crossing $J2$ is defined as the *inverse alpha*. These alphas may be written as

$$\alpha_{1I} = \gamma_2\beta_1, \tag{2.107}$$

$$\alpha_{2I} = (1 - \gamma_2)\beta_2. \tag{2.108}$$

By the use of superposition, the equations describing the current flow within the device can now be written. This is accomplished by applying voltage across each junction separately and then adding the currents at each junction which result from each voltage V_1, V_2, and V_3.†

With $V_1 > 0$, $V_2 = V_3 = 0$, the currents at each junction are

$$I_1 = I_{S_1} \left[\exp \left(\frac{qV_1}{nkT} \right) - 1 \right], \tag{2.109}$$

$$I_2 = \alpha_{1N} I_{S_1} \left[\exp \left(\frac{qV_1}{nkT} \right) - 1 \right], \tag{2.110}$$

$$I_3 = 0. \tag{2.111}$$

† The exponent of the expression $[\exp (qV/kt) - 1]$ used in equation 1.85 has been modified by the constant n; it is now qV/nkT to allow for deviation from simple theory. The value of n varies from 1 to 2 and depends on the current level, the density of the trapping sites and their energy levels.[3,17,18,22]

With $V_3 > 0$, $V_1 = V_2 = 0$:

$$I_1 = 0, \tag{2.112}$$

$$I_2 = \alpha_{2N} I_{S_3} \left[\exp \left(\frac{qV_3}{nkT} \right) - 1 \right], \tag{2.113}$$

$$I_3 = I_{S_3} \left[\exp \left(\frac{qV_3}{nkT} \right) - 1 \right]. \tag{2.114}$$

With $V_2 < 0$, $V_1 = V_3 = 0$:

$$I_1 = -\alpha_{1I} I_{S_2} \left[\exp \left(-\frac{qV_2}{nkT} \right) - 1 \right], \tag{2.115}$$

$$I_2 = -I_{S_2} \left[\exp \left(-\frac{qV_2}{nkT} \right) - 1 \right], \tag{2.116}$$

$$I_3 = -\alpha_{2I} I_{S_2} \left[\exp \left(-\frac{qV_2}{nkT} \right) - 1 \right]. \tag{2.117}$$

For the case where V_1, V_2, and V_3 are all different from zero, the total current across each junction can be found by superposition of the above results and

$$I_1 = I_{S_1} \left[\exp \left(\frac{qV_1}{nkT} \right) - 1 \right] - \alpha_{1I} I_{S_2} \left[\exp \left(-\frac{qV_2}{nkT} \right) - 1 \right], \tag{2.118}$$

$$I_2 = \alpha_{1N} I_{S_1} \left[\exp \left(\frac{qV_1}{nkT} \right) - 1 \right] - I_{S_2} \left[\exp \left(-\frac{qV_2}{nkT} \right) - 1 \right]$$
$$+ \alpha_{2N} I_{S_3} \left[\exp \left(\frac{qV_3}{nkT} \right) - 1 \right], \tag{2.119}$$

$$I_3 = -\alpha_{2I} I_{S_2} \left[\exp \left(-\frac{qV_2}{nkT} \right) - 1 \right] + I_{S_3} \left[\exp \left(\frac{qV_3}{nkT} \right) - 1 \right]. \tag{2.120}$$

With the device in the conducting state and with current flowing out of only the two end terminals, then $I_1 = I_2 = I_3$. To obtain the relationship between terminal current and voltage, the equations above are solved for the $[\exp (qV/nkT) - 1]$ functions and give the following expressions:

$$I_{S_1} \left[\exp \left(\frac{qV_1}{nkT} \right) - 1 \right] = \left(\frac{1 - \alpha_{2N}\alpha_{2I} + \alpha_{2N}\alpha_{1I} - \alpha_{1I}}{1 - \alpha_{1N}\alpha_{1I} - \alpha_{2N}\alpha_{2I}} \right) I = A_1 I, \tag{2.121}$$

$$I_{S_2} \left[\exp \left(-\frac{qV_2}{nkT} \right) - 1 \right] = \left(\frac{\alpha_{1N} + \alpha_{2N} - 1}{1 - \alpha_{1N}\alpha_{1I} - \alpha_{2N}\alpha_{2I}} \right) I = A_2 I, \tag{2.122}$$

$$I_{S_3} \left[\exp \left(\frac{qV_3}{nkT} \right) - 1 \right] = \left(\frac{1 - \alpha_{1N}\alpha_{1I} + \alpha_{1N}\alpha_{2I} - \alpha_{2I}}{1 - \alpha_{1N}\alpha_{1I} - \alpha_{2N}\alpha_{2I}} \right) I = A_3 I. \tag{2.123}$$

Rearranging these equations, we get

$$V_1 = \frac{nkT}{q} \ln \left(\frac{A_1 I}{I_{S_1}} + 1 \right),$$ (2.124)

$$V_2 = - \frac{nkT}{q} \ln \left(\frac{A_2 I}{I_{S_2}} + 1 \right),$$ (2.125)

$$V_3 = \frac{nkT}{q} \ln \left(\frac{A_3 I}{I_{S_3}} + 1 \right).$$ (2.126)

In the ON state $(AI/I_S) \gg 1$. In addition, if $(AI/I_S) > 1$, V_2 must be negative in order to satisfy equation (2.125). This means that V_2 must be forward-biased when the device is in the conducting state. Hence, the total voltage drop across the device can be written

$$V_T = V_1 + V_2 + V_3 = \frac{nkT}{q} \left[\ln \left(\frac{A_1 A_3}{A_2} \right) + \ln \left(\frac{I_{S_2} I}{I_{S_1} I_{S_3}} \right) \right].$$ (2.127)

Since the forward drop across a p-n diode is equal to $(nkT/q)(\ln I/I_S)$, we see that the total drop across all three junctions will be greater than that across a p-n junction by $(nkT/q)(\ln A_1 A_3/A_2)$. For a device constructed as described in Chap. 3, the alpha values at normal load currents might be $\alpha_{1N} = 0.7$, $\alpha_{2N} = 0.9$, $\alpha_{1I} = 0.6$, and $\alpha_{2I} = 0.1$. Thus, $(A_1 A_3/A_2) = (1.73)(1.14)/(1.22) = 1.62$. Using the experimental value of $n = 1.5$ shown in Fig. 2.25, we find that $nkT/q(\ln A_1 A_3/A_2) = 0.02$ v. Thus, one would expect the voltage drop across the device to be only slightly higher than that of a conventional p-n junction if resistive drops within the device can be neglected. Using the same values of alpha and calculating the voltage drops across the device, we find that for a current density of 50 amp/cm^2, $V_1 = 0.96$ v, $V_2 = -0.95$ v, and $V_3 = 1.13$ v, giving a combined voltage drop across the device of 1.14 v.

At high current densities nonlinear resistive drops are expected to occur within the body of the p and n regions. An ohmic drop is not necessarily expected, since all four regions are conductivity-modulated owing to minority-carrier injection.[35] Moreover, if the emitter efficiency of either $J1$ or $J3$ drops appreciably, then the minority-carrier current collected at $J2$ will provide insufficient drive for the opposite base region. If this situation exists, the device will become unsaturated and behave much the same way as a transistor with insufficient base drive to drive it into saturation. Thus, the voltage drop across the device will increase rapidly with increasing current, and increased gate drive will cause the voltage drop across the device to decrease.

If both emitters are sufficiently heavily doped, then the voltage drops within the device could be expected to be of the same general form as that which occurs for p^+-n-n^+ devices.[20,21,22] That is, one would expect the forward voltage drop characteristic at high current densities to be of the form

$(V - V_0) = K\sqrt{I}$, where V_0 is the built-in potential of the device and K is a constant. At much higher load currents, lead resistances will become important, and $(V - V_0) \sim IR_0$. Combining these expressions with equation (2.127), we get

$$V = \frac{nkT}{q}\left[\ln\left(\frac{I}{I_S}\right) + \ln\left(\frac{A_1 A_3}{A_2}\right)\right] + K_F\sqrt{I} + IR_0. \qquad (2.128)$$

As can be seen from Fig. 2.25, the agreement between an equation of this form and experimental data is quite reasonable and probably to some extent accidental.

2.6 Dynamic Operation

In studying the transient operation of *p-n-p-n* devices, it is convenient to consider them to be controlled by charge rather than by current.[23] In the case of most transistors this approach is particularly advantageous, since control over the electronic charge within their base layers can be maintained by external means (i.e., a base connection is provided).[24,25,26] With a *p-n-p-n* structure, little external control can be exercised, because of the positive feedback effects within the device and because one base region is floating. Nevertheless, a great deal of insight into *p-n-p-n* operation can be gleaned by studying its charge distribution and the charge motion which results from electric fields and diffusion effects.

2.6.1 TURN-OFF OR RECOVERY TIME

When a *p-n-p-n* is in the conducting state, all three junctions are forward-biased, as shown in Fig. 2.9. Consequently, both bases and, in some cases, one or both emitter regions contain excess minority- and majority-carrier charge, which increases with forward current. To switch back to the blocking state this excess† stored charge must be swept out by an electric field or decay by recombination. In a circuit sense, this turn-off process is generally initiated by reducing the load current to a value less than the holding current or by reversing the current flow through the structure. Another possibility is turn-off by removal of base current from the gate lead, but this technique is limited to low currents or specially designed devices (see Sec. 2.7).

If the voltage is reversed across the structure shown in Fig. 2.9, the two outer junctions *J*1 and *J*3 are driven into reverse bias, whereas the center junction remains forward-biased. Because of the high impurity concentrations usually on both sides of junction *J*3, it will have a relatively low avalanche-breakdown voltage as compared to junctions *J*1 and *J*2. Moreover, the center

† For this situation, excess charge is defined as the difference between the mobile charge in the device during forward conduction and that found in the blocking state.

junction will be a relatively good emitter of holes, because in many *p-n-p-n* device designs the equilibrium concentration of holes in *p2* is much greater than that of electrons in *n1*. If the reverse voltage which is applied is greater than the breakdown voltage of *J3*, then the resulting current waveforms and charge distributions assume the configurations shown in Fig. 2.27.

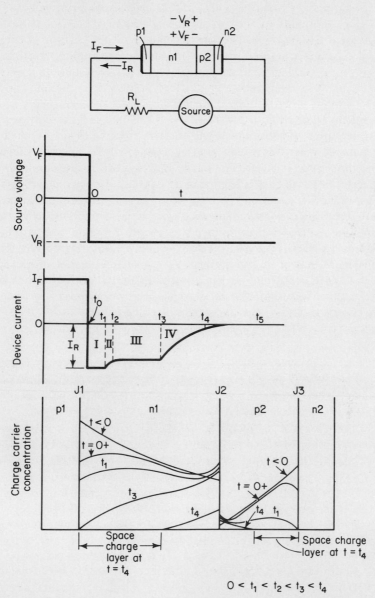

$$0 < t_1 < t_2 < t_3 < t_4$$

Fig. 2.27 Current waveforms and charge distributions during turn-off.

The current waveform can be divided into four regions. In region I the current is limited only by the external circuit impedance. During this period, the minority-carrier concentration at the junctions is sufficiently high for the load current to flow by diffusion without space-charge-layer buildup. When the excess minority carrier concentration at junction $J3$ reaches zero (time t_1), its space-charge layer begins to widen and $J3$ becomes reverse-biased. As the voltage across $J3$ builds up, the current through the circuit decays as shown in region II until the avalanche-breakdown voltage of the junction is reached. At time t_2 the voltage across $J3$ becomes essentially a constant voltage drop in series with the remaining $p2$-$n1$-$p1$ portion of the device, which still looks like a short circuit. As a consequence of $J2$'s high hole-emitter efficiency, most of the current which flows through it during the reverse recovery phase is comprised of hole current injected from $p2$ into $n1$. Thus, as holes diffuse across $n1$ to $J1$ and are swept into the anode emitter, other holes are supplied into the $n1$ base by means of injection at junction $J2$. On the other hand, as electrons diffuse across $p2$ to $J3$ and are swept into the cathode emitter, only a small fraction of the base current near $J2$ consists of electrons injected into $p2$. Thus, we have a situation in which electrons are being swept out of base $p2$ by $J3$ at a much faster rate than they are injected by $J2$. Therefore, holes are being injected into region $n1$ by $J2$ at almost the same rate as they are being swept out by $J1$. The result is that regions $p2$ and $n2$ are swept free of charge prior to that of $n1$. After time t_2 the $p2$-$n2$-$p1$ portion of the device continues to look like a short circuit, as indicated in III, until the excess holes at $J1$ reach zero. When this occurs, the voltage across $J1$ begins to build up, and the current decays to its steady-state blocking value.

The time from 0 to t_1 is called the *first storage time* t_{s_1}; that from t_1 to t_2, the *first decay time* t_{d_1}; from 0 to t_3, the *second storage time* t_{s_2}; and that from t_3 until the current reaches 10 per cent of its value at t_3, the *second decay time* t_{d_2}. Note that if the reverse supply voltage is less than the breakdown voltage of $J3$, then one sees only the storage and delay time associated with that junction.

By considering the device to be charge-controlled, an analysis of the transient operation of the device can be obtained. If we assume that the regions between the junction space-charge layers are essentially in space-charge balance (i.e., neutral), then the excess holes and electrons in a given base region are equal. Thus, the holes which are injected into region $n1$, minus the holes removed from region $n1$, must be equal to the number which recombine plus those stored. Mathematically, this statement, for a "small volume," reduces to one of the continuity equations,

$$-\nabla \cdot \mathbf{J}_p = q\,\frac{\partial p}{\partial t} + q\left(\frac{p - p_0}{\tau_p}\right) \qquad (1.58a)$$

or

$$\nabla \cdot \mathbf{J}_n = q\,\frac{\partial n}{\partial t} + q\left(\frac{n - n_0}{\tau_n}\right). \qquad (1.58b)$$

Integrating equation (1.58a) over the volume of the neutral region of base n_1, we can find the number of excess holes, Q_1, in the $n1$ base layer. Thus

$$\int_{\text{vol. of } n1} -\nabla \cdot \mathbf{J}_p \, dv = \frac{Q_1}{\tau_p} + \frac{\partial Q_1}{\partial t},$$

where

$$Q_1 = \int_{\text{vol. of } n1} q(p - p_0) \, dv. \tag{2.129}$$

From Gauss' Law we get

$$I_{B_1} = \frac{Q_1}{\tau_p} + \frac{\partial Q_1}{\partial t}, \tag{2.130}$$

where I_{B_1} is the net number of holes times the electronic charge q which flows into base region $n1$. The same type of equation holds for the excess electrons of base region $p2$. With the device in the forward conducting state and a steady d-c current flowing, $\partial Q/\partial t = 0$; therefore, the charge and base current relation can be determined from equation (2.130) to be $\tau_p I_{B_1 F} = Q_{1F}$. $I_{B_1 F}$ can be found by using equations (2.121) and (2.122). The hole current injected into $n1$ is

$$I\left[\gamma_1\left(\frac{1 - \alpha_{2N}\alpha_{2I} + \alpha_{2N}\alpha_{1I} - \alpha_{1I}}{1 - \alpha_{1N}\alpha_{1I} - \alpha_{2N}\alpha_{2I}}\right) + \gamma_2\left(\frac{\alpha_{1N} + \alpha_{2N} - 1}{1 - \alpha_{1N}\alpha_{1I} - \alpha_{2N}\alpha_{2I}}\right)\right], \tag{2.131}$$

and the hole current removed by collection is

$$I\left[\alpha_{1N}\left(\frac{1 - \alpha_{2N}\alpha_{2I} + \alpha_{2N}\alpha_{1I} - \alpha_{1I}}{1 - \alpha_{1N}\alpha_{1I} - \alpha_{2N}\alpha_{2I}}\right) + \alpha_{1I}\left(\frac{\alpha_{1N} + \alpha_{2N} - 1}{1 - \alpha_{1N}\alpha_{1I} - \alpha_{2N}\alpha_{2I}}\right)\right]. \tag{2.132}$$

Thus the net base current, i.e., (2.131) minus (2.132), is

$$I_{B_1} = I\{(\gamma_1 - \alpha_{1N}) + [\alpha_{1I}(\gamma_1 - \alpha_{1N}) + (\gamma_2 - \alpha_{1I})]A_0\}, \tag{2.133}$$

where

$$A_0 = \frac{\alpha_{1N} + \alpha_{2N} - 1}{1 - \alpha_{1N}\alpha_{1I} - \alpha_{2N}\alpha_{2I}}. \tag{2.134}$$

For simplicity, let us assume that all the emitter efficiencies of the device that we will analyze are unity and that $\alpha_{1N} = \alpha_{1I}$. Equation (2.133) then becomes

$$I_{B_1 F} = \alpha_{2N} I_F, \tag{2.135}$$

and, using equation (2.130), we see that

$$Q_{1F} = \tau_p \alpha_{2N} I_F \tag{2.136}$$

if we suddenly reverse the voltage across the device at $t = 0$. At first the current will be determined only by the series resistance of the circuit. The excess electrons in base region $p2$ are swept out as they diffuse to junction $J3$. Since we have assumed that $J2$ is a perfect emitter of holes, no electrons are injected into the $p2$ base region; thus, it recovers rather quickly, as a base width limited diode does. However, the transistor formed by $p2$-$n1$-$p1$ does not recover quickly, since holes swept out of $n1$ by the field across $J1$ are immediately replaced by holes injected by $J2$. The hole current through the structure is then proportional to the charge in base $n1$. Charge balance requires that the excess hole and electron concentration be equal. With $\gamma_2 = 1$ electrons can escape from base region $n1$ only by recombining with the excess holes. With these assumptions the hole current injected into the base at $J2$ is equal to that collected at $J1$, so I_{B_1} (the net base current) is now zero. Using equation (2.130), we have

$$\frac{Q_1}{\tau_p} + \frac{\partial Q_1}{\partial t} = 0, \tag{2.137}$$

and, integrating, we get

$$Q_1 = A \exp\left(-\frac{t}{\tau_p}\right). \tag{2.138}$$

At $t = 0$, $Q_1 = Q_{1F}$; therefore,

$$Q_1 = Q_{1F} \exp\left(-\frac{t}{\tau_p}\right), \tag{2.139}$$

and using equation (2.136), we see that

$$Q_1 = \tau_p \alpha_{2N} I_F \exp\left(-\frac{t}{\tau_p}\right). \tag{2.140}$$

Now, since the hole current through the structure is proportional to the excess charge in base $n1$, we can say that

$$I = I_F \exp\left(-\frac{t}{\tau_p}\right), \tag{2.141}$$

if at $t = 0$, $I = I_F$.

Thus we see that for this simple case the current decay is exponential and highly dependent on the minority-carrier lifetime in base layer $n1$. Moreover, it should also be apparent that the excess charge in $n1$ must drop nearly to zero before forward voltage can be reapplied; otherwise, the device will switch immediately into conduction. In fact, we know that the current must drop below the holding current I_H for the device to block forward voltage when it is reapplied. Thus, the turn-off time will be

$$t_{\text{off}} \cong \tau_p \ln \frac{I_F}{I_H}, \tag{2.142}$$

if dv/dt effects are assumed to be negligible.

We see that the turn-off time (i.e., the time which must elapse after conduction before the device will block reapplied forward voltage) is strongly dependent on the lifetime of the high-resistivity base layer. It should be pointed out that our assumptions are quite restrictive; nevertheless, they are not too unrealistic for most high-voltage SCR's now being produced. To obtain high forward and reverse blocking voltages, the donor impurity concentration of region $n1$ must be quite low. In practical devices the net impurity concentrations in regions $p1$ and $p2$ are usually much greater than that of $n1$. The result is that junctions $J1$ and $J2$ act as good hole emitters when forward-biased. As a consequence, the excess charge in base $p2$ can be swept out, whereas the excess charge in region $n1$ must decay by recombination. Thus, the anode turn-off time of an SCR is determined primarily by recombination in base $n1$, so lifetime is the primary controlling factor. Generally, the lifetime of this region can be controlled by diffusing gold into the wafer during the manufacturing process.

2.6.2 dv/dt TRIGGERING

By applying a rapidly rising positive voltage to the anode of a p-n-p-n device, it can be made to "turn on" if the rate of rise of voltage, dv/dt, and the applied voltage are sufficiently great.[5,6,27] This phenomenon can be particularly troublesome when transients occur in the SCR circuitry and cause undesired switching of the device.

A simple understanding of the problem can be gleaned through the use of the two-transistor analogue used in Sec. 2.2.1. In the previous analysis, no consideration was given to the effect of junction capacitances. If these capacitances are considered, then Fig. 2.4 can be redrawn as shown in Fig. 2.28. With the system in the blocking state a rapidly rising voltage applied to the anode lead will cause current to flow through the base-to-emitter junction of each of the transistors and collector-junction capacitance C_{J2}. Since the

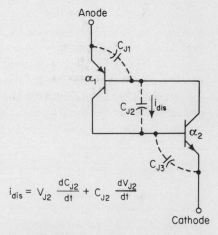

$$i_{dis} = V_{J2} \frac{dC_{J2}}{dt} + C_{J2} \frac{dV_{J2}}{dt}$$

Fig. 2.28 Two-transistor analogue showing junction capacitance.

alphas increase with emitter current, the current which flows as a result of a rapid change in voltage may cause the alpha sum to become unity. Switching then occurs.

To examine the physical operation in greater detail, let us assume an SCR to be in an equilibrium state, as shown in Fig. 2.6. In this case the charge owing to the uncompensated donor and acceptor impurities that make up the space-charge layer of $J2$ is $q = K_0\sqrt{V_0}$, where V_0 is the built-in potential and is determined by the impurity distribution at $J2$. If a rapidly rising positive voltage is applied to the anode of the device, $J1$ and $J3$ become forward-biased and $J2$ reverse-biased, as depicted by Figs. 2.7 and 2.8. Because Poisson's equation must be satisfied, mobile charge is removed from the vicinity of the junction $J2$ to permit blocking voltage to build up across it. Thus, depending on the magnitude of voltage rise applied across the device, a finite quantity of electrons will be removed from the donor impurities in the vicinity of $J2$ and will flow toward $J1$. An equal number of holes near $J2$ must flow toward $J3$. As described in Sec. 2.2, these excess majority carriers in the base regions of $p2$ and $n1$ momentarily upset space-charge neutrality and cause junctions $J1$ and $J3$ to be highly forward-biased. Consequently, minority carriers are injected into the base regions to re-establish charge neutrality. The injected minority carriers diffuse toward $J2$, some of them recombining en route and the remainder being collected at $J2$. If the resulting current which flows through the device is sufficient for the sum of the alphas to rise to unity, then the *p-n-p-n* device will trigger into the conducting state. For rating and application purposes, the dv/dt capability of a device is defined as the maximum rate of rise of forward voltage that a *p-n-p-n* will support without triggering.

Assuming that the junctions are abrupt, we can determine the displacement current through the device as follows. Since the space-charge layer that supports the voltage across $J2$ is formed by removing electrons from the n-side and holes from the p-side of the junction, the charge which is removed from either side of $J2$ as a function of voltage can be calculated. Thus, for any potential V, the number of electrons which must be removed from the vicinity of $J2$ to form the space-charge layer will be $N_d a$, as shown in Fig. 2.7. Since the electrons are displaced from the $n1$-side of junction $J2$, an equal number of holes must be displaced from the $p2$-side. Using equations (2.56) and (2.59), we find that the charge which must be removed to support a given voltage is

$$\mathcal{Q} = qAN_d a = \sqrt{\frac{2K\epsilon_0 A^2 q N_d V}{\left(1 + \dfrac{N_d}{N_a}\right)}}, \tag{2.143}$$

where

$V = V_0 + V_A$ (i.e., V is the sum of the built-in and applied voltage).
A = the area of the junction.

Thus the displacement current as a function of the rate of rise of voltage is

$$I_{\text{DIS}} = \frac{dq}{dt} = \frac{dV}{dt} \sqrt{\frac{K\epsilon_0 A^2 q N_d}{2V\left(1 + \dfrac{N_d}{N_a}\right)}}. \tag{2.144}$$

For a constant rate of rise of voltage, $dv/dt = m = \dfrac{dV}{dt}$, we get

$$I_{\text{DIS}} = \frac{mK_1}{\sqrt{V}}. \tag{2.145}$$

This displaced charge results in excess charge in both bases $n1$ and $p2$. The displaced electrons lower the potential of $n1$ with respect to $p1$, causing holes to be injected from emitter $p1$ through junction $J1$ to base $n1$ in order to re-establish electrical neutrality. The injected holes diffuse toward collector junction $J2$, the amount collected being dependent on the excess charge in base $n1$. In the same manner, displaced holes raise the potential of $p2$ with respect to $n2$, causing electrons to be injected into $n2$ by $J3$. The injected electrons diffuse toward $J2$, the amount collected being dependent on the excess charge in base $p2$. Those electrons collected by $J2$ are swept into base $n1$ where they tend to upset electrical neutrality conditions and cause junction $J1$ to inject more holes into base $n1$. Of course, the holes collected by $J2$ cause additional electrons to be injected into $p2$ by $J3$. As explained in the turn-off time discussion, this excess charge must recombine or be stored if the emitter efficiencies of $J1$ and $J3$ are equal to unity. Thus, Q_1 and Q_2, the excess charge in the bases, will be

$$\frac{dQ_1}{dt} + \frac{Q_1}{\tau_p} = \frac{mK_1}{\sqrt{V}} + f_2(Q_2), \tag{2.146}$$

$$\frac{dQ_2}{dt} + \frac{Q_2}{\tau_n} = \frac{mK_1}{\sqrt{V}} + f_1(Q_1), \tag{2.147}$$

where τ_p is the lifetime of holes in base $n1$, τ_n that of electrons in $p2$, and $f_2(Q_2)$ is the functional relationship between the excess charge in base $p2$ and the electrons collected by $J2$. Similarly, $f_1(Q_1)$ is the function which relates excess charge in base $n1$ to the holes collected by $J2$. Although these equations are nonlinear, some insight into the device's characteristics can be obtained from them.

Consider the case where the rate of voltage rise is so rapid that negligible recombination of the excess base charge occurs. In this case equation (2.146) can be written

$$\frac{dQ_1}{dV} \cong \frac{K_1}{\sqrt{V}} + \frac{f_2(Q_2)}{m}. \tag{2.148}$$

In equation (2.148) dt has been replaced by dV/m to eliminate time as a variable.

Integrating the applied voltage from 0 to V_M, we get

$$Q_1 \cong 2K_1(\sqrt{V_0 + V_M} - \sqrt{V_0}) + \int_{V_0}^{V_0 + V_M} \frac{f_2(Q_2)}{m} \, dV \tag{2.149}$$

for the excess charge in base $n1$.

A similar equation can be written for the excess charge Q_2 in base $p2$. We notice now that $f_2(Q_2) = I\alpha_2(Q_2)$† and $f_1(Q_1) = I\alpha_1(Q_1)$, where I is the

† The relationship between emitter current and excess base charge was discussed in Chap. 1.

current through the device and $\alpha_2(Q_2)$ and $\alpha_2(Q_1)$ are the charge dependent current gains for the *n2-p2-n1* and the *p1-n1-p2* sections, respectively. We expect at least one of the alphas to be quite small for values of Q up to some critical value Q_c. When the charge in the base increases above Q_c, then α will

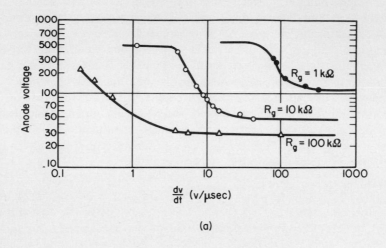

(a)

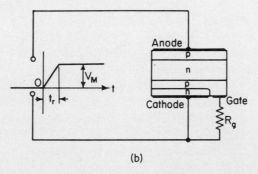

(b)

Fig. 2.29 (a) *dv/dt* capability versus voltage for a small-area *p-n-p-n* device at 25°C (area is 15×10^{-3} cm²); (b) measurement scheme for obtaining *dv/dt* capability. An input pulse having a variable rise time t_r and a maximum value V_M is applied across the device. t_r is then decreased until the device will no longer block the voltage V_M. The *dv/dt* capability is then defined as V_M/t_r (with voltage starting from zero bias), since the rate of rise is linear with time. Because the data shown above were obtained on a small device, the effect of the gate resistor was quite significant.

rise rapidly with further charge increase and as a consequence the device will trigger into conduction. Note that under these conditions the charge in the base is only a function of voltage and not the rate of rise of voltage. Experimental data substantiate this deduction, as can be seen in Fig. 2.29.

At the other extreme, the rate of change of voltage can be so small that dQ/dt is much smaller than the recombination current Q/τ. As the applied voltage continues to rise, avalanche breakdown will occur, causing the device to trigger, as already described in the section on voltage triggering. Figure 2.29 also shows the voltage triggering level. A very effective way to increase the dv/dt capability of a p-n-p-n device is by incorporating the "shorted emitter" in the construction of the device, as described in Sec. 3.7.[5,28] By means of this technique, the capacitive current can be shunted around the emitter junction so that turn-on will not occur unless the displacement current is exceedingly high. It should be pointed out that the dv/dt capability can be enhanced by lowering the minority-carrier lifetime. The result is that for a given current level, the emitter efficiencies and transport factors are reduced, so more displacement current is required to trigger the device.

2.6.3 Gate Turn-on

Earlier in this chapter, gate triggering was discussed under the assumption that transient effects could be neglected. Actually, the load current through a p-n-p-n device does not respond immediately to the application of gate current.[5,6] If the device is placed in the circuit shown in Fig. 2.30, then the load current I_A can be characterized by a delay period and a rise period.

When the load current is large compared to the gate trigger current, the delay period will depend strongly on the gate drive current. Using Fig. 2.31, we can visualize the turn-on process by thinking of it in step fashion. Let us assume that the gate is biased with a step function of current. This results in immediate injection of electrons into base $p2$, where they begin diffusing toward $J2$. However, as was pointed out in Sec. 1.8.5, it takes a finite period of time for these electrons to cross base layer $p2$. This period of time is referred to as the base transit time and can be calculated by using equation (1.106). Thus, after a short time,†

$$t_{t_2} = \frac{W_{B_2}^2}{2D_n}. \tag{2.150}$$

Following the application of gate current, electrons will arrive at collector junction $J2$. Since the anode current must equal the electron and hole current collected by $J2$, the anode current becomes equal to the gate current after a period of time t_{t_2}. Because the electrons swept into $n1$ are majority carriers,

---

† R. Davies has derived a more accurate expression for base transit time which includes the effect of lifetime; i.e.,

$$t_t = \frac{4W^2}{\pi^2 D\left(1 + \dfrac{4W^2\tau}{\pi^2 D}\right)}.$$

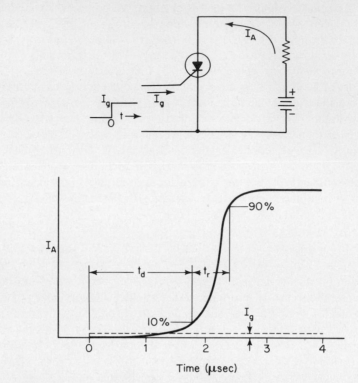

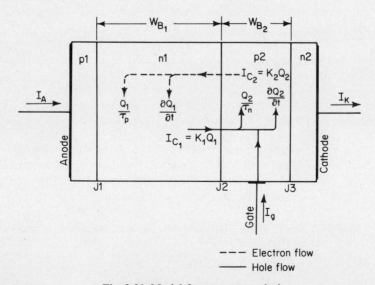

Fig. 2.30 Delay and rise time during gate turn-on.

Fig. 2.31 Model for turn-on analysis.

they cause a potential to develop across $J1$, so holes are injected from $p1$ into $n1$. Again, we must wait for a finite period of time,

$$t_{t_1} = \frac{W_{B_1}^2}{2D_p},\qquad(2.151)$$

for the holes to diffuse across the $n1$ region to be collected by $J2$. When they arrive and are swept by $J2$ into $p2$, the holes cause a further increase in injected electron current by $J3$. This process continues until the current reaches its steady-state load current level. Thus, we see that the minimum delay time is equal to the sum of the base transit times. Moreover, the delay time can be quite dependent on the gate drive current and the base-layer width of the device. It should be mentioned that, as a consequence of their wide base widths, high voltage SCR's have longer delay and turn-on times than devices designed for low-voltage service.

During gate turn-on, a p-n-p-n device begins conducting in the immediate vicinity of the emitter edge nearest the gate lead.[5,29,30,31,42] Hence, with large-area devices, that portion of the device nearest the gate may be turned on prior to the remainder of the device. As a consequence, nonuniform current distribution may become a serious problem when large-area devices are used in pulse application.[32]

Basically, a p-n-p-n device is charge-operated. Consequently, the same approach as was used in the previous section to analyze turn-off time can be used to study the one-dimensional turn-on process. Consider Fig. 2.31 and note that the base current driving the $n2$-$p2$-$n1$ portion of the device can be written

$$I_g + I_{C_1} = I_{B_2},\qquad(2.152)$$

where I_g is the gate current and I_{C_1}, the holes collected by $J2$. The electrons collected by $J2$ drive the base of the $p1$-$n1$-$p2$ transistor so that

$$I_{C_2} = I_{B_1}.\qquad(2.153)$$

If the minority-carrier transit time across the base is short compared to the anode-current rise time, then the hole current collected is proportional to the excess charge in base $n1$, and the collected electron current is proportional to the excess charge in base $p2$. Thus, we can write

$$I_{C_1} = K_1 Q_1,\qquad(2.154)$$

and

$$I_{C_2} = K_2 Q_2,\qquad(2.155)$$

where K is the proportionality constant relating the excess base charge to the collected current, as described in Sec. 1.8 of Chap. 1. The base current for each transistor either recombines or is stored; therefore,

$$I_{B_1} = \frac{Q_1}{\tau_p} + \frac{\partial Q_1}{\partial t},\qquad(2.156)$$

and

$$I_{B_2} = \frac{Q_2}{\tau_n} + \frac{\partial Q_2}{\partial t}. \qquad (2.157)$$

Combining equations (2.153), (2.155) with (2.156), and (2.152), (2.154) with (2.157), we get

$$K_2 Q_2 = \frac{Q_1}{\tau_p} + \frac{\partial Q_1}{\partial t}, \qquad (2.158)$$

$$I_g + K_1 Q_1 = \frac{Q_2}{\tau_n} + \frac{\partial Q_2}{\partial t}. \qquad (2.159)$$

These equations can be solved through the use of Laplace transforms.[33]
Assuming no excess charge in the bases prior to turn-on, we obtain

$$Q_1(t) = K_2 I_g \left[\frac{1}{ab} + \frac{\exp(-at)}{a(a-b)} + \frac{\exp(-bt)}{b(b-a)} \right] \qquad (2.160)$$

and

$$Q_2(t) = \frac{I_g}{\tau_p} \left[\frac{1}{ab} + \frac{(1-a\tau_p)}{a(a-b)} \exp(-at) + \frac{(1-b\tau_p)}{b(b-a)} \exp(-bt) \right], \qquad (2.161)$$

where

$$a, b = \frac{\tau_p + \tau_n}{2\tau_p \tau_n} \left[1 \pm \sqrt{1 + \frac{4K_1 K_2 \tau_p^2 \tau_n^2 - 4\tau_p \tau_n}{(\tau_p + \tau_n)^2}} \right].$$

for the solution to the excess charge in the $n1$ base at time t. The anode current is determined by noting that the total collected current at $J2$ must be equal to I_A. Using equations (2.154) and (2.155), we get

$$I_A(t) = K_1 Q_1(t) + K_2 Q_2(t). \qquad (2.162)$$

Figure 2.32 shows an experimental curve along with a calculated curve using equation (2.162). A small-area device was chosen to minimize two-dimensional effects. Although the calculated and experimental curves do not match perfectly, they do show reasonable agreement with respect to shape and order of magnitude.

Let us now consider the two-dimensional effects during turn-on of a large-area SCR. As was pointed out in the section on gate triggering, lateral biasing plays a strong role during the turn-on interval. In Fig. 2.19 we note that when the gate switch is closed, electrons are injected from the cathode emitter into base $n1$ in the region nearest the gate connection. Because of the lateral base resistance in the $p2$ base, it is apparent from equation (2.40) that areas remote from the gate lead are not much affected by the gate pulse. Electrons are injected by $J3$ in a small area near the gate contact and diffuse

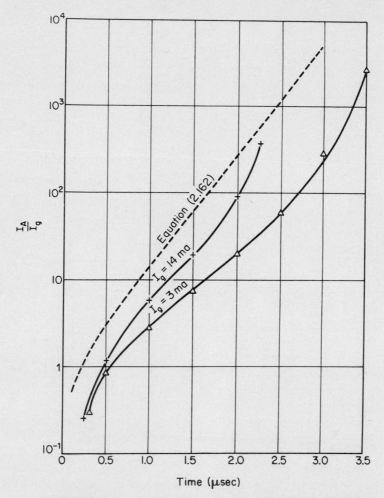

Fig. 2.32 Ratio of anode-gate current versus time for a small-area SCR (15×10^{-3} cm^2) for two different values of gate current. Calculations were based on the assumptions that the device had electron and hole lifetimes of 2 and 5 μsec. respectively and that the p- and n-layer thicknesses and doping concentrations were the same as those shown in Fig. 3.4.

$J2$. Upon being collected by $J2$ and swept into $n1$, the electrons lower the potential of $n1$ with respect to $p1$, causing $J1$ to be forward-biased in the area adjacent to the region of $J2$ where the electrons were collected. Consequently, holes are injected from $p1$ to $n1$ to maintain charge balance. These holes diffuse across base $n1$ in a time of approximately $W_{B_1}^2/2D_p$ and are collected

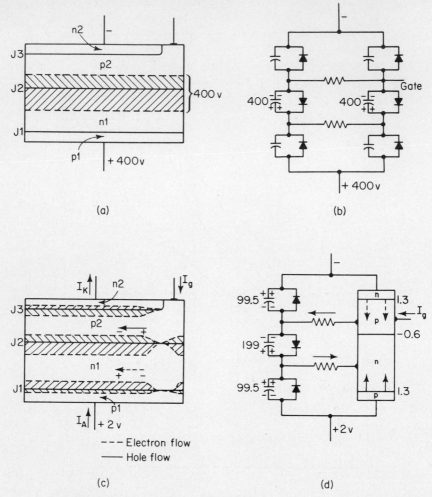

Fig. 2.33 Turn-on mechanism.

by *J*2 and swept into base region *p*2.†[(34,35)] The collected holes cause a further increase in forward bias across *J*3 and more electrons are injected, etc. This process continues until the current is limited by the load.

As the region of the device near the gate switches to the conducting state, the load current rises, the voltage across the load builds up, and the voltage across the SCR drops. Thus, part of the device is ON and the remainder is OFF.

† If the *n*1 base is relatively wide and of rather high resistivity, the electrons collected at *J*2 establish an "ohmic field" in *n*1 which causes the holes injected at *J*1 to drift as well as diffuse toward *J*2. Thus, the transport factor will be greater than diffusion theory would predict, and the transit time is shorter.

The situation can be visualized by considering Fig. 2.33. In schematic (a) the SCR is in the blocking state, with $J2$ supporting the voltage. An equivalent circuit in (b) represents the junctions as diodes with the junction capacitance shown separately. When the device is triggered, the region nearest the gate turns on, the anode-to-cathode voltage drops, and the junction capacitances are discharged. However, in the regions remote from the gate, the rapid fall in anode-to-cathode voltage causes the charge on the center junction to be partially redistributed onto the emitter junctions. As a consequence, $J2$ becomes less reverse-biased, whereas the two emitter junctions go from forward

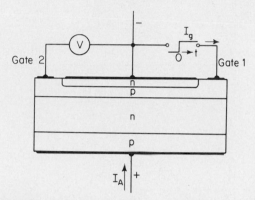

Fig. 2.34 SCR with two gates for measuring speed of current propagation.

to reverse bias. This causes very large lateral voltage drops and high current densities in the base regions. Although the process of discharging the junction capacitances is quite rapid, the time required for this process for an SCR one-half inch in diameter may exceed fifty microseconds.

Figure 2.34 is a diagram of a device having two gate leads. A trigger pulse was applied to one of the gates, while the voltage with respect to the cathode was measured on the other one. The result is shown in Fig. 2.35. Note that the voltage drop across the SCR is several volts, even though a part of it is conducting. The current during this period is space-charge limited by the mobile carriers. Consequently, fast-rising currents cause heat to be generated at a very rapid rate and can readily cause failure in a large-area device owing to a hot spot.[29,30]

2.7 Gate Turn-off

A *p-n-p-n* device is maintained in the conducting state by the two component transistors which comprise the device, each providing base drive for the other. This system is regenerative and thus constitutes a positive feedback

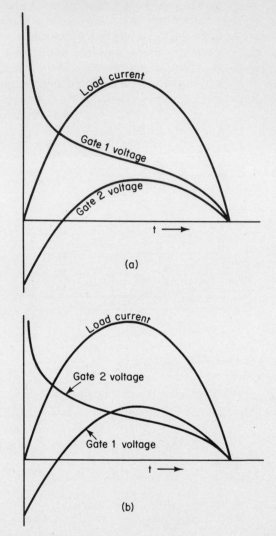

Fig. 2.35 Waveshapes resulting from triggering the two-gated SCR of Fig. 2.34 with gate 1, as shown in (a), and gate 2, as shown in (b).

loop. One method used for turning the device off is to remove the base drive from one of the transistor sections, as shown in Fig. 2.36. However, this technique is not generally effective on most SCR's, particularly those rated for higher current, because of lateral biasing effects resulting from the gate turn-off current. Consequently, gate turn-off devices are specifically designed and rated to overcome the problems associated with lateral base-biasing and related effects. By proper design, *p-n-p-n* devices can be switched off with considerable gain.[36,37,39,40]

Although the turn-off mechanism is a two-dimensional process involving lateral emitter-biasing effects, a simple one-dimensional analysis provides a great deal of insight into the device's operation.[36,37,38,39] By referring to Figs. 2.36 and 2.37, we see that the base current supplied to the *n-p-n* section

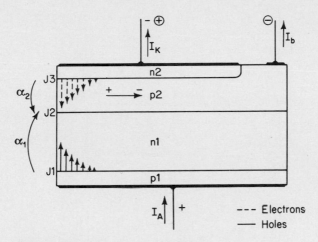

Fig. 2.36 Turn-off by means of the gate.

consists of the hole current collected at $J2$ minus that removed via the gate. Thus

$$I_p = \alpha_1 I_A + I_{pd} + I_{sc} - I_b, \qquad (2.163)$$

whereas the drive required by the *p2* base is

$$I_{B_2} = (1 - \alpha_2)I_K - I_{nd}. \qquad (2.164)$$

If the hole current supplied to the *p2* base region is more than that needed for recombination with electrons in it, as denoted by equation (2.164), then the *n2-p2-n1* section will drive the *n1* base of the *p1-n1-p2* section with more electron current than it requires for hole recombination; the result is that both regions are driven into saturation, so junction $J2$ becomes forward-biased. As a consequence of the forward bias, holes will be injected from *p2* to *n1* and electrons from *n1* to *p2*, causing the minority-carrier concentration gradients to be lower across the two base regions; this effectively lowers the alphas until the base drive provided by each transistor section is just equal to the other transistor section-recombination current requirements. Thus with a *p-n-p-n* in the ON state, the sum of the alphas would exceed unity if junction $J2$ were not forward-biased.

To turn the device off, the current drive to the *p2* base I_p must be less than that required to keep the *n2-p2-n1* transistor section in saturation. Thus, using equations (2.163) and (2.164), we obtain

$$\alpha_1 I_A + I_{pd} + I_{sc} - I_b < (1 - \alpha_2)I_K - I_{nd}. \tag{2.165}$$

By Kirchhoff's law we see that $I_A = I_K + I_b$, and then

$$I_b > \frac{(\alpha_1 + \alpha_2 - 1)I_A + I_d + I_{sc}}{\alpha_2}, \tag{2.166}$$

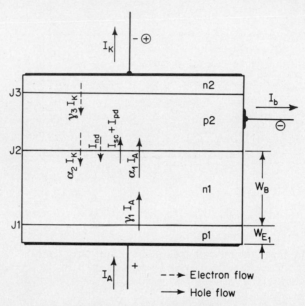

Fig. 2.37 *p-n-p-n* model for turn-off analysis.

where $I_d = I_{nd} + I_{pd}$, and I_b is the current which must be extracted from the gate to achieve turn-off.

If we define the turn-off gain as the ratio of current flowing in the load when the switch is on to the base current required to turn the switch off, then

$$G_{\text{OFF}} = \frac{I_A}{I_b} = \frac{\alpha_2}{(\alpha_1 + \alpha_2 - 1)}, \tag{2.167}$$

where we have neglected thermally generated currents. Thus, high turn-off gains can be achieved in three-terminal *p-n-p-n* devices if they are designed so that, when ON (with the voltage across *J2* equal to zero), the alpha sum just exceeds unity and α_2 remains reasonably high. Figure 2.38 shows a plot of turn-off gain as a function of current for a two-ampere device.

Now consider the design parameters which determine the magnitude of the alphas and their variation with current density. When in the ON state, the load current I_A will be determined principally by the supply voltage and the load resistance. To remain in the conducting mode, the holes supplied to base region $p2$ must be greater than or equal to the electrons which recombine, whereas the electrons supplied to base region $n1$ must be greater than or

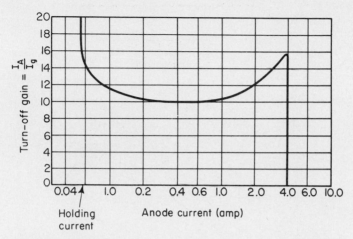

Fig. 2.38 Turn-off gain versus load current for a two-ampere p-n-p-n device.

equal to the holes which recombine in that region. Using equations (2.163) and (2.164) and relation $I_A = I_K + I_b$, we see that, for turn-off,

$$I_A(1 - \alpha_1) - I_d - I_{sc} = \alpha_2 I_K, \qquad (2.168)$$

where $I_d = I_{pd} + I_{nd}$, and the alphas are the values which would exist if not altered by forward injection of $J2$. Since the alphas vary nonlinearly with emitter currents, turn-off gain is most easily visualized in graphical form. Thus, if the alphas are assumed to vary with emitter current, as shown in Fig. 2.39(a), the solution to equation (2.168) can be determined graphically. The left- and right-hand sides of the equation are plotted as a function of I_A and I_K, respectively, in Fig. 2.39(b). Next, the load current at which the turn-off gain is desired is selected and a vertical line constructed to intersect the $(1 - \alpha_1)I_A - I_d - I_{sc}$ curve. For turn-off to occur, the $\alpha_2 I_K$ must have the same value as that of the intersection at point four. Thus a horizontal line is drawn from point two until it intersects the $\alpha_2 I_K$ curve at point three. A vertical line is then dropped to the abscissa to obtain the cathode current I_K. I_b is the separation between the two vertical lines, since $I_b = I_A - I_K$. The resulting gate turn-off gain is shown in Fig. 2.39(c).

The values of the alphas and their variation with emitter current can be

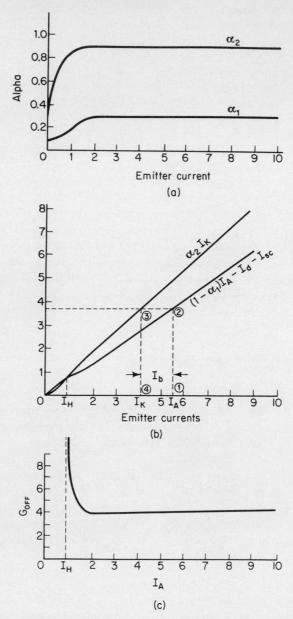

Fig. 2.39 Graphical determination of turn-off gain.

varied by means of the minority-carrier lifetimes, the doping levels, and the geometry. As an example, α_1 can be lowered to increase turn-off gain [see equation (2.167)] by carefully controlling the emitter efficiency of junction $J1$.

At moderate current densities the emitter efficiency γ_1 is given by the expression [see equation (1.80) of Chap. 1]

$$\gamma_1 \approx \left(1 + \frac{\sigma_{n_1} W_{B_1}}{\sigma_{p_1} W_{E_1}}\right)^{-1},$$

where σ_{n_1} and σ_{p_1} are the conductivities of bases $n1$ and $p1$, respectively, W_{B_1} the width of base $n1$ and W_{E_1} the width of emitter $p1$. Thus, by control of the widths and doping of the two regions, γ_1 can be varied over a wide range. Moreover, considerable variation can be expected with current density if the doping in the base layer is moderately low, owing to conductivity modulation of the high-resistivity $n1$ base region.[3] As a result, the turn-off gain will increase with load current. However, as base current is withdrawn from the gate of the device, the lateral base-voltage drop causes emitter junction $J3$ to become reverse-biased in the vicinity of the gate region. This situation occurs even though the opposite end of the emitter junction is in a forward-biased state. As more and more gate current is withdrawn from the base, that region of the cathode emitter junction adjacent to the gate connection finally avalanches, with the result that a shunt path for the current develops between gate and cathode. Consequently, higher anode currents cannot be turned off by removal of gate current; therefore, the turn-off gain drops to zero, as shown in Fig. 2.38.

REFERENCES

1. J. L. Moll, M. Tanenbaum, J. M. Goldey, N. Holonyak, Jr., "*p-n-p-n* Transistor Switches," *Proc. I.R.E.*, Vol. **44** (September, 1956), pp. 1174–82.

2. W. Fulop, "Three Terminal Measurement of Current Amplification Factors of Controlled Rectifiers," *I.E.E.E. Transactions on Electron Devices*, Vol. **ED-10** (May, 1963), pp. 120–33.

3. A. Nussbaum, *Semiconductor Device Physics*. Englewood Cliffs, N.J.: Prentice-Hall, Inc., 1962.

4. M. Wolf, "Limitations and Possibilities for Improvement of Photovoltaic Solar Energy Converters," *Proc. I.R.E.*, Vol. **48** (July, 1960), pp. 1246–63.

5. F. Gentry, "Recent Advances in *p-n-p-n* Devices," I.E.E.E. Conference Paper, No. 63-430 (January, 1963).

6. A. K. Jonscher, "Notes on the Theory of Four-Layer Semiconductor Switches," *Solid State Electronics*, Vol. **2** (1961), pp. 143–48.

7. W. Shockley, "Problems Related to *p-n* Junctions in Silicon," *Solid State Electronics*, Vol. **2** (1961), pp. 35–67.

8. I. M. Mackintosh, "The Electrical Characteristics of Silicon *p-n-p-n* Triodes," *Proc. I.R.E.*, Vol. **46** (June, 1958), pp. 1229–35.

9. W. Shockley and R. C. Prim, "Space Charge Limited Emission in Semiconductors," *Physical Review*, Vol. **90**, No. 5 (June 1, 1953), pp. 753–58.

10. R. Emeis and A. Herlet, "The Blocking Capability of Alloyed Silicon Power Transistors," *Proc. I.R.E.*, Vol. **46** (June, 1958), pp. 1216–20.

11. J. Maserjian, "Determination of Avalanche Breakdown in *p-n* Junctions," *Jour. Appl. Phys.*, Vol. **30** (1959), p. 1613.

12. R. Davies and F. Gentry, "Control of Electric Fields at the Surface of *p-n* Junctions," I.R.E. Electron Device Conference, Sheraton Park Hotel, Washington, D.C., October 25–27, 1962. To be published in I.E.E.E. *Transactions on Electron Devices* (July, 1964).

13. C. G. B. Garrett and W. H. Brattain, "Some Experiments on, and a Theory of, Surface Breakdown," *Jour. Appl. Phys.*, Vol. **27**, No. 3 (March, 1956), pp. 299–306.

14. R. L. Batdorf, A. G. Chynoweth, G. C. Dacey, and P. W. Foy, "Uniform Silicon *p-n* Junctions, I. Broad Area Breakdown," *Jour. Appl. Phys.*, Vol. **31**, No. 7 (July, 1960), pp. 1153–60.

15. D. R. Muss and C. Goldberg, "Switching Mechanism in the *n-p-n-p* Silicon Controlled Rectifier," *I.E.E.E. Transactions on Electron Devices*, Vol. **ED-10** (May, 1963), pp. 113–20.

16. E. M. Pell, "Reverse Current and Carrier Lifetime as a Function of Temperature in Germanium Junction Diodes," *Jour. Appl. Phys.*, Vol. **26** (June, 1955), pp. 658–65.

17. C. T. Sah, R. N. Noyce, and W. Shockley, "Carrier Generation and Recombination in *p-n* Junctions and *p-n* Junction Characteristics," *Proc. I.R.E.*, Vol. **45** (September, 1957), pp. 1228–43.

18. H. S. Veloric and M. B. Prince, "High Voltage Conductivity Modulated Rectifiers," *Bell System Tech. Jour.*, Vol. **36** (July, 1957), pp. 975–1004.

19. Leopoldo B. Valdes, *The Physical Theory of Transistors*. New York: McGraw-Hill Book Co., 1961, pp. 297–99.

20. A. K. Jonscher, "Analysis of Current Flow in a Planar Junction Diode at High Forward Bias," *Jour. of Electronics and Control*, Vol. **5** (1958), p. 5.

21. A. K. Jonscher, "Measurement of the Voltage-Current Characteristics of Junction Diodes at High Forward Bias," *Jour. of Electronics and Control*, Vol. **5**, p. 226.

22. J. Shields, "The Forward Characteristics of p^+-n-n^+ Diodes in Theory and Experiment," *Proc. I.E.E.*, Vol. **105**, Part B (1959).

23. A. N. Baker, J. M. Goldey, and I. M. Ross, "Recovery Time of *p-n-p-n* Diodes," *I.R.E. Wescon Convention Record*, Part 3, August 18–21, 1959, pp. 43–47.

24. R. Beaufoy and J. J. Sparkes, "The Junction Transistor as a Charge-Controlled Device," *Proc. I.R.E.*, Vol. **45** (December, 1957).

25. C. LeCan, K. Hort, and C. DeRuyter, *The Junction Transistor as a Switching Device*. New York: Reinhold Publishing Corp., 1962.

26. J. J. Sparkes, "A Study of the Charge Control Parameters of Transistors," *Proc. I.R.E.*, Vol. **48** (October, 1960), pp. 1696–1705.

27. G. E. McDuffie and W. L. Chadwell, "An Investigation of the Dynamic Switching Properties of Four-Layer Diodes," A.I.E.E. Conference Paper, CP 59-671.

28. R. W. Aldrich and N. Holonyak, Jr., "Two-Terminal Asymmetrical Silicon Negative Resistance Switches," *Jour. Appl. Phys.*, Vol. **30** (November, 1959), pp. 1819–24.

29. N. Mapham, "The Rating of SCR's When Switching into High Currents," I.E.E.E. Conference Paper, CP 63-498, I.E.E.E. Winter General Meeting, January 27–February 1, 1963.

30. N. Mapham, "Overcoming Turn-on Effects in Silicon Controlled Rectifiers," *Electronics*, Vol. **35** (August 17, 1962), pp. 50–51.

31. R. L. Longini and J. Melngailis, "Gated Turn-on of Four-Layer Switch," *I.E.E.E. Trans.*, Vol. **ED-10** (May, 1963), p. 178.

32. K. Hubner, M. Melehy, and R. L. Biesele, "Uniform Turn-on in Four-Layer Diodes," *I.R.E. Trans.*, Vol. **ED-8** (November, 1961), pp. 461–64.

33. S. Goldman, *Transformation Calculus and Electrical Transients*. Englewood Cliffs, N.J.: Prentice-Hall, Inc., 1949.

34. R. W. Aldrich and N. Holonyak, Jr., "Multi-terminal *p-n-p-n* Switches," *Proc. I.R.E.*, Vol. **46** (June, 1958), pp. 1236–39.

35. J. A. Hoerni and R. N. Noyce, "*p-n-π-n* Switches," *I.R.E. Wescon Convention Record*, Part 3 on Electron Devices, August, 1958, p. 172.

36. J. M. Goldey, I. M. Mackintosh, and I. M. Ross, "Turn-Off Gain in *p-n-p-n* Triodes," *Solid State Electronics*, Vol. **3** (September, 1961), pp. 119–22.

37. J. Moyson and J. Petruzella, "Investigation of Electronically Controllable Turn-Off Controlled Rectifiers," General Electric Co. Final Report, Signal Corps Contract DA-36-039-SC-85062 (June, 1961).

38. H. F. Storm, "Introduction to Turn-Off Silicon Controlled Rectifiers," I.E.E.E. Conference Paper 63-321, Winter General Meeting, New York, N.Y., January 27, 1963.

39. R. H. van Ligten and D. Navon, "Base Turn-Off of *p-n-p-n* Switches," *I.R.E. Wescon Convention Record*, Part 3 on Electron Devices, August, 1960, pp. 49–52.

40. T. A. Longo, M. Miller, A. L. Derek, and J. D. Eknaian, "Planar Epitaxial *p-n-p-n* Switch With Gate Turn-Off Gain," *I.R.E. Wescon Convention Record*, Part 3, August, 1962.

41. W. M. Webster, "On the Variation of Junction-Transistor Current Amplification Factor with Emitter Current," *Proc. I.R.E.* (June, 1954), pp. 914–20.

42. T. Misawa, "Turn-On Transient of *p-n-p-n* Triode," *Jour. of Electronics and Control*, Vol. **7** (December, 1959), pp. 523–33.

CHAPTER 3

DESIGN AND FABRICATION OF p-n-p-n DEVICES

3.1 Introduction

p-n-p-n devices can be produced by a number of different junction-forming techniques. Methods such as alloying, diffusion, and epitaxial and rate growth are all potentially useful methods. However, diffusion and alloying have proved to be the most popular methods, because they lend themselves to economical mass production. A simplified outline of some of the methods and problems encountered in the manufacture of SCR's is presented to aid in understanding the limitations and capabilities of these devices.

As p-n-p-n applications have grown more sophisticated, a need for enhancement of specific characteristics has developed. As a consequence, specific device improvements are being realized by means of such innovations as the "shorted emitter,"[1] gold diffusion, contoured surfaces,[2] etc. The latter portion of this chapter includes some of these specialized devices.

3.2 p-n Junction Formation

A cross-sectional representation of a typical medium-current SCR is shown in Fig. 3.1. Fabrication begins by selecting silicon of the proper resistivity and dimensions. Using Fig. 2.22 as a guide, we choose an n-type starting material which will provide the required reverse breakdown and forward breakover voltages. The n-type base which remains after the junction has been formed is generally selected to be as narrow as possible, commensurable with reasonable forward drop, gate sensitivity, and blocking voltages. Lifetime also plays a significant role in the determination of the base widths, as was pointed out in Chap. 2, and must be carefully controlled by proper processing.

132

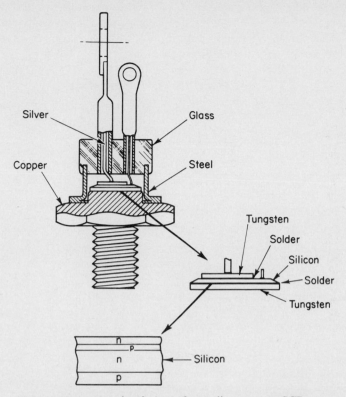

Fig. 3.1 A cross-sectional view of a medium-current SCR.

For purposes of illustration, we shall assume that two of the junctions are formed by diffusion and the other by alloying. In preparation for diffusion, the silicon slice is lapped and etched to the desired thickness. At this stage, a typical slice for a 600 v device would be less than 0.010 in. thick.

The diffusion step consists of placing the silicon slice in a quartz enclosure along with a *p*-type impurity such as gallium, as shown in Fig. 3.2. An inert gas such as argon is used as a carrier for the impurity. The pressure of the gallium vapor surrounding the silicon is controlled by regulating the temperature of the acceptor source. Under these conditions, the gallium atoms slowly

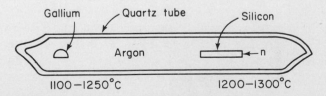

Fig. 3.2 Gallium diffusion.

diffuse into the silicon slices to a depth of a few thousandths of an inch after several hours.[3,4] For the type of diffusion processes generally used, the impurity concentration decreases rapidly with distance from the surface of the slice and can be described by the equation†

$$N_a = N_S \operatorname{erfc} (x/2\sqrt{Dt}),$$

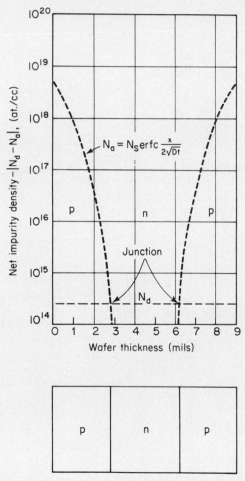

Fig. 3.3 Typical impurity density profile resulting from gallium diffusion.

† $$\operatorname{erfc} (x/2\sqrt{Dt}) = 1 - \operatorname{erf} (x/2\sqrt{Dt})$$
$$= 1 - \frac{2}{\sqrt{\pi}} \int_0^{x/2\sqrt{Dt}} \exp (-\lambda^2)\, d\lambda.$$

where

    N_a = the acceptor impurity concentration.

    N_S = the concentration of impurities at the surface of the slice.

    D = the diffusion constant of the diffusing impurity.

    x = the distance from the surface of the slice.

    t = diffusion time.

The junction is located at the point where the acceptor density is exactly equal to the donor density (where $N_a - N_d = 0$). Thus the net concentration, $N = N_a - N_d$, becomes

$$N = N_S \operatorname{erfc} (x/2\sqrt{Dt}) - N_d,$$

where

$$N_d = \text{the donor impurity density.}$$

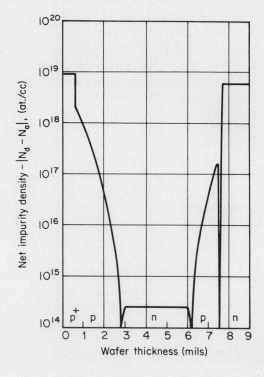

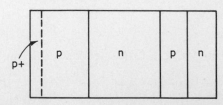

Fig. 3.4 Typical impurity density profile of an alloy-diffused SCR.

This process results in a *p-n-p* wafer impurity profile, as shown in Fig. 3.3.

With the *p-n-p* portion of the device now complete, the next step is to form an *n*-type emitter in one of the diffused *p*-type layers. This can be accomplished by another diffusion step in which the anode *p*-side is masked with silicon dioxide, or it can be made by alloying. Since a diffusion process has already been described, let us consider an alloy process. In this case, the slice is cut into pellets of the desired size and chemically cleaned. A suitable alloy foil (for example, gold foil), containing a small percentage of antimony, is placed on one side of the wafer while aluminum is placed on the other and held in position by a suitable fixture made of carbon, ceramic, quartz, etc. When raised to a temperature of 600 to 700°C, the gold antimony and the aluminum will alloy with the silicon to a depth determined by the temperature and the foil thickness. If cooled in the correct manner, the molten silicon-gold alloy containing both acceptor and donor atoms will solidify, forming a layer of single-crystal silicon which grows at the solid-liquid interface. The relatively high concentration of donor impurities in the melt, as compared to the *p*-type dopant, results in an *n*-type regrowth layer. On the other side of the wafer, the molten aluminum-silicon cools in a similar manner and forms a p^+-p junction. The transition plate is often also attached, the aluminum-silicon layer being used as a solder. The resultant net impurity concentration is shown in Fig. 3.4. Thus, the *p-n-p-n* structure has been formed; the remainder of the fabrication process is for the purpose of making lead attachments, dissipating the heat which is generated during operation, and protecting the junctions from adverse environments.

3.3 Lifetime and Geometry Control

In Chaps. 1 and 2, the relationship between the electrical characteristics, minority-carrier lifetime, and the dimensions of the SCR were discussed. Reasonable control over both the dimensions of the *p*- and *n*-regions and the impurity density is required in order to realize good device characteristics. Dimensions are controlled by careful attention to furnace temperatures, gas purity, fixture design, and the tolerances of the silicon and the alloy foils. Minority-carrier lifetime is controlled by controlling the purity of all materials used in the fabrication process, by "gettering" unwanted impurities, and/or by introducing suitable "lifetime killers," such as gold, during or following the diffusion operation.

3.4 Heat Transfer and Electrical Contact Consideration

It is essential that a suitable heat-transfer path be provided between the silicon pellet and the heat sink. Moreover, the electrical contacts and lead wires should have negligible resistance. The design in Fig. 3.1 meets these requirements. A stud-mounted cell is provided for ease in mounting to a heat sink or fin. Except for transition plates between the silicon and the copper stud and the top lead, the majority of the heat and electrical conducting paths are copper. Copper has excellent thermal and electrical conductivity, but it has two undesirable characteristics for this application; its coefficient of expansion is four times greater than that of silicon, and it has relatively low yield strength. As a result of the difference in coefficients of expansion, transition plates are employed to prevent fracture of the silicon. The low yield strength of copper requires that a severe restriction be placed on the amount of torque which can be applied to the stud when it is screwed into a heat sink. If this limit is exceeded, the threads may be stripped or the silicon wafer damaged.

3.5 Mechanical Stresses and Thermal Fatigue

Silicon has a linear thermal-expansion coefficient of 4×10^{-6} cm/(cm × °C), whereas copper has a coefficient of 17×10^{-6} cm/(cm × °C). If the silicon is soldered directly to the copper, then as the temperature is lowered below the freezing point of the solder, the silicon would be placed in compression along with a bending moment that is dependent on the dimensions and symmetry of the assembly. If a very ductile solder is used, little mechanical stress is transmitted to the silicon, because the solder flows with each temperature cycle; that is, its elastic limit is exceeded and plastic deformation results in each cycle. This type of action leads to thermal fatigue failure; it is discussed in more detail in Sec. 4.3. A nonductile solder will often cause the silicon to fracture. Thus, direct attachment of the silicon to the copper results in some serious disadvantages.

The assembly shown in Fig. 3.1 utilizes tungsten transition plates between the silicon and the copper. The coefficient of expansion of tungsten very nearly matches that of silicon. Moreover, it has a high modulus of elasticity, a high yield strength, and good thermal and electrical conductivity; it is also relatively inert in most acids. Consequently, tungsten is an excellent counter-electrode material for preventing mechanical stress from being transferred to the silicon and causing it to fracture at low temperature. However, care must still be exercised in mounting the tungsten-silicon subassembly to the copper stud or lead. If a "soft solder," such as lead-tin, is used between the tungsten and the copper, the stress on the silicon will be reduced, but it may still fatigue under cycling conditions. Many presently available devices such as the one shown in Fig. 3.1 utilize "hard solders"† for all joints to avoid thermal-fatigue problems.

---

† A hard solder as defined here is one whose elastic limit is not exceeded over the operating temperature range of the SCR.

3.6 Surface Protection

After the junctions of a *p-n-p-n* device are formed, they must be kept free of contamination to insure reliability. Thus, it is essential that the surface of the silicon be kept free of ionizable impurities during the life span of the device. Moisture is particularly troublesome, and, as a consequence, a hermetically sealed package is necessary if a high degree of reliability is expected. For high-power SCR's, it is common practice to use ceramic insulators because of their high strength and impact resistance. For smaller and less expensive devices, glass seals are more often used.

To prevent surface degradation owing to transient overvoltage, avalanche breakdown should be restricted to the interior of the device rather than the surface. As pointed out in Sec. 2.4.3, the silicon lattice is disrupted at the surface, so a smaller magnitude of electric field is required to initiate avalanche breakdown there than is required in the body of the device. As a consequence, the device should be designed so that the potential gradient is lower at the surface. This can be accomplished by proper lapping, grinding, or etching to achieve the correct surface contour.[2] Moreover, the use of an inert insulating material having a dielectric constant and breakdown capability higher than that of silicon on the junction surfaces will aid in preventing dielectric breakdown of the gases surrounding the junction space-charge layers.

3.7 The Shorted Emitter

The "shorted emitter"[1] is a construction method whereby the emitter efficiency of a *p-n* junction is controlled structurally instead of by means of the impurity concentration between emitter and base. Such a structure is shown in Fig. 3.5. Note that with the anode biased positively, the hole current collected at $J2$ will flow laterally beneath the emitter junction until the voltage drop reaches a sufficient level to cause $J3$ to emit electrons into the base region. Thus, we have an emitter which has essentially a zero emitter efficiency

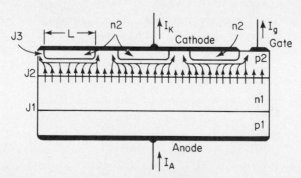

Fig. 3.5 *p-n-p-n* device with shorted emitter.

at very low currents, but as the current through the structure increases, the emitter efficiency increases. By controlling the sheet resistance of the $p2$ layer and the lateral dimension L of emitter $n2$, the effective emitter efficiency as a function of current can be regulated. Such control is needed in SCR's and is particularly advantageous in improving the dv/dt capability of a device. By providing the shunt path around the emitter, the space-charge layer capacitance of $J2$ can be charged without sufficient electrons being injected by the cathode emitters to trigger the device. Moreover, such a configuration is only slightly more costly than an ordinary all-diffused device.

3.8 Bilateral Diode Switch

One shortcoming of the SCR is its inability to conduct current bilaterally; i.e., when it is in the ON state the current is limited to one direction of flow. By extending the shorted-emitter concept as shown in Fig. 3.6, a symmetrical two-terminal switch can be fabricated.[1] Note that the device consists essentially of two p-n-p-n sections in parallel but arranged in opposite order. Thus, when in the ON state, one section conducts current in one direction, whereas the other section conducts when the current reverses. Devices of this type can be triggered by rapidly raising the applied voltage, by raising the applied voltage above the avalanche voltage of the blocking junction, or by increasing the junction temperature to a sufficiently high level.

To visualize the operation of the device, let us apply a positive voltage to electrode 1 with respect to electrode 2. Note that junctions $J2$ and $J4$ will tend

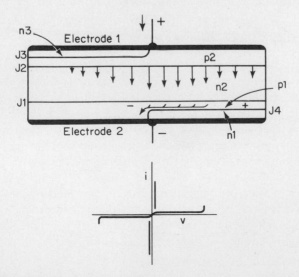

Fig. 3.6 Bilateral diode switch.

to be forward-biased, whereas $J1$ will be reverse-biased. As we continue to increase the applied voltage, junction $J1$ will finally avalanche, and any further increase in voltage will result in a substantial current flow across $J1$. The current flow across junction $J3$ will be negligible, because with electrode 1 biased positively, $J3$ will be reverse-biased. Consequently, any current which flows across the left-hand portion of the device shown in Fig. 3.6 must overcome the lateral resistance of $p2$. As the current through the device increases, junction $J2$ will become forward-biased; holes will be injected from $p2$ into $n2$ and diffuse across $n2$ to be collected by junction $J1$. The holes collected by $J1$ on the right-hand side of the device are swept into region $p1$, where they raise its potential with respect to electrode 2 and region $n1$. At low-current levels the hole current will flow parallel to junction $J4$ to reach electrode 2, since that is the path of least resistance. However, as the current increases, the lateral voltage drop will become large enough to forward-bias junction $J4$, which causes electrons to be injected from $n1$ to $p1$. As the current through the device is further increased, enough current will flow through junction $J4$ so that the $p2-n2-p1-n1$ section will switch from the blocking to the conducting state in the manner described in Chap. 2.

If electrode 2 is made positive with respect to electrode 1, the left-hand section of the device (i.e., $p1-n2-p2-n3$) will switch in the same manner as that just described for the right-hand section. The trigger operation just described results from applying a voltage in excess of the avalanche-breakdown capability of the blocking junctions.

Triggering can also be accomplished by rapidly increasing the applied voltage across the device at a level below the avalanche-breakdown value.† The operation is much the same as that described for voltage triggering, except that the current through the device is initiated by charging the capacitance of the blocking junction instead of by avalanche multiplication. Thus, with electrode 1 positive, displacement current causes a lateral voltage bias in region $p1$, which forward-biases junction $J4$.

The bilateral diode switch has a number of interesting and unique features. Because of its physical symmetry, its electrical characteristics are quite symmetrical, and its fabrication is relatively inexpensive. By suitable oxide masking and diffusion techniques the structure shown in Fig. 3.6 can be produced readily.[3.4] For example, junctions $J1$ and $J2$ can be formed simultaneously by diffusing gallium into an *n*-type slice of silicon. The slice can then be masked by thermally growing an SiO_2 layer on the surface and then chemically removing part of the oxide layer in selected areas, as shown in Fig. 3.7. The oxide layer acts as a mask and prevents phosphorus from diffusing into the silicon, so *n*-layers can be located precisely where they are required. As a consequence of the simultaneous formation of junctions which perform the same function, the blocking junctions ($J1$ when electrode 1 is positive and $J2$ when electrode 2 is positive) will

† This is commonly referred to as dv/dt triggering and is discussed in detail in Sec. 2.6.2.

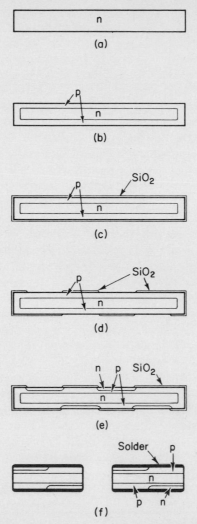

Fig. 3.7 Diffusion and oxide-masking steps for fabrication of a bilateral diode switch: (a) obtain silicon slice of proper type, size,
and impurity concentration; (b) diffuse in an inert gas containing
gallium vapor; (c) thermally grow a silicon dioxide layer by heating
slice in a high-temperature oxidizing atmosphere; (d) mask surface
with wax and chemically remove SiO_2 in select areas; (e) diffuse
in an atmosphere containing phosphorus; (f) remove remaining
SiO_2 and apply ohmic contacts. Cut slice into pellets.

have very nearly the same characteristics. By maintaining the areas of the two
sections identical, devices can be made which have electrical characteristics
which are completely symmetrical. In addition, less silicon is required than
for a three-terminal device, since there is no area required for a gate terminal.

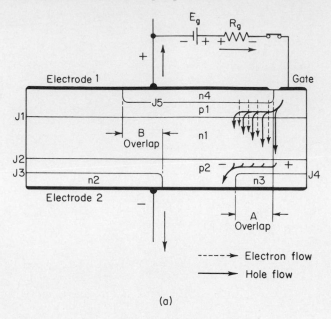

(a)

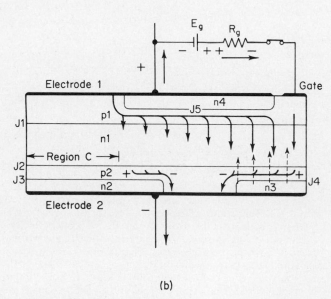

(b)

Fig. 3.8 Bilateral triode switch.

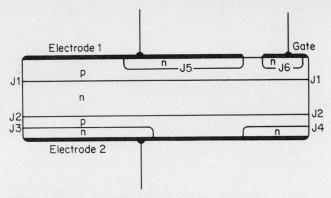

Fig. 3.9 Bilateral triode switch which can be triggered with either negative or positive gate pulses.

3.9 Bilateral Triode Switches and Related Structures

3.9.1 Introduction

For many alternating current applications it is desirable to have an a-c switch which can be triggered into conduction by means of a pulse of current into a gate lead in a manner similar to that of an SCR. Such a device can be fabricated by judiciously arranging the p- and n-regions, as shown in Figs. 3.8 or 3.9.[5] These devices can be triggered into conduction in either direction by the application of a low-voltage, low-current pulse between the gate terminal and the adjacent load-current terminal. Since the device will conduct on both alternations of an a-c current, only one heat sink is required, and the trigger circuitry can be simplified, as compared to that required for two SCR's connected in parallel but in opposite directions.

The operation of a bilateral triode switch is easier to visualize if we first consider the "building blocks" which are the basis of their operation. The next three sections will deal with the three fundamental elements required for most bilateral triode switches.

3.9.2 The Junction Gate

A device which has a junction gate[6] is shown in Fig. 3.10. To develop insight into its operation, let us bias the anode positive with respect to the cathode, and assume that the device is in the blocking state. Next, we will apply a negative voltage to the gate with respect to the cathode. As a result, hole current will flow from the emitter short toward the junction gate so that $p2$ is biased positive with respect to $n3$. Thus, $n3$ injects electrons into $p2$, and the $p1$-$n1$-$p2$-$n3$ portion of the device in region A begins to turn on in the

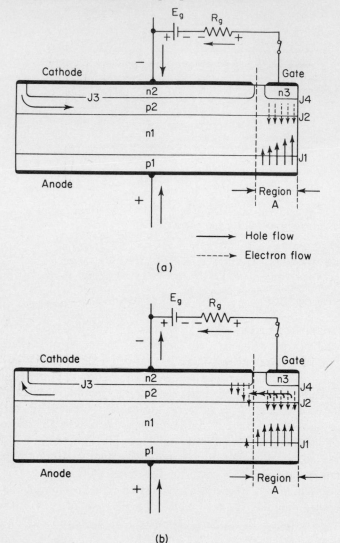

(a)

(b)

Fig. 3.10 *p-n-p-n* device with a junction gate.

manner of a conventional *p-n-p-n* device. However, as it begins to switch, current will build up through the gate circuit until the voltage drop across R_g exceeds E_g.

Region $p2$ is then driven quite positive with respect to the cathode in the vicinity of region A. The result is that hole current flows toward the cathode junction, as shown in Fig. 3.10b, and junction $J3$ becomes forward-biased. With $J3$ forward-biased, the remainder of the device turns on in the same manner as a conventional SCR.

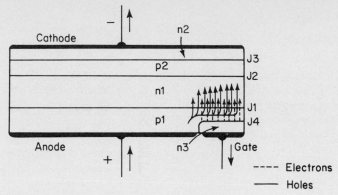

Fig. 3.11 *p-n-p-n* device with a remote gate.

3.9.3 THE REMOTE GATE

The remote gate is a novel arrangement of *p*- and *n*-regions which allows switching from the anode side of the device as shown in Fig. 3.11.[5] Assume that the anode is biased positive with respect to the cathode and that the device is in the blocking state. When a negative voltage is applied to the gate lead, electrons are injected from *n3* to *p1* and diffuse toward junction *J1*. Those electrons which are collected† lower the potential of *n1* with respect to *p1* (forward-biasing *J1*), so holes are injected from *p1* to *n1*. These holes diffuse across *n1*, and those collected at *J2* raise the potential of *p2* with respect to *n2* (thus forward-biasing *J3*), causing electrons to be injected from *n2* to *p2*. These electrons diffuse toward *J2*, where those collected lower the potential of *n1* with respect to *p1*, so more holes are injected from *p1* into *n1*. This process continues until the device turns on.

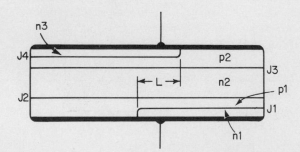

Fig. 3.12 Bilateral diode switch with an "overlap."

---

† It should be borne in mind that the electric field in the space-charge layer of a forward-biased junction is in the same direction as that of a reverse-biased junction and is quite adequate for collection of minority carriers.

3.9.4 THE OVERLAP

The overlap is a scheme whereby majority-carrier current is diverted by strategic lateral placement of junctions. For example, by making regions $n1$ and $n3$ of the bilateral diode switch of Fig. 3.6 overlap as shown in Fig. 3.12, we can make the device trigger at a lower current level. From the description of the two-terminal device's operation in Sec. 3.7, it should be apparent that the lateral voltage drops, caused by majority-carrier current flow in regions $p1$ and $p2$, determine the trigger sensitivity of the device. Thus, by varying the amount of overlap L, the trigger current can be varied for the device.

3.9.5 BILATERAL TRIODE SWITCHES

By combining the three innovations just described along with the conventional SCR there are several types of a-c switches which can be fabricated.[5]

First, we shall describe the operation of the device shown in Fig. 3.8. Assume that the device is in the blocking state, with positive voltage applied to electrode 1 while electrode 2 remains at ground potential. By applying a positive voltage to the gate with respect to electrode 1, the potential of $p1$ is raised with respect to $n4$ in the vicinity of $J5$, near the gate lead. As a consequence, electrons are injected from $n4$ to $p1$ and diffuse toward $J1$. Those electrons collected at $J1$ lower the potential of $n1$ with respect to $p1$, causing $p1$ to inject holes into $n1$. The holes diffuse toward $J2$, and those collected flow toward the ohmic contact. The resulting hole-current flow creates a voltage drop which causes $n3$ to inject electrons into $p2$—when the hole current reaches sufficient magnitude for junction $J4$ to be forward-biased by a few tenths of a volt. The degree of forward bias across $J4$ is proportional to the sheet resistance of the $p2$-base-region which is between $n3$ and $n1$ and also by the amount of overlap in region A. With junction $J4$ in forward bias, $n3$ injects electrons into $p2$, where they diffuse toward junction $J2$. Those electrons collected at junction $J2$ lower the potential of $n1$ with respect to $p1$ in region A and cause additional holes to be injected from $p1$ to $n1$. Thus, the device begins to turn on in region A. However, as current begins to build up through the gate lead, the voltage across R_g (as shown in Fig. 3.8b) will rise, causing hole current to flow from the shorted region of $p1$ laterally toward region A, where it is injected from $p1$ to $n1$. Thus, the structure consisting of $p1$-$n1$-$p2$-$n3$ begins to turn on, with junction $J2$ acting as a collector for the electrons injected by $n3$ which diffuse across $p2$ and as a collector for the holes injected from $p1$ to $n1$ which diffuse across $n1$. As junction $J2$—which was in a blocking state—starts to switch, the electrons injected from $n3$ into $p2$ increase, and thus the collected electron current which flows into $n1$ increases, causing further drop in potential of $n1$ with respect to $p1$. Since the sheet resistance of $p1$ is reasonably high, holes will also be injected from $p1$

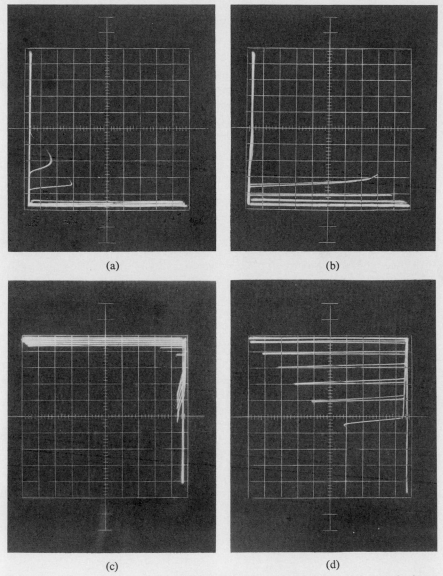

(a)   (b)

(c)   (d)

Fig. 3.13 Voltage-current characteristics (25°C) for the bilateral triode switch shown in Fig. 3.9: (a) Electrode 2 positive with respect to electrode 1 (horizontal scale 10 volts/cm, vertical scale 1 ma/cm), gate positive with respect to electrode 1 (1 ma gate current steps); (b) Electrode 2 positive with respect to electrode 1 (horizontal scale 10 volts/cm, vertical scale 5 ma/cm), gate negative with respect to electrode 1 (2 ma gate steps); (c) Electrode 2 negative with respect to electrode 1 (horizontal scale 10 volts/cm, vertical scale 50 ma/cm), gate positive with respect to electrode 1 (20 ma gate steps); (d) Electrode 2 negative with respect to electrode 1 (horizontal scale 10 volts/cm, vertical scale 5 ma/cm), gate negative with respect to electrode 1 (2 ma gate steps).

into $n1$ in region B, where they will diffuse across $n1$ and be collected at junction $J2$, thus raising the potential of $p2$ with respect to $n2$ in region B. This causes electrons to be injected from $n2$ to $p2$. Thus, region C becomes conductive. It should be pointed out that conductivity modulation aids this process by lowering the resistance of layer $n1$.

If the device shown in Fig. 3.8 has a positive potential applied to electrode 2 with electrode 1 at ground potential, it will behave in much the same manner as a conventional SCR. With a positive bias applied to the gate with respect to electrode 1, emitter $n4$ will inject electrons into base $p1$, and those collected by blocking junction $J1$ will lower the potential of $n1$ with respect to $p2$ so that holes are injected from $p2$ to $n1$, etc. Thus, we have a device which can be triggered with a positive gate current pulse when either electrode is positive.

By the addition of a junction gate, as shown in Fig. 3.9, we can construct an a-c switch which can be triggered into conduction with load current of either direction by means of either a positive or a negative pulse. If the gate is biased positively, junction $J6$ will tend to be reverse-biased, so current will flow through the shorted region to forward-bias junction $J5$. The device will then trigger in the same manner as described in the previous paragraphs. With the gate biased negatively, it behaves as a junction gate when electrode 2 is positive with respect to electrode 1, and as a remote gate when electrode 1 is positive with respect to electrode 2. The resulting voltage-current characteristics of such a device are shown in Fig. 3.13.

REFERENCES

1. R. W. Aldrich and N. Holonyak, Jr., "Two-Terminal Asymmetrical and Symmetrical Silicon Negative Resistance Switches," *Jour. Appl. Phys.*, Vol. **30** (November, 1959), 1819–24.

2. R. Davies and F. Gentry, "Control of Electric Fields at the Surface of *p-n* Junctions." *I.E.E.E. Transactions on Electron Devices*, Vol. **ED-8**, No. 7 (July, 1964), pp. 313-23.

3. R. W. Aldrich and N. Holonyak, Jr., "Silicon Controlled Rectifiers From Oxide Masked Diffused Structures," *A.I.E.E. Trans., Communication and Electronics*, No. 40 (January, 1959), pp. 952–54.

4. F. M. Smits, "Formation of Junction Structures by Solid-State Diffusion," *Proc. I.R.E.*, Vol. **46** (June, 1958), pp. 1049–61.

5. F. E. Gentry, R. I. Scace, and J. Flowers, "A Three Terminal A.C. Switch," I.E.E.E. Electron Device Conference, Washington, D.C., October 31– November 1, 1963. To be published.

6. J. Moyson and F. E. Gentry, "A Junction Gate Controlled Rectifier," Semiconductor Device Research Conference, June 13–15, 1962, Carnegie Institute of Technology.

CHAPTER 4

RATINGS, SPECIFICATIONS, AND CHARACTERISTICS

4.1 Introduction

Well-developed ratings and specifications are exceedingly important design tools which bridge the gap between the designer of the semiconductor device and the user of the device. Ratings establish the bounds within which the component can be used without damage to the device or malfunction harmful to the equipment in which it is used. Component characteristics are provided so that inherent variations of properties with temperature, voltage, current, etc., can be taken into consideration by the equipment designer. Nothing catastrophic is likely to occur if a rating is exceeded by a slight amount. However, maximum ratings do warn of encroaching reliability problems if those ratings are exceeded. Thus, the steps in establishing a specification are as follows:

1. Characterization and measurement of parameters.
2. Determination of failure mechanisms.
3. Establishment of rating which will permit reliable operation.
4. Maintenance of adequate production testing to assure that rating and reliability levels can be met on a continual basis.

For detailed specifications and values the reader should refer to the manufacturer's specifications, since rather wide ratings are possible. This chapter deals with the characterization, measurement, failure mechanisms, and the establishment of ratings for SCR's.

149

4.2 Electrical Characteristics

To establish *p-n-p-n* device ratings, it is first necessary to obtain the electrical characteristics for the current, voltage, and temperature range over which the device is likely to be applied. The nature and the variations of many of these characteristics were discussed and their governing equations derived in Chaps. 1 and 2. However, for purposes of rating and application, the electrical characteristics of a device should be obtained experimentally (so that they apply to the real situation) and presented in analytical and graphical form.[1,2,3]

4.2.1 ANODE-TO-CATHODE VOLTAGE-CURRENT CHARACTERISTICS—GENERAL

The anode-to-cathode voltage-current characteristic of a *p-n-p-n* device has a number of complex regions which require additional description and definition. An instantaneous forward and reverse voltage-current characteristic of an SCR is shown in Fig. 4.1. The regions may be described as follows. In region 0–1 and 0–6, the device is in the blocking state. By applying sufficient gate trigger current, the device can be triggered from the forward blocking state to its forward conducting state, which lies between points 3 and 5. Normally, it will not revert back to the blocking condition unless the anode

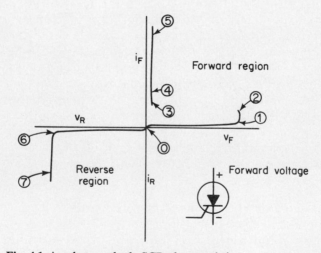

Fig. 4.1 Anode-to-cathode SCR characteristic:
- 0–2 Forward blocking state.
- 1–2 Forward avalanche region.
- 2   Forward breakover point.
- 2–4 Negative resistance region.
- 3–5 Forward conducting characteristic.
- 3   Holding current.
- 0–7 Reverse blocking characteristic.

current is reduced below the holding current, which is indicated by point 3. However, specialized devices may be designed which can be turned off by reverse-biasing the gate-cathode junction (see Sec. 2.7). For the case of a device having a p-gate (as shown in Fig. 4.1), current would be extracted from the gate lead by means of a negative gate bias.

To assure positive triggering, it is usually necessary that the load current level be greater than the holding current. Such a condition results because the alphas over the whole area of the device are not uniform, or because the device has not had time to turn on fully during the duration of a short gate pulse. This minimum current which must flow in the anode circuit to assure switching is referred to as the latching current and is shown in Fig. 4.3.

When in the blocking state an SCR will switch to the ON state if the forward voltage exceeds the forward breakover voltage, as indicated by point 2. The reverse avalanche region is much the same as that for a rectifier, and switching will not normally occur. However, devices can be designed to switch in either direction, as described in Sec. 3.8.

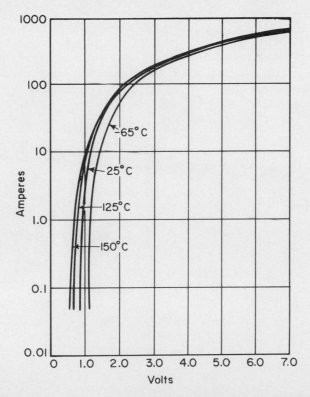

Fig. 4.2 Forward conducting characteristic of a 25 amp SCR with temperature as a parameter (effective junction area 0.14 cm²).

4.2.2 Forward Conducting Characteristic

In Sec. 2.5 the forward characteristic equation for the conducting state was derived for a *p-n-p-n* structure and found to be of the form

$$v_F = \frac{nkT}{q} \ln (K_1 i_F) + K_2 \sqrt{i_F} + i_F R. \tag{4.1}$$

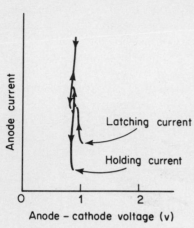

Fig. 4.3 A SCR characteristic showing multiple conducting states.

An experimentally obtained set of forward characteristics for a medium current SCR is shown in Fig. 4.2 with temperature as a parameter. From Fig. 4.2 we see that the constants of equation (4.1) are somewhat temperature-dependent. In Sec. 4.4.4 we shall study and use this temperature dependence to measure junction temperature. Although equation (4.1) is generally accurate in the higher current regions, some deviation is expected near the holding current region because of alpha variations with current. In fact, multiple conducting states may be encountered, as shown in Fig. 4.3, when different areas of the device switch into conduction.

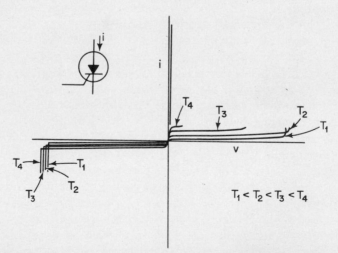

Fig. 4.4 Effect of temperature on the anode-cathode characteristic of a SCR.

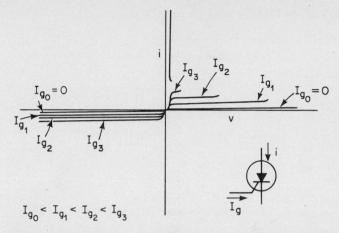

Fig. 4.5 Effect of gate current on anode-to-cathode characteristic of a SCR.

4.2.3 FORWARD AND REVERSE BLOCKING CHARACTERISTICS

Forward and reverse blocking currents of conventional SCR's are very dependent on temperature and gate drive and increase greatly with temperature and gate drive as shown in Figs. 4.4 and 4.5. During normal operation, forward bias of the gate junction is applied to the device only when it is to be triggered. If the gate-to-cathode junction of a small-area conventional SCR is reverse-biased, the high-temperature capability and its ability to withstand sudden application of anode voltage without being triggered will improve. However, this improvement is usually negligible with high-current devices because of lateral base resistance effects. On the other hand, forward bias of the gate-to-cathode junction while the device is in the OFF state causes the blocking current to increase so that the heat generated is increased measurably (see Fig. 4.5). In this case the device behaves as if it were a remote base transistor,[4] with the cathode emitter providing base drive for the *p-n-p* transistor portion of the device.

The temperature dependence of the forward and reverse blocking current is of an exponential nature. A typical current density plot as a function of temperature is shown in Fig. 2.11. By replotting as shown in Fig. 4.6, we see that over a limited temperature range the current density can be represented by an equation of the form $i = K \exp aT$, where a and K are constants. This rapid increase of blocking current in conjunction with increases in the alphas as a result of temperature leads to a steep drop-off in the ability of the SCR to block forward current without triggering[5] as shown in Fig. 4.4. Breakover voltage as a function of temperature for a typical SCR is shown in Fig. 2.12.

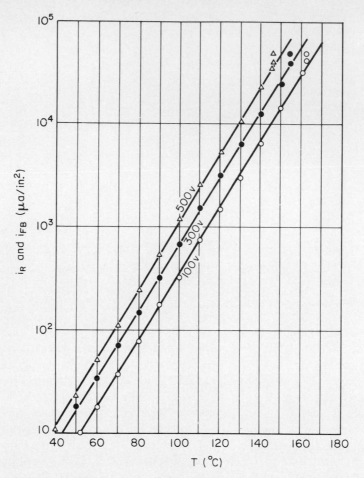

Fig. 4.6 Forward and reverse blocking current density of a typical high-current SCR.

4.2.4 GATE-TRIGGER CHARACTERISTICS

The theory of gate triggering has already been discussed in some detail in Chap. 2. From equation (2.31) we note that the gate current required to trigger a *p-n-p-n* into conduction is determined by the variation of the device alphas with current density or injected charge level. With increasing gate current the alphas rise until the device switches to the ON state, and the blocking junction goes from reverse to forward bias, as shown in Fig. 4.5.[6,7,8,9,10] As a consequence, the gate characteristic changes abruptly, because the alphas are now determined by the load current I_L. The gate voltage-current characteristic of a small-area *p-n-p-n* device in both the ON and OFF states is shown in

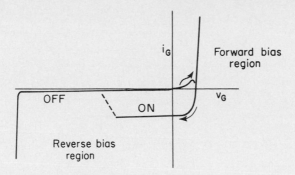

Fig. 4.7 Gate voltage-current characteristic of a *p-n-p-n* device in the ON and OFF states.

Fig. 4.7. By using equations (2.118), (2.119), and (2.120) and noting that $I_L = I_1 = I_2$ and that $I_3 = I_L + I_g$, we can obtain the relation

$$I_g = \frac{I_{S_3}[\exp(qV_3/nkT) - 1](1 - \alpha_{1N}\alpha_{1I} - \alpha_{2N}\alpha_{2I})}{(1 - \alpha_{1N}\alpha_{1I})}$$

$$- \frac{I_L[1 - \alpha_{1N}(\alpha_{1I} - \alpha_{2I}) - \alpha_{2I}]}{(1 - \alpha_{1N}\alpha_{1I})} \tag{4.2}$$

Note that, prior to switching, the load current I_L is very small, so the right-hand term of the equation is negligible. Thus we would expect a gate characteristic such as the one shown for the OFF condition in Fig. 4.7. However, when the device switches, I_L becomes large and causes the gate current to reverse and flow into the gate supply. By increasing or decreasing the gate supply voltage after the device is conducting, the gate current can be made to increase or decrease. If the gate current is decreased and then reversed sufficiently, the device may even be turned off—provided the two-dimensional effects discussed in Sec. 2.7 are not too limiting.

If a *p-n-p-n* device is to be triggered on with a pulse of current, it should be recognized that the structure is essentially charge-operated, as was pointed out in Sec. 2.6. This means that as the trigger pulse width is decreased the gate current required for triggering must be increased when the pulse duration approaches the minority-carrier lifetime or the transit time of the device. From equations (2.160) and (2.161) it can be seen that the gate current required for triggering is a rather complex function of time. Figure 4.8 shows the gate current and voltage required to trigger a typical SCR as a function of pulse duration. It should be mentioned that inductance in the load circuit will prevent an SCR from triggering if the gate pulse duration is too short. This results because the buildup of anode current may be so slow that the latching current is not reached before the gate current ceases.

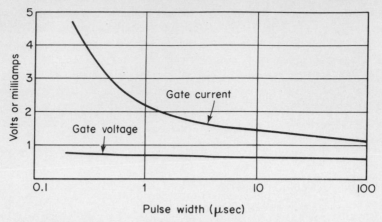

Fig. 4.8 Gate current and voltage required to trigger a typical SCR as a function of trigger pulse width.

To turn off a *p-n-p-n* by means of the gate requires the removal of sufficient charge from one of the bases of the device so that both bases of the SCR are taken out of the saturated state. This requires that the lateral resistance of the base to which the gate is attached be small enough so that the emitter-to-base

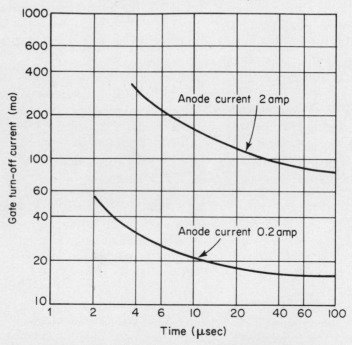

Fig. 4.9 Gate turn-off current as a function of gate turn-off pulse duration for a two-ampere turn-off *p-n-p-n* device.

breakdown voltage is not greatly exceeded during the removal of current from the gate lead. If the gate-to-cathode junction is taken into the avalanche region, a shunt path (due to avalanche in a local region) will develop at a point near the gate lead; further increase in gate current will not turn the device off. If a pulse is used to turn the device off, the current which must be removed increases sharply with decreasing pulse duration as the pulse width approaches the lifetime of the minority carriers. Gate voltage and current are shown as a function of turn-off pulse duration for a two ampere gate turn-off switch in Fig. 4.9.

4.2.5 Dynamic Characteristics

The current and voltage waveshapes depicted by Fig. 4.10 will be used to illustrate three of the more important dynamic characteristics of an SCR which must be considered in the designing of circuits. These characteristics are commonly referred to as turn-on time, turn-off time, and dv/dt capability.[11,12]

First consider the device to be in the blocking state at point 1. At point 2, a gate trigger pulse is applied (also see Fig. 2.30). However, a short delay period t_d results while the anode current builds up to 10 per cent of its final value. This delay period is quite dependent on the gate drive current, as was noted in Sec. 2.6.3. The rise time from 10 per cent to 90 per cent of final load current in a pure resistive circuit exhibits little dependence on gate current if

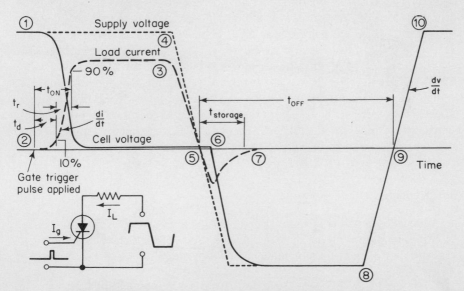

Fig. 4.10 Current and voltage waveshapes during turn-on and turn-off.

the load current is much greater than the gate current. In this case experimental turn-on-current data can be approximated by the expression

$$i = A \exp a(t - t_d),\qquad(4.3)$$

where t is the time variable, t_d the delay time, and A and a are constants. It should be recognized that turn-on is initiated in a small area near the gate lead[13] and that in very low-inductance systems it may be desirable to limit the rate of rise of anode current by introducing some inductance[14] to limit excessive heat dissipation in local regions during turn-on.

At point 3 the SCR is in steady-state conduction. If at point 4 we drop the supply voltage, the current through the device will start to fall until it reaches zero at point 5. However, because the base regions still are saturated with minority charge carriers, the device does not block current immediately but acts as a low impedance in the reverse direction as the supply voltage builds up negatively until the bases are no longer saturated at point 6. At that point the device begins to block reverse voltage; the recovery current drops as described in Sec. 2.6.1. At point 7 the recovery current has dropped to a negligible value. If the device is again to block forward voltage, the reverse voltage must remain applied for a short duration to permit the remainder of the carriers in the base regions to recombine, or the device will switch immediately into forward conduction with the reapplication of forward voltage. At point 8 we again start to reverse the external supply voltage so that the reverse voltage across the device begins to drop until it passes through zero at point 9, and then rises toward point 10 in the forward direction. The time interval between when the forward current decreases to zero at point 5 and when the voltage reaches zero at point 9 is defined as the turn-off interval. The rate at which the voltage rises from point 9 to point 10 is referred to as reapplied dv/dt. If the OFF interval is too short to allow the base regions of the device to be cleared of minority carriers or if the rate of rise of reapplied voltage is too great, the SCR will not block the applied forward voltage but will switch into conduction. Since both the OFF time and the rate of rise of voltage affect the charge-carrier density in the base layers, these parameters are interdependent. Thus, when the turn-off time of an SCR is specified,† the rate of rise of voltage must also be specified. During the period from point 6 to point 7 the recovery current is exponential in nature, as described in Sec. 2.6.1.

4.3 Mechanisms of Failure

There are a number of basic mechanisms leading to semiconductor-device failure. The design of the devices and the care with which they are manufactured has a great deal of influence on the magnitude of stress (voltage,

† The turn-off time of an SCR and the circuit OFF time should not be confused. Turn-off time is the minimum circuit OFF time which will allow the SCR to block when forward voltage is reapplied.

temperature, current, etc.) required to promote failure. However, the level and nature of stress which will degrade a particular design must be known if the device is to be rated properly. After this information has been assembled, a device is rated by selecting operating conditions which will not result in degradation. Although other mechanisms may exist, past experience has shown that the various modes discussed in the following paragraphs include almost all SCR failures which have been identified.

4.3.1 SURFACE DEGRADATION

Generally, surface degradation failure results from ionic contaminants within the device housing which accumulate in the vicinity of the *p-n* junctions. They may form ionic conducting paths which shunt the junction space-charge region, or they may create surface states that distort the *p-n* junction space-charge layer near the surface to form inversion surfaces (i.e., change conductivity type from *p* to *n* or vice versa) or accumulation surfaces (i.e., change from *n* to n^+ or *p* to p^+). As a result of these changes, the saturation currents, breakdown voltages, current gains, etc., can change drastically. Thus, it is essential that very close control of gases, assembly cleanliness, and the like, be maintained during manufacture of the device in much the same manner as is required in electron-tube manufacture.

Unfortunately, correlation between initial device characteristics and surface failures is rather poor. This is not too surprising, however, since many of the contaminants may be trapped on the walls of the housing and might not have had an electrical or other stress applied which will enhance their accumulation near the junctions. Like most other components, temperature will accelerate this mode of failure. High temperatures promote chemical activity and cause those contaminants within the package to accumulate in the high electric field regions near the junctions at a faster rate. For transistors and diodes, it has been shown[15,16] that the rate of failure as a function of temperature often follows the empirical equation

$$R = A \exp(-E/kT),$$

where T is the junction temperature (in degrees Kelvin), E is an activation energy, k is Boltzmann's constant, R is the rate of failure, and A is a constant whose value is determined by the amount of "contamination" present. Two obvious alternatives, or a combination of both, can be used to prevent this mode of failure. One is to limit the device temperature to low enough values so that the chemical activity is reduced to a negligible rate.[16,17] The other approach is to eliminate the contaminants from possible contact with the surface of the junction. This can be accomplished by suitable care in handling, cleaning, surface coatings, bakeout, gettering, and hermetic sealing during the fabrication process.

Voltage and current also accelerate failure by surface degradation.[16,17,18]

As might be expected, the high field in the junction space-charge layer which results from the application of voltage attracts mobile ionized impurities to the junction region which subtends the surface. Moreover, the dielectric strength of the surface coatings or surrounding gases are not the same as that within the silicon. Consequently, transient voltages can be particularly troublesome if the surface region breaks down or avalanches at a lower voltage than the junction in the body of the device. Because of the relative nonuniformity of surface regions, surface breakdown will occur in very small areas, so heat cannot be readily dissipated; the result is that the localized temperature rise is likely to damage the device. This mode of failure can be prevented by use of proper junction geometry, which keeps the field near the surface lower than that within the bulk of the device.[19]

Degradation may also occur as a result of the flow of injected current through an SCR. In the conducting state, the minority-carrier concentration within the structure is raised by orders of magnitude. These carriers may interact with the surface states to cause increased saturation current or changes in the α's of the device.[18] This type of degradation is often more severe at low junction temperatures than at higher ones.

Obviously, great care must be exercised by the manufacturer in device designs to keep the surface fields low and in fabrication processes to keep contaminants to a very low level. For high voltages, hermetically sealed junctions are a necessity if highly reliable operation under severe ambient conditions is to be expected.

4.3.2. THERMAL FATIGUE

Within an SCR many materials of greatly differing coefficients of expansion must be soldered, brazed, or alloyed together. As a consequence, when the device is cycled over a wide temperature range, the solders are placed under a great deal of stress. If any of the materials are strained beyond their elastic limits, i.e., into the plastic strain region, then fatigue failure is quite likely to result. The number of cycles necessary to cause failure is dependent on the degree of plastic deformation and the nature of the material being deformed. In general, the number of cycles required to cause failure to occur is given by the expression[20]

$$N = \frac{C_1}{(\Delta\epsilon_p)^2},\tag{4.4}$$

where $\Delta\epsilon_p$ is the change in plastic strain per cycle, N the number of cycles to cause failure, and C_1 a constant which is determined by the material's being plastically deformed. It turns out that $\Delta\epsilon_p$ is a function of ΔT, where ΔT is the temperature rise per cycle above that required to induce plastic strain. For a given SCR, the relationship between $\Delta\epsilon_p$ and ΔT, as a first approximation, can be expressed as [21]

$$\Delta\epsilon_p = C_2\Delta T,\tag{4.5}$$

where

$\Delta T = T - T(\infty)$ for $T > T(\infty)$.

$T(\infty) =$ temperature rise at which plastic flow begins. Below $T(\infty)$ the elastic limit of the materials is not exceeded, whereas for temperature rises above $T(\infty)$ plastic flow occurs.

$C_2 =$ constant which is a function of the area of the joint, its location, and the properties of the materials in the device.

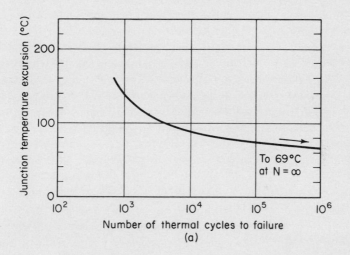

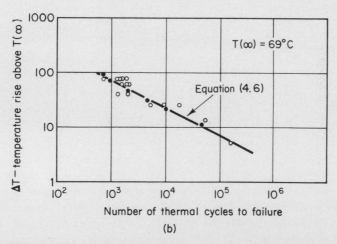

Fig. 4.11 Thermal fatigue failure curves for a typical soft soldered rectifier: (a) junction temperature excursion versus number of cycles required to cause device failure; (b) temperature rise above $T(\infty)$ required to cause failure.

By substituting equation (4.5) in (4.6), we get

$$N = \frac{C_3}{(\Delta T)^2}. \tag{4.6}$$

Thus it is evident that with greater temperature excursion the cycling problem becomes more severe. This problem can be alleviated by either a reduction in the temperature excursion or by designing the SCR so that none of the materials are strained beyond their elastic range. Curves of thermal cycles to cause failure versus temperature excursion for a large-area rectifier with a soft-solder joint is shown in Figs. 4.11(a) and 4.11(b). By using hard solders and designing the device so that none of the materials are plastically strained during a complete temperature cycle, failure caused by thermal fatigue can be minimized or eliminated.[21]

The first evidence of thermal-fatigue damage is usually an increase in the thermal resistance between the junction and the case. Very small cracks appear in the solder and continue to grow as the number of cycles increase. The increase in thermal resistance causes the temperature excursion to increase until the device eventually is overheated to the point of destruction.

4.3.3 FRACTURE

Silicon is a very brittle material and, as is common with most brittle materials, has a low yield strength when shear or tension stress is applied. Because it is desirable to maintain a low thermal resistance, the silicon should be placed as near the heat sink as possible. Molybdenum or tungsten is commonly placed between the silicon and the copper stud or lead to act as a stress buffer. Because molybdenum and tungsten closely match the coefficient of expansion of the silicon and have a high modulus of elasticity, the bimetallic stress is not readily transmitted to the silicon.[22]

When the solders or alloys which are used to attach the subassembly to the stud solidify during the brazing cycle, any further contraction below the solidification temperature introduces stress into the silicon through the molybdenum or tungsten back-up plates. Thus, this high-stress condition is aggravated by very low temperatures. Moreover, the larger the diameter of the device, the greater will be the stress at the periphery of the silicon, because of the differences in the expansion coefficients of the materials. Poor or incomplete wetting of solders between parts also causes unequal stress distributions, and these regions of high-stress concentration tend to aggravate the problem. Consequently, fracture is often the failure mechanism which limits low-temperature operation.

"Stud torque ratings" are generally required to prevent too much bending moment applied to the junction by mechanical means when the device is mounted into a heat sink.

Current surges at low temperature may also cause fracture.[23] With an

SCR initially at low temperature a great deal of mechanical stress will be exerted on the materials owing to their differences in expansion. The sudden application of a large load current will cause thermal gradients, which can cause additional mechanical stress in the semiconductor. As a consequence, surge current failures which occur at low temperatures may be the result of fracture rather than melting.

4.3.4 MELTING AND OVERTEMPERATURE

Current surges or thermal runaway can easily cause characteristic changes owing to localized melting of the silicon or the adjoining alloys.[23] With current surges the damage may be progressive, if the surge level is not so great as to cause complete melting. In general, the forward and reverse blocking characteristics are the first to degrade with current surges. Thermal runaway will occur when device degradation or a high junction temperature causes the blocking current to increase to a high level. This subject is discussed in detail in Sec. 4.6.3.

Transient overvoltages may also result in sufficiently high temperatures at either the surface or within the bulk of the device to cause failure by melting. Overvoltage in the forward blocking direction should not cause failure but should result in the device's turning itself on, *provided* the *surface* breakdown voltage of the forward blocking junction is greater than that within the body of the device. However, if an SCR is not specifically designed and constructed so that voltage breakdown occurs within the body of the device instead of at the surface, then localized heating at a point on the periphery of the junction is quite likely to cause damage.

4.3.5 RADIATION DAMAGE

Nuclear radiation of sufficient intensity and duration will damage SCR's. The result is increased voltage drop in the conducting state, lower gate sensitivity, faster recovery times, and finally increased reverse current. Fast neutrons, protons, electrons, and gamma rays all can cause sufficient damage to the silicon lattice so that the lifetime of the device suffers materially. An integrated neutron dose of about 10^{12} *nvt* is usually sufficient to cause noticeable permanent changes in device characteristics.[24,25,26] However, by proper design and selection of doping agents, this threshold can be increased with some sacrifice in other device parameters. The lifetime of minority carriers in the base of the SCR after neutron irradiation can be expressed by the relation

$$\frac{1}{\tau} = \frac{1}{\tau_0} + \frac{\Phi}{K},$$

where $K = 3 \times 10^{12}$ *nvt*-μsec, τ_0 is the initial lifetime in μsec, and Φ is the integrated neutron dosage in *nvt*.[26]

4.3.6 TEMPERATURE

Temperature affects many of the device characteristics. Its most noticeable effect is on forward and reverse blocking current, which, as noted in Sec. 2.4, increases exponentially with increasing temperature. As a consequence, the reverse and forward blocking power dissipation increases with increasing temperature and may cause thermal runaway if the temperature is sufficiently high. In addition, the forward breakover voltage first increases slightly because of an increase in avalanche breakdown and then decreases with further increases of temperature owing to rapidly increasing blocking current.

Such a forward breakover curve versus temperature for a typical SCR is shown in Fig. 2.12. The effect on forward drop in the ON state is shown in Fig. 4.2. Anode-commutated turn-off is also adversely affected by increasing temperature caused primarily by increases in lifetime and increased minority-carrier concentrations. Figure 4.12 illustrates the effects of temperature on

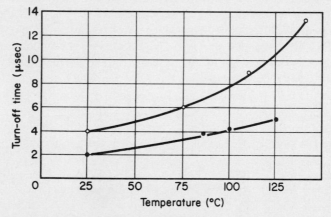

Fig. 4.12 Typical variation of turn-off time versus temperature for two different SCR's.

anode turn-off time. In addition, gate trigger current and voltage decrease with increasing temperature. Thus, the inherent device design characteristics generally determine the maximum allowable operating junction temperature of an SCR.

The chemical activity of surface contaminants and the rate at which entrapped contaminants outdiffuse from the materials inside the package increase markedly with temperature, as was discussed in Sec. 4.3.1. It is essential that life-tests be conducted to determine the degree to which contaminants affect SCR's fabricated by a given process. If fabricated properly, contamination-initiated surface degradation will be negligible under normal operating conditions. If it is desirable to have the maximum storage temperature higher than the operating junction temperature, the storage temperature is usually selected to achieve adequate reliability, or it may be limited by the melting temperature of the solders which are used to fabricate the device.

The low-temperature limit for the device is usually set at a value which will not cause fracture of the silicon or rupture of the insulating seals owing to differences in thermal expansion between these materials and the metals to which they are attached. In addition, the gate current required to trigger an SCR increases with decreasing temperature, whereas reverse breakdown and forward breakover voltages decrease. As a consequence, most specifications limit SCR operation to $-65°C$.

4.3.7 VOLTAGE

Voltage-induced failure usually results from hot spots caused by high electric fields, which result in localized avalanche breakdown within the junctions or on their surfaces. Increased blocking voltage also raises the electric field at the semiconductor surface, so surface impurities become more mobile and easier to ionize. Moreover, for a given device, the higher will be the blocking power generated and thus the lower the margin of thermal stability (see Sec. 4.6).

To lower electric fields at the surface during normal operation, two alternative approaches are possible:

1. In designing the SCR the surface can be properly contoured or the electric field otherwise altered so that it is significantly lower at the surface than in the body of the silicon.[19]
2. The SCR can be rated so that the critical surface-breakdown voltage is never exceeded.

Because impurities and lattice disturbances at the surface of the junctions are not uniformly distributed, breakdown in this region is very likely to result in localized hot spots, thereby damaging the SCR even though the current into the device is very low. Consequently, surface breakdown should be avoided if possible. Irregularities in a junction, such as those produced by poorly alloyed regions, nonuniformly diffused junctions, or the presence of metallic or oxygen precipitates, all cause highly localized electric fields.[27,28] If these irregularities are severe, hot spots will cause destructive internal breakdown.

4.3.8 CURRENT

Failure owing to current generally manifests itself by causing the temperature of the semiconducting material to rise excessively. In many instances, such as during triggering, it is impossible accurately to measure or calculate the temperature rise, because the current may be nonuniformly distributed over the junction area. Also, for current-surge conditions, it may be exceedingly difficult accurately to calculate the temperature rise.[23] As a result, experimental tests are often the quickest and most exact method of establishing limit points for rating curves. If the mode of failure and a few limit points are known, the rating curves under other conditions can usually be predicted with good accuracy.[1,2,37]

Another mode of failure which sometimes occurs after prolonged direct-current forward conduction is an increase in blocking current owing to changes in the surface states near the junction-surface interface. This phenomenon is usually caused by minority-carrier trapping at the surface so that inversion or accumulation layers are formed. This situation results in a high leakage current across the junctions or leads to surface breakdown with the application of blocking voltage. Such a condition is rare and is the result of improper surface conditioning.

4.3.9 MECHANICAL ENVIRONMENT

Most mechanical failures are the result of obvious mishandling or mechanical weaknesses. One of the most common mechanical-type failures results from leaky packages. Minute leaks are difficult to detect and yet are often large enough to permit moisture and other harmful materials to enter the device and degrade the surface of the junctions. The usual method of determining mechanical capability of an SCR is by testing it in a simulated environment.

4.4 Thermal Resistance

4.4.1 INTRODUCTION

The heat generated within the semiconducting material of an SCR must be dissipated into a heat sink, or for short periods it can be stored in the heat capacity of the cell materials. Because the materials through which the heat flows have both thermal resistance and capacitance, the thermal behavior of the device is quite analogous to that of an electrical RC transmission line. As a consequence, the thermal impedance between the junctions and the heat sink is time-dependent as shown in Fig. 4.13. At normal load current levels virtually all the heat is generated within the semiconducting material. Losses which occur elsewhere in the device are generally negligible.

4.4.2 HEAT GENERATION

The question which naturally arises in studying an SCR is that of where the heat is generated in a p-n-p-n structure. Unfortunately, both the mode of operation and the construction of the device itself cause the location of heat generation to vary widely throughout the semiconductor

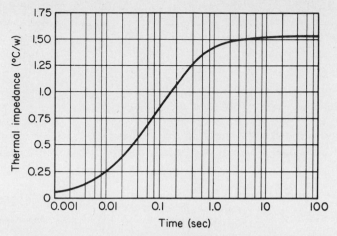

Fig. 4.13 Transient thermal impedance for a medium-current SCR.

When an SCR is in the reverse or forward blocking state, heat is generated in the space-charge region by carriers colliding with the lattice while they are being swept across by the electric field. If the voltage is raised sufficiently to cause avalanche breakdown, the collisions during transit of the depletion region will cause secondary carriers to be dislodged from the lattice and accelerated, as was discussed in Chap. 1. If the electric field in the space-charge region is badly perturbed by junction irregularities or by impurity precipitates, avalanche microplasmas will be confined to a few localized regions so that heat is liberated in small "hot spots."[27,28]

In the conducting state all the junctions of an SCR are forward-biased. With forward current passing through a *p-n* junction, electrons and holes evaporate over the potential hill and diffuse away from the junction until they recombine or are collected, thus releasing energy. As a consequence, heat is liberated where the minority carriers recombine.[29,30] In addition, joule heat is produced in the body of the semiconductor owing to majority current voltage drop. Furthermore, heat is generated at contacts and in the current-carrying terminals by ohmic losses.

Switching losses often tend to be localized owing to the nonuniform distribution of carriers across the area of a *p-n-p-n* device under transient conditions.[28] In three-terminal *p-n-p-n* structures, switching losses generally occur near the gate lead, causing "hot spots" on the emitter junction near the gate connection.[13] This phenomenon is discussed in Sec. 2.6.

Because of the complex nature of heat generation in the semiconducting material of a *p-n-p-n* device, it is essential that simplifying assumptions be made so that the problem can be made tractable. By assuming that all the electrical losses in an SCR are transformed into heat which is liberated in a plane through the center of the silicon wafer, parallel to the center junction, we can obtain a reasonably valid solution. Such an assumption is permitted if hot spots are not in evidence and if the time is long compared to l^2/D_T, where D_T is the thermal diffusitivity of the silicon wafer and l is its thickness.[23] For a wafer of silicon 0.010 in. thick, $l^2/D_T = 1.4$ msec.

4.4.3 Heat Dissipation and Thermal Resistance

The equivalent thermal circuit of the SCR can be represented as shown in Fig. 4.14. For planar junctions two principal network branches emanate from

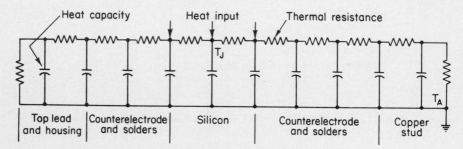

Fig. 4.14 Equivalent thermal circuit of a SCR.

the semiconductor to the heat sink. One branch path goes through the top lead to the heat sink, whereas the other goes through the stud. By making use of the assumptions outlined in the next section on heat generation and by neglecting i^2R losses outside of the junction, we can simplify the circuit shown in Fig. 4.14 to that shown in Fig. 4.15.

For the individual with an electrical background, it may be easier to visualize the thermal circuit operation in terms of its electrical analogue.[23,31,32] Heat capacitance is analogous to electrical capacitance, thermal resistance to electrical resistance, power (heat) to current, and temperature to voltage. Thus, one can apply many of the same methods of analysis used in electrical RC network analysis.

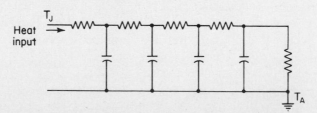

Fig. 4.15 Simplified equivalent thermal circuit for a SCR.

If a heat-dissipating assembly, such as an SCR, is initially in a quiescent state, the time function of temperature at the input in response to the application of a unit step of power is called the *transient thermal impedance*. Thus, when a step input of power is applied to such a network, the temperature rise can be expressed by the equation[2,32,33]

$$T(t) = P\theta(t), \tag{4.7}$$

where

  $T(t)$ = temperature rise above ambient, $T_J - T_A$, °C.
  P = step input of heat, w.
  $\theta(t)$ = transient thermal impedance, °C/w.
  T_J = junction temperature, °C.
  T_A = ambient temperature, °C.

With the application of the step of heating power in the semiconducting material as shown in Fig. 4.16, the junction temperature will rise at a rate

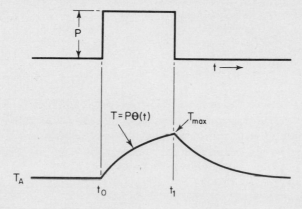

Fig. 4.16 Junction temperature rise resulting from a step input of power.

determined by the thermal network. The size, shape, and material which go to make up the SCR, along with the heat sink or fin to which it is attached, determine the thermal characteristics of the device. A typical thermal resistance curve for an SCR rated at 25 amp is shown in Fig. 4.13. For steady power input, the transient thermal resistance approaches a constant value; that is, the $\lim_{t \to \infty} \theta(t) = \theta(\infty)$, the steady-state thermal resistance. From the average power dissipation and the steady-state thermal resistance, the average temperature rise of the device can be found. However, because the heat capacity of SCR's is small, overloads will cause the internal temperature to rise very rapidly in comparison to most other electrical equipment of about the same rating, such as transformers and motors. As a consequence, it is generally advisable to determine the maximum junction temperature. By proper use of the transient thermal resistance curve and the superposition principle, the peak junction temperature can be found for any arbitrary pulse shape or train of pulses.

An arbitrary waveshape of power input can be described by a series of step inputs and is of the form

$$P(\tau) = P(0)U(\tau) + \Delta_1 PU(\tau - \Delta_1\tau) + \cdots$$
$$+ \Delta_{n-1}PU(\tau - t + \Delta_n\tau) + \Delta_n PU(\tau - t), \qquad (4.8)$$

where $U(\tau - \Delta_1\tau)$ is a unit step function having a value of zero for times less than $\tau - \Delta_1\tau$ and a value of unity for times greater than $\tau - \Delta_1\tau$. This equation is represented in Fig. 4.17. The temperature response to this input will be

$$T(\tau) = P(0)\theta(\tau) + \Delta_1 P\theta(\tau - \Delta_1\tau) + \Delta_2 P\theta(\tau - \Delta_1\tau - \Delta_2\tau) + \cdots$$
$$+ \Delta_{n-1}P\theta(\tau - t + \Delta_n\tau) + \Delta_n P\theta(\tau - t), \qquad (4.9)$$

where $\theta(\tau - \Delta_1\tau - \Delta_2\tau)$ is the transient thermal resistance at time $\tau - \Delta_1\tau - \Delta_2\tau$; for values of time less than $\Delta_1\tau + \Delta_2\tau$, the function takes on a value of zero.

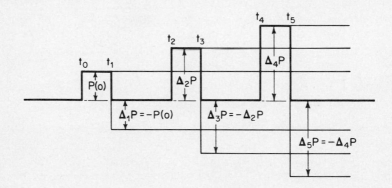

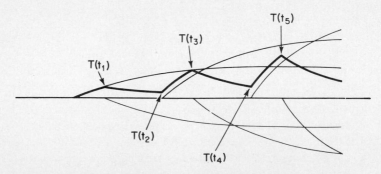

Fig. 4.17 Use of superposition to determine junction temperature.

From Fig. 4.17 it can be seen that if n is permitted to increase independently and all $\Delta\tau \to 0$, then

$$\Delta P = \frac{\partial P(\tau)}{\partial \tau} \Delta\tau, \tag{4.10}$$

provided ΔP is continuous as τ increases. As a consequence, equation (4.8) becomes

$$P(t) = P(0)U(t) + \int_0^t \frac{\partial P(\tau)}{\partial \tau} U(t - \tau) \, d\tau, \tag{4.11}$$

and equation (4.9) becomes

$$T(t) = P(0)\theta(t) + \int_0^t \frac{\partial P(\tau)}{\partial \tau} \theta(t - \tau) \, d\tau. \tag{4.12}$$

Alternative forms of these equations can be derived[34] and are expressed as follows:

$$T(t) = \frac{d}{dt} \int_0^t P(\tau)\theta(t - \tau)d\tau, \tag{4.13}$$

$$T(t) = P(t)\theta(0) + \int_0^t P(\tau) \frac{\partial \theta(t - \tau)}{\partial \tau} \, d\tau. \tag{4.14}$$

Thus, in principle, if the power input at the junction and the transient thermal resistance are known, the temperature at any given time can be calculated. Since much of semiconductor rating theory evolves by keeping the junction temperature below a specified limit, these equations, used in conjunction with those which describe heat generation in the device, constitute a major portion of the expressions required to rate an SCR.

4.4.4 Measurement of Thermal Resistance

The most straightforward techniques for measurement of thermal resistance consist of placing a thermocouple at or near the p-n junction (assumed to be the heat source) and on the heat sink to which the device is mounted. D-C current is then passed through the device in the forward direction to produce the desired heat generation, and the temperature difference between the two thermocouples is recorded. The thermal resistance between the junction and the heat sink is defined as

$$\theta(t) = \frac{T_J - T_S}{VI} \quad (°C/w), \tag{4.15}$$

where

T_J = junction temperature (°C).
T_S = heat-sink temperature (°C).
V = voltage drop across device (v).
I = d-c current through device (amp).

This technique is not completely satisfactory because of the small dimensions encountered in many p-n-p-n devices and because of the inaccessibility of the junctions to thermocouples without damaging or destroying the device. Moreover, thermocouple errors are quite troublesome if transient thermal impedance data are needed.

Fortunately, *p-n* junctions can be used as temperature indicators, since their characteristics are quite temperature-sensitive. With germanium devices it is usual to use the reverse *I-V* characteristic to detect temperature changes. However, because the reverse saturation current of a silicon junction is exceedingly small over much of the temperature range of interest, surface leakage currents often predominate and vary in an unpredictable manner with temperature. The forward characteristic is much less affected and is a reasonably reliable indicator which does not vary widely from unit to unit of the same type. As a consequence, it can be used to determine temperature to a reasonable degree of accuracy without separate temperature-voltage calibration runs being required.† With calibration, very accurate measurements usually can be made.

The relationships between temperature and forward voltage drop for an SCR can be derived from the equation developed in Sec. 2.5.

$$v_F = \frac{nkT}{q}\left[\ln\left(\frac{i_F}{I_S}\right) + \ln\left(\frac{A_1 A_3}{A_2}\right)\right]. \tag{4.16}$$

Because of thermal generation of hole-electron pairs, I_S varies with temperature according to the equation[35,36]

$$I_S = KT^{5/2}\exp\left(-\frac{q\varphi}{nkT}\right), \tag{4.17}$$

where

K = constant dependent on area, geometry, and lifetime of the device
T = temperature in °K
φ = band gap voltage (1.12 ev for silicon)
k = Boltzmann's constant
q = electron charge (1.6 × 10⁻¹⁹ coulombs)
n = constant determined by density and level of trapping sites and the current level.

Substituting equation (4.17) in (4.16), we get

$$v_F = \varphi + \left(\frac{nkT}{q}\right)\left[\ln i_F - \frac{5}{2}\ln KT + \ln\left(\frac{A_1 A_3}{A_2}\right)\right]. \tag{4.18}$$

If the current is held constant, the rate of change of forward voltage drop v_F with respect to temperature T can be obtained by differentiating equation (4.18).

$$\frac{\partial v_F}{\partial T} = -\frac{nk}{q}\left[-\ln i_F + \frac{5}{2}\ln(KT) - \ln\left(\frac{A_1 A_3}{A_2}\right) + \frac{5}{2} - \frac{\partial}{\partial T}\ln\left(\frac{A_1 A_3}{A_2}\right)\right]. \tag{4.19}$$

† The accuracy of this method of measurement may be inadequate for SCR's which have "shortened emitter" construction (sec. 3.7).

The quantity in brackets varies very slowly with changes in temperature, and for most practical cases can be regarded as a constant, provided the temperature excursion is not too great. Thus, the rate of change in forward drop with temperature can be written, by definition, as

$$\frac{\partial v_F}{\partial T} \equiv -a.$$ (4.20)

By substituting equation (4.18) in equation (4.19), we find that

$$a = -\frac{\partial v_F}{\partial T} = \frac{\varphi - v_F}{T} + \left[\frac{5}{2} - \frac{\partial}{\partial T}\ln\frac{A_1 A_3}{A_2}\right]\frac{nk}{q}.$$ (4.21)

In actual practice, the forward current used for this measurement is about one per cent of the rated forward current. For silicon devices the slope, a, is generally of the order of two mv per °C. Hence, the forward characteristic of a *p-n-p-n* junction device can serve as a relatively good thermometer for determining its own temperature.

To measure the transient impedance, a thermocouple is attached to the heat sink, stud, or other reference point to which the thermal impedance is to be measured. A low level of d-c forward current is passed through the device, and the forward conducting drop $v_F(t = 0)$ is recorded. Since the heat generated with this small current is negligible, the junction and heat sink temperature are essentially the same. Next, a step of forward current of a high level is passed through the device to raise the junction temperature, and the system is allowed to reach equilibrium. Forward voltage drop and current are then recorded and the input power, $V \times I$, is computed. The current is then instantaneously dropped back to the low-level value of current, and the voltage is monitored as a function of time. Because of minority-carrier storage, the values of voltage for times less than about twenty times the minority-carrier lifetime must be disregarded; to find the low-level forward drop to be used for determining the temperature at the instant that the current was dropped ($t = 0$), it is necessary to extrapolate back to zero time. The junction temperature fall is

$$T_J(t) - T_S = \frac{v_F(\infty) - v_F(t)}{a}.$$ (4.22)

Thermal impedance is then given by

$$\theta(t) = \frac{T_J(t) - T_S}{VI}$$ (4.23)

where

T_J = junction temperature.
T_S = heat-sink temperature.
VI = heat dissipated at junction area.

This equation is defined for *rising* temperature produced by a step input of heat. In the case just discussed, the temperature drops after heat generation ceases. Hence, thermal resistance can be obtained by combining equations (4.22) and (4.23).

$$\theta(t) = \frac{v_F(t) - v_F(\infty)}{aVI} \quad °C/w, \qquad (4.24)$$

where

$v_F(t)$ = the low-level voltage drop for $t > 0$.
$v_F(\infty)$ = the low-level voltage drop for $t \to \infty$.
VI = watts of heat being dissipated for $t < 0$.

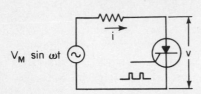

This transformation from a cooling curve to a heating curve is permitted if the thermal properties of the materials in the device are linear and bilateral and if the heating occurs all in the same plane.

4.5 Heat Generation Calculations

4.5.1 INTRODUCTION

Electrical energy is converted to heat, which must be dissipated to the heat sink, because of the following electrical power losses:

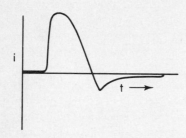

1. Forward voltage drop during load current conduction.
2. Forward leakage current during forward blocking.
3. Reverse leakage current during reverse blocking.
4. Losses in gate region owing to trigger energy.
5. Losses owing to switching and transients.

At high frequencies all these loss components can be observed. Figure 4.18 shows the voltage, current, and power loss waveforms for such a condition.

4.5.2 FORWARD-CONDUCTION HEAT DISSIPATION

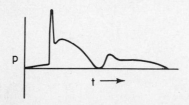

Fig. 4.18 Current, voltage, and power dissipation waveforms for an SCR.

Forward-conduction losses are the largest contributor to heating of the device for most applications. In Sec. 2.5 the equation for the forward drop in an SCR was approximated as

$$v_F = \frac{nkT}{q} \ln \left(\frac{I_{S_2} i_F}{I_{S_3} I_{S_1}} \right) + K\sqrt{i_F} + Ri_F. \tag{4.25}$$

From this expression, $\bar{P}_F$, the average forward heat generated during a half sine wave of current is determined by integration of $V \times I$ over a period of one cycle.

With the substitutions

$$i_F = I_M \sin \theta, \tag{4.26}$$

$$I^* = \frac{I_{S_3} I_{S_1}}{I_{S_2}}, \tag{4.27}$$

$$\beta = \frac{q}{nkT}, \tag{4.28}$$

$$\theta = \omega t, \tag{4.29}$$

the expression for average forward power is

$$P_{F(AV)} = \bar{P}_F$$

$$= \frac{I_M}{2\pi} \int_{\theta_1}^{\theta_2} \left[\frac{1}{\beta} (\sin \theta) \ln \left(\frac{I_M}{I^*} \sin \theta \right) + K\sqrt{I_M} (\sin \theta)^{3/2} + RI_M \sin^2 \theta \right] d\theta. \tag{4.30}$$

Integration of this expression yields

$$\bar{P}_F = \frac{I_M}{2\pi} \left\{ \frac{1}{\beta} \left[-\cos \theta \right]_{\theta_1}^{\theta_2} \ln \frac{I_M}{I^*} + I_M R \left[\frac{\theta}{2} - \frac{1}{4} \sin 2\theta \right]_{\theta_1}^{\theta_2} + \frac{\varphi_1(\theta)}{\beta} \Big|_{\theta_1}^{\theta_2} \right.$$

$$\left. + \varphi_2(\theta) \Big|_{\theta_1}^{\theta_2} K\sqrt{I_M} \right\}, \tag{4.31}$$

where

$$\varphi_1(\theta) \Big|_{\theta_1}^{\theta_2} = \int_{\theta_1}^{\theta_2} (\sin \theta \ln \sin \theta) \, d\theta, \tag{4.32}$$

$$\varphi_2(\theta) \Big|_{\theta_1}^{\theta_2} = \int_{\theta_1}^{\theta_2} \sin^{3/2} \theta \, d\theta. \tag{4.33}$$

φ_1 and φ_2 are intractable except for the definite interval $\theta = 0$ to $\theta = \pi/2$, where

$$\varphi_1 \Big|_0^{\pi/2} = (\ln 2 - 1) = -0.307,$$

$$\varphi_2 \Big|_0^{\pi/2} = \frac{\sqrt{\pi}}{2} \frac{\Gamma(\frac{5}{4})}{\Gamma(\frac{7}{4})} = 0.876,$$

where

$$\Gamma(n) = \int_0^\infty x^{(n-1)}[\exp{(-x)}]\,dx.$$

Thus, for forward conduction from $\theta_1 = 0$ to $\theta_2 = \pi/2$ or from $\theta_1 = \pi/2$ to $\theta_2 = \pi$, the heat generated in the device is

$$\bar{P}_F = \frac{I_M}{2\pi}\left[\frac{\ln{(I_M/I^*)}}{\beta} + \frac{\pi I_M R}{4} - \frac{0.307}{\beta} + 0.876K\sqrt{I_M}\right]. \tag{4.34}$$

The heat generated for 180 deg conduction ($\theta = 0$ to $\theta = \pi$) is exactly double the 90 deg conduction value, since the current wave is symmetrical about the 90 deg point. From equation (4.31) and Fig. 4.19 the average heat

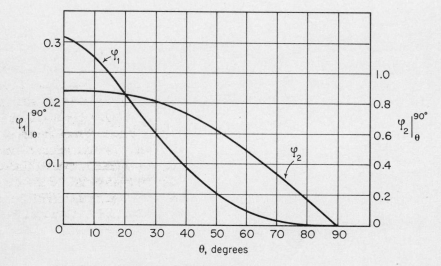

Fig. 4.19 φ_1 and φ_2 for interval θ to $90°$.

generated over any conduction angle may be determined. For example, the heat generated as a result of conduction from $\theta_1 = \pi/3$ to $\theta_1 = \pi$ is determined by making use of symmetry as follows:

$$\bar{P}_F = \frac{I_M}{2\pi}\left\{\left[-\frac{\cos\theta}{\beta}\right]_{\pi/3}^{\pi} + I_M R\left[\frac{\theta}{2} - \frac{1}{4}\sin 2\theta\right]_{\pi/3}^{\pi} + \frac{\varphi_1}{\beta}\bigg|_{\pi/3}^{\pi/2} + \frac{\varphi_1}{\beta}\bigg|_0^{\pi/2}\right.$$
$$\left. + K\sqrt{I_M}\,\varphi_2\bigg|_{\pi/3}^{\pi/2} + K\sqrt{I_M}\,\varphi_2\bigg|_0^{\pi/2}\right\}, \tag{4.35}$$

$$\bar{P}_F = \frac{I_M}{2\pi}\left(\frac{1.5}{\beta} + 0.831 I_M R - \frac{0.307}{\beta} - \frac{0.022}{\beta} + 0.590K\sqrt{I_M} + 0.876K\sqrt{I_M}\right), \tag{4.36}$$

$$\bar{P}_F = \frac{I_M}{2\pi}\left(\frac{1.171}{\beta} + 0.831 I_M R + 1.466K\sqrt{I_M}\right). \tag{4.37}$$

The average forward power dissipated as a function of conduction angle can be derived by following this procedure. Usually the power is computed as a function of average forward current or rms current, where

$$I_{F(AV)} = \bar{I} = \frac{1}{2\pi} \int_{\theta_1}^{\pi} I_M \sin \theta \, d\theta = \frac{I_M}{2\pi} \left[-\cos \theta \right]_{\theta_1}^{\pi} = \frac{I_M}{2\pi} \left(1 + \cos \theta_1 \right). \quad (4.38)$$

The root mean square (rms) value of current can also be found from the equation

$$I_{rms} = \sqrt{\frac{I_M^2 \int_{\theta_1}^{\theta_2} (\sin \theta)^2 \, d\theta}{\int_0^{2\pi} d\theta}} = \frac{I_M}{\sqrt{2\pi}} \sqrt{\int_{\theta_1}^{\theta_2} \sin^2 \theta \, d\theta} \quad (4.39)$$

$$I_{rms} = \frac{I_M}{2\sqrt{\pi}} \sqrt{\theta - \tfrac{1}{2} \sin 2\theta} \, \Big|_{\theta_1}^{\theta_2}. \quad (4.40)$$

Forward power dissipation for other load current waveshapes can be calculated in a similar manner.

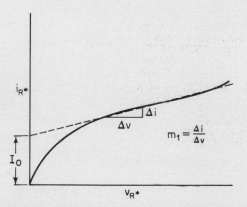

Fig. 4.20 Approximation used to determine reverse power dissipation.

4.5.3 REVERSE OR FORWARD BLOCKING HEAT GENERATION

Reverse or forward blocking current at any given junction temperature as a function of voltage can be approximated by the expression (see Fig. 4.20)

$$i_{R*} = I_0 + m_1 v_{R*}, \quad (4.41)$$

where

I_0 = intercept current with no gate current
m_1 = slope of the current as a function of voltage
v_{R*} = instantaneous reverse voltage = $E_M \sin \theta$.

The instantaneous reverse power then is

$$P_{R*} = v_{R*}i_{R*} = (E_M \sin \theta)(I_0 + m_1 E_M \sin \theta), \tag{4.42}$$

and the average power over a complete cycle of single-phase voltage is

$$P_{R(AV)} = \bar{P}_R = \frac{E_M}{2\pi} \int_{\theta_1}^{\theta_2} [I_0 \sin \theta + m_1 E_M \sin^2 \theta] \, d\theta, \tag{4.43}$$

$$\bar{P}_R = \frac{E_M I_0}{2\pi} \left[-\cos \theta \right]_{\theta_1}^{\theta_2} + \frac{m_1 E_M^2}{4\pi} \left[\theta - \frac{1}{2} \sin 2\theta \right]_{\theta_1}^{\theta_2}. \tag{4.44}$$

In many single-phase circuits, the reverse voltage is applied for a full 180 deg. Under this condition the reverse power dissipation in the cell will be

$$P_{R(AV)} = \frac{E_M I_0}{\pi} + \frac{m_1 E_M^2}{4}. \tag{4.45}$$

Blocking power dissipation for other voltage waveshapes can be calculated in a similar manner.

Both the reverse and forward blocking characteristics are significantly increased by the application of forward bias across the gate-to-emitter junction, as was pointed out in Sec. 4.2. In this case, the SCR characteristic behaves in a manner very similar to that of a transistor with the gate acting as a base lead. Actually, the device is a "remote-base" transistor.[4] In Figs. 4.5 and 2.2, an SCR is shown which is biased so that the gate will cause the cathode emitter junction to inject electrons into the adjacent p-type base. These electrons diffuse across the p-type region and are collected at J2. The resulting majority carriers bias J1 so that the p-n-p region behaves as a transistor with a base drive of $\alpha_{npn}I_K$. Using the nomenclature of Sec. 2.5, the reverse current is

$$i_{R*} = \frac{I_{co} + \alpha_{2N}i_g}{1 - \alpha_{1I}}, \tag{4.46}$$

and the forward blocking current is

$$i_{F*} = \frac{I_{co} + \alpha_{2N}i_g}{1 - \alpha_{1N} - \alpha_{2N}}. \tag{4.47}$$

Thus, equation (4.41), which expresses instantaneous reverse or forward current, must be modified during the period when the gate-to-emitter junction is forward-biased. The effect is to increase the saturation value so that (4.41) becomes

$$i_{R*} = I_0 + \frac{\alpha_{2N}i_g}{1 - \alpha_{1I}} + m_1 v, \tag{4.48}$$

and

$$i_{F*} = I_0 + \frac{\alpha_{2N}i_g}{1 - \alpha_{1N} - \alpha_{2N}} + m_1 v, \tag{4.49}$$

when the alphas are evaluated with a few volts across the device.

4.5.4 GATE POWER DISSIPATION

The heat generated in the gate region of an SCR can be calculated in much the same manner and by using the same techniques as outlined for anode-to-cathode heat calculations. As noted in Sec. 4.2, the gate current-voltage characteristic is generally very similar to that of a small, low-voltage diode—except that there is interaction with the anode current when the device triggers. However, heating which results from the gate triggering pulse or the current build-up during turn-on tends to be localized in the vicinity of the gate lead. In addition, the gate trigger pulse is often of short duration. *As a consequence, the peak rather than the average power should generally be used for calculation of heating.* For rating purposes it is usually sufficient to approximate the actual gate power with a square pulse of the same magnitude and adjusted in duration so as to contain the same energy.

Caution should be exercised in triggering an SCR when fast-rising anode current wavefronts are prevalent, since the spot heating which results may seriously limit the device's power-handling capability.[13,14] It should also be remembered that a great deal of heat can be generated in the gate circuit if the reverse avalanche voltage of the gate-to-cathode junction is exceeded.

4.5.5 TRANSIENT HEATING

The heat which is generated during the periods when the current through an SCR is changing rapidly (usually less than fifty μsec for most SCR's) is complicated by the difficulty of accurately predicting the SCR voltage-current characteristic resulting from transient carrier distributions. Moreover, the heating effects can be very localized, depending on the circumstances. As a consequence, transient ratings are most often determined empirically. Several situations are discussed in the following paragraphs.

SCR Conducting—Surge Current Applied: If an SCR is initially in the conducting state with no gate drive being supplied, and the load impedance is lowered or the source voltage raised, the current will rise quickly to the new steady-state value. This condition is typical of the usual surge condition, and the heat generated can generally be calculated by using equation (4.31). However, if the load impedance or source voltage is instantaneously changed, the anode-to-cathode voltage-current relationship cannot be described by equation (4.25). Instead, a high voltage which decays exponentially with time will develop across the SCR, as depicted in Fig. 4.21. This situation results because a finite time is required for minority carriers to traverse the base regions of the SCR.

The sequence of events prior to equation (4.25)'s becoming valid can be visualized by considering Fig. 2.9. When the load impedance is suddenly lowered, more electrons must flow toward $p1$ and more holes toward $n2$ for the current to rise. As a consequence of the delay required for the minority

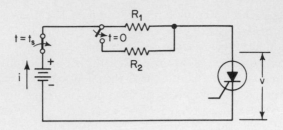

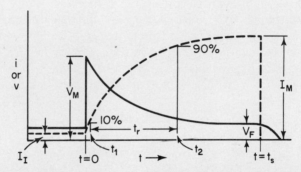

Fig. 4.21 Voltage and current resulting from an instantaneous change in load impedance.

carriers to cross their respective bases, the excess holes and electrons in the space-charge layer of forward-biased junction $J2$ are removed, causing the device to be temporarily taken out of the saturated state, so junction $J2$ becomes reverse-biased. However, as the injected carriers from junctions $J1$ and $J3$ begin to reach $J2$, its space-charge layer again becomes charged, and $J2$ becomes forward-biased. Once the carriers have reached an essentially steady-state condition† equation (4.25) can be used.

If the circuit impedance is small enough so that the current is limited by the SCR (i.e., for rise time of about ten μsec or less), the current can be expected to build up exponentially, and the power dissipated during this transient can be calculated by referring to Fig. 4.21 as follows:

$$i \cong (I_M - I_I)[1 - \exp(-2.2t/t_r)] + I_I, \qquad (4.50)$$

$$v \cong (V_M - V_F) \exp(-2.2t/t_r) + V_F, \qquad (4.51)$$

† For steady-state condition to exist, the time should be significantly long compared to the transit time. The transit time is approximately $W^2/2D$, where W is the smallest base width and D is the diffusion constant for minority carriers in that base [see Chap. 1, equation (1.106)].

where

V_M = instantaneous maximum voltage across the SCR at the beginning of switching.

I_M = steady-state value of current.

t_r = time for current $I_M - i$ to rise from 10 per cent to 90 per cent of its final value.

I_I = current prior to switching.

The heat generated in the device will be

$$P = vi = V_F I_M [1 - \exp(-2.2t/t_r)]^2$$
$$+ (V_F I_I + V_M I_M)[1 - \exp(-2.2t/t_r)] \exp(-2.2t/t_r)$$
$$+ V_M I_I \exp(-4.4t/t_r). \qquad (4.52)$$

The average power can be determined by integrating equation (4.52) over the surge period.

$$P_{\text{avg}} = \frac{1}{t_s} \int_0^{t_s} vi \, dt. \qquad (4.53)$$

If $t_s \gg t_r$ and $I_M \gg I_I$, then

$$P_{\text{avg}} \cong \left(\frac{V_M I_M}{4.4} - \frac{3V_F I_M}{4.4} \right) \frac{t_r}{t_s} + V_F I_M. \qquad (4.54)$$

If the change in current resulted from a change in load impedance or supply voltage, the heat generated will usually be distributed over the area of the device in a reasonably uniform manner. However, if the current rise resulted from gate triggering, the heat is almost certain to be localized.

Circuit-commutated turn-off: When an SCR is in the conducting state and reverse voltage is suddenly applied across the cell, the initial current will be limited only by the external load. Minority carriers are removed from the two bases as described in Sec. 2.7. However, one of the transistor sections always recovers before the other does. As a consequence, all the current must flow across a reverse-biased junction which is in avalanche or zener breakdown. This high voltage in conjunction with high commutating current can cause considerable heating.

4.6 Calculation of Rating—Based on Junction Temperature

4.6.1 INTRODUCTION

An effective approach to the rating of an SCR must take into consideration the more desirable device characteristics and all the mechanisms of failure and their interrelationships. With the determination of the characteristics and the establishment of the modes of failure, operating conditions which will assure reliable performance during the desired life of the device can be derived. From the discussion on failure mechanisms in Sec. 4.3, it is apparent that many stress factors contribute to failure. Each stress factor may produce or accelerate degradation by one or more mechanisms. As a consequence, the effect of each stress should be examined to determine its contribution toward possible malfunction of the device. The contribution made by temperature, voltage, current, and the mechanical environment to each mechanism of failure must be quantitatively established, and a rating must be derived which will provide an adequate factor of safety. In addition, the characteristics of the SCR must be maintained within limits which are reasonable for the intended application. Since the equipment designer has control only over temperature, voltage, current, and the SCR's mechanical environment, the ratings must be established in terms of these measurable parameters.

Junction temperature is a cornerstone around which an SCR is rated.[2] Since temperature affects voltage and current capability, along with contributing to several of the failure mechanisms discussed in Sec. 4.3, ratings are usually based on maintaining the peak junction temperature below a value determined by characteristics, life tests, and the device designer's judgment. By combining the results derived in the preceding sections, calculations can be made which relate maximum junction temperature to load current under various load conditions and heat-sink temperatures.

Under steady-state conditions the generation of heat owing to the losses discussed in Sec. 4.5 is balanced by the flow of heat through the thermal resistance of the device to the heat sink. This flow of heat causes the junction temperature to rise above that of the heat sink or ambient by an amount equal to the product of the power dissipated in the SCR and the thermal resistance between the junctions and the ambient. Because the junction temperature varies cyclically with the load current (i.e., for 60 cycle duty the temperature rises and falls during every cycle), ratings should be based on the peak rather than the average temperature. This can be accomplished by approximating the thermal resistance with a simple RC circuit,[2] or, to be more accurate, the transient thermal impedance curve should be used to calculate instantaneous junction temperature. The next section describes a method for converting arbitrary waveshapes into equivalent square-wave pulses for use with the transient thermal impedance curve so that peak junction temperature can be calculated. Although such a task can be quite laborious if done manually, a computer solution is extremely rapid.[37]

Under transient overload conditions, the heat generated in the semiconducting material may not have sufficient time to reach the heat sink; nevertheless, the junction temperature can be determined by using the concept of transient thermal impedance. In addition, it must be remembered that the reverse and forward blocking currents are very temperature-dependent. Care must be exercised that the heat input does not reach a level which will cause the device thermally to "run away." This problem is treated in Sec. 4.6.3.

4.6.2 IRREGULARLY SHAPED POWER PULSES

In Sec. 4.4 it was shown that by the use of superposition and a knowledge of transient thermal impedance, the temperature rise owing to any arbitrarily shaped power pulse could be calculated. In most practical applications it is exceedingly difficult to consider the exact shape of the power pulse without the problem's becoming intractable. From the approximation that the actual power pulse can be transformed into an equivalent rectangular form, calculations of junction temperature can be more easily accomplished. Figure 4.22 illustrates a recurring power pulse which is of arbitrary waveshape. It has

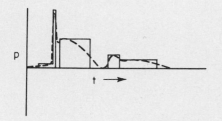

Fig. 4.22 Conversion of power waveforms to equivalent rectangular waves.

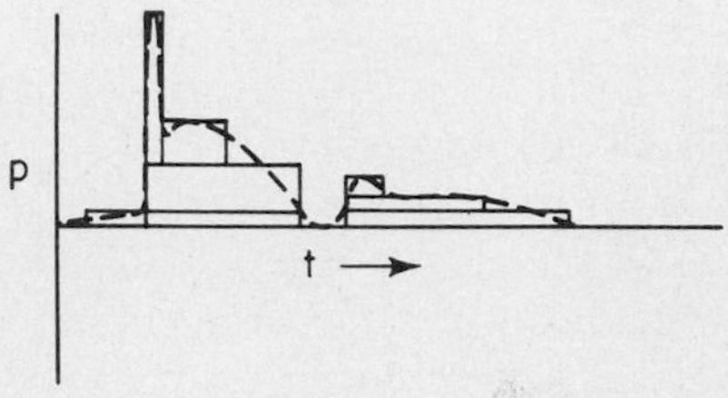

Fig. 4.23 Superposition of rectangular waves to achieve accuracy.

a peak power value of P_M watts and a full cycle-average of P_{avg}, but the rectangular pulse duration is altered by a constant, N, to maintain the proper peak-to-average relationships, where

$$N = \frac{P_{avg}}{P_M}. \tag{4.55}$$

Conversion of arbitrary waveshapes into rectangular waveshapes by this method results in a worst-case approximation, since a rectangular pulse of power will always raise the temperature higher than any other pulse shape having the same peak and average value. A rectangular pulse concentrates the heat into a shorter period of time, thus reducing the amount which can escape by diffusion to the heat sink.

A more accurate method of converting complex waveforms is to superimpose several rectangular waves, as shown in Fig. 4.23. This method is particularly useful for the calculation of temperature where switching losses are predominant.

When power pulses follow each other closely, the temperature will rise with the application of pulse power and fall when it is removed until the next pulse occurs, as shown in Fig. 4.17. The temperature rises for various combinations of repeated pulses have been derived by superposition and are shown in Fig. 4.24.[3]

Basic Load Current Rating Equations

Load condition	Waveform of power loss at junction	Waveform of junction temperature rise (T_R = reference temp.)	Solution for junction temperature and power loss θ = steady-state thermal resistance. $\theta_{(t_1)}$ = transient thermal impedance at time t_1. $\theta_{(t_2-t_1)}$ = transient thermal impedance at time (t_2-t_1), etc.
Continuous load			$T_J - T_R = P_0\theta$ $P_0 = \dfrac{T_J - T_R}{\theta}$
Single load pulse	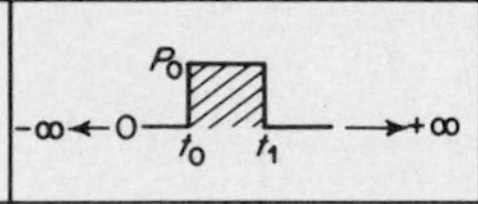	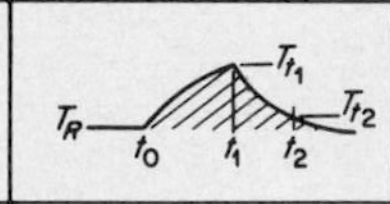	$T_1 - T_R = P_0\theta_{(t_1)}$ $T_2 - T_R = P_0\left[\theta_{(t_2)} - \theta_{(t_2-t_1)}\right]$ $P_0 = \dfrac{T_1 - T_R}{\theta_{(t_1)}}$
Short train of load pulses (equal amplitude)	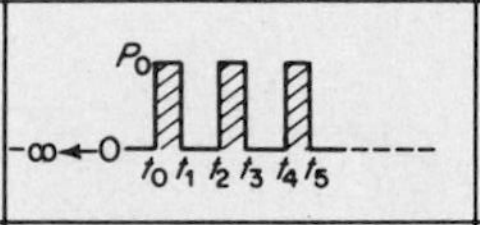	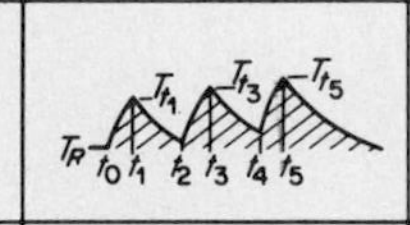	$T_1 - T_R = P_0\theta_{(t_1)}$ $T_3 - T_R = P_0\left[\theta_{(t_3)} - \theta_{(t_3-t_1)} + \theta_{(t_3-t_2)}\right]$ $T_5 - T_R = P_0\left[\theta_{(t_5)} - \theta_{(t_5-t_1)} + \theta_{(t_5-t_2)} - \theta_{(t_5-t_3)} + \theta_{(t_5-t_4)}\right]$ etc.
Train of unequal amplitude load pulses	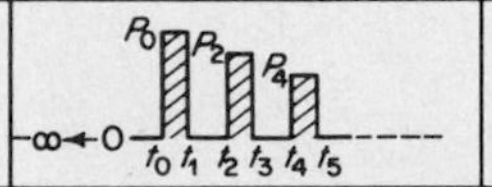		$T_1 - T_R = P_0\theta_{(t_1)}$ $T_3 - T_R = P_0\theta_{(t_3)} - P_0\theta_{(t_3-t_1)} + P_2\theta_{(t_3-t_2)}$ $T_5 - T_R = P_0\theta_{(t_5)} - P_0\theta_{(t_5-t_1)} + P_2\theta_{(t_5-t_2)} - P_2\theta_{(t_5-t_3)} + P_4\theta_{(t_5-t_4)}$
Long train of equal amplitude load pulses (approx. solution)	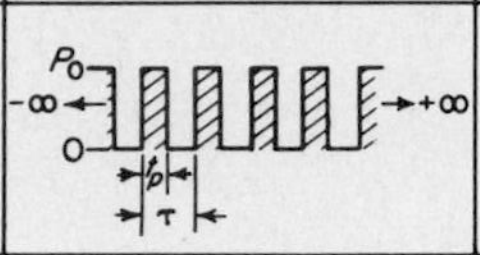		$T_J - T_R = P_0\left[\dfrac{t_p\theta}{\tau} + \left(1 - \dfrac{t_p}{\tau}\right)\theta_{(\tau + t_p)} - \theta_{(\tau)} + \theta_{(t_p)}\right]$ $P_0 = \dfrac{T_J - T_R}{\dfrac{t_p\theta}{\tau} + \left(1 - \dfrac{t_p}{\tau}\right)\theta_{(\tau + t_p)} - \theta_{(\tau)} + \theta_{(t_p)}}$
Overload following continuous duty (nonpulsed)	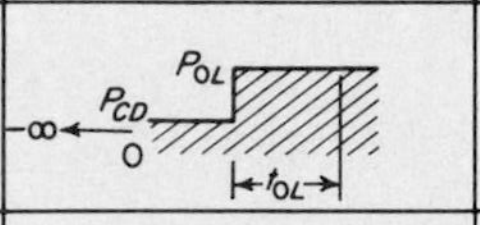	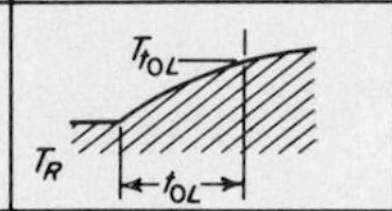	$T_{OL} - T_R = P_{CD}\theta + (P_{OL} - P_{CD})\theta_{(t_{OL})}$ $P_{OL} = \dfrac{T_{OL} - T_R - P_{CD}\theta}{\theta_{(t_{OL})}} + P_{CD}$
Overload following continuous duty (pulsed) (approx. solution) $P_0\dfrac{t_p}{\tau} > P_{CD}$	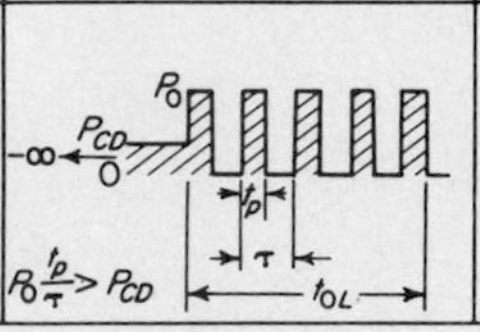	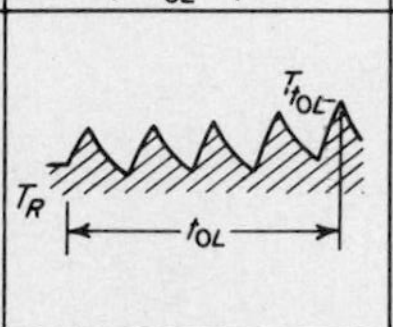	$T_{OL} - T_R = P_{CD}\theta + P_0\left\{\left[\dfrac{t_p}{\tau} - \dfrac{P_{CD}}{P_0}\right]\theta_{(t_{OL})} + \left(1 - \dfrac{t_p}{\tau}\right)\theta_{(\tau + t_p)} - \theta_{(\tau)} + \theta_{(t_p)}\right\}$ $P_0 = \dfrac{T_{OL} - T_R - P_{CD}\theta}{\left(\dfrac{t_p}{\tau} - \dfrac{P_{CD}}{P_0}\right)\theta_{(t_{OL})} + \left(1 - \dfrac{t_p}{\tau}\right)\theta_{(\tau + t_p)} - \theta_{(\tau)} + \theta_{(t_p)}}$

Fig. 4.24

4.6.3 THERMAL RUNAWAY

Under steady-state conditions the generation of heat owing to the losses discussed in Sec. 4.5 is balanced by the flow of heat through the thermal resistance to the heat sink. This heat flow causes the junction temperature to rise above that of the heat sink by an amount equal to the product of the power dissipated in the device and the thermal resistance between the junction and the heat sink. However, each of the power-loss components is temperature-sensitive to some degree. Blocking current is particularly sensitive to temperature and has an exponential dependence, as noted in Sec. 4.2. Thus, with moderately high applied voltages, heat may be generated more rapidly than it can be dissipated.

For the device to be thermally stable, the cell's ability to dissipate heat, P_D, must be equal to or greater than the heat generated, P_G.[36] If on a steady-state basis the heat generated exceeds that dissipated, then the temperature of the device will rise without bound. This will cause the device to turn on if it is in the forward blocking state; or if it is biased in the reverse direction, the temperature may rise sufficiently for the solders or junction to melt. The maximum heat which can be dissipated and the resulting temperature rise can be determined by equating the heat dissipation to the heat generation. Neglecting gate triggering and transient losses, we note from Sec. 4.2 that the forward and reverse blocking current is exponential in nature, so the heat generated while in the blocking state is of the form

$$P_B = P_R + P_{FB} = (P_{R_A} + P_{FB_A}) \exp\left[a(T_J - T_A)\right], \qquad (4.56)$$

where

P_{R_A} = the heat generated in the reverse direction at heat-sink temperature T_A,

P_{FB_A} = the forward blocking heat generated at temperature T_A.

The heat generated in the conducting state, P_F, is essentially constant with temperature,† so for the total heat generated we can write

$$P_G = P_F + (P_{R_A} + P_{FB_A}) \exp\left[a(T_J - T_A)\right]. \qquad (4.57)$$

Since we are attempting to determine if the device will remain stable under steady-state conditions, we write for the power dissipation

$$P_D = \frac{(T_J - T_A)}{\theta(\infty)}. \qquad (4.58)$$

Under steady-state conditions, $P_D = P_G$, so we equate (4.57) and (4.58) to get

$$\frac{(T_J - T_A)}{\theta(\infty)} = P_F + (P_{R_A} + P_{FB_A}) \exp\left[a(T_J - T_A)\right]. \qquad (4.59)$$

---

† Actually, forward conducting power decreases slightly with increasing temperature because the forward voltage drop has a negative temperature coefficient up to quite high currents, as can be seen in Fig. 4.2.

This equation has two solutions under normal operation, as shown in Fig.

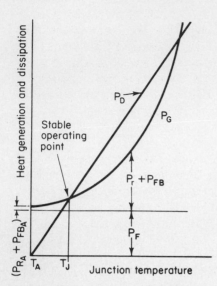

4.25. It can also have one solution, the condition for the maximum junction temperature which can be tolerated without thermal runaway, and no solution, the condition for thermal runaway. To determine the maximum power which can be dissipated, the dissipation curve should just touch (be tangent to) the heat-generation curve. These solutions can be obtained by equating the derivatives (slopes) of (4.57) and (4.58). Thus,

$$\frac{\partial P_D}{\partial T_J} = \frac{1}{\theta(\infty)}, \tag{4.60}$$

and

$$\frac{\partial P_G}{\partial T_J} = a(P_{R_A} + P_{FB_A})\exp{[a(T_J - T_A)]}, \tag{4.61}$$

Fig. 4.25 Heat generation and dissipation as a function of junction temperature.

so the maximum permissible temperature rise for stability is

$$(T_J - T_A)_{\max} = \frac{1}{a}\ln{\left[\frac{1}{a\theta(\infty)(P_{R_A} + P_{FB_A})}\right]}. \tag{4.62}$$

Substituting equation (4.56) into (4.61) and equating with (4.60), we obtain

$$P_{B_{\max}} = \frac{1}{a\theta(\infty)}. \tag{4.63}$$

From this equation we see that if the device is overloaded so that the blocking losses of the device exceed $P_{B_{\max}}$ for a period of time much longer than the thermal time constant of the device, then thermal runaway will occur. The result will be either failure to block in the forward blocking mode or destruction if the device "runs away" in the reverse direction.

4.6.4 DETERMINATION OF CURRENT RATING

From the theory developed in the previous sections in conjunction with maximum junction temperature (determined for reliable operation), a load current versus stud (case) temperature curve can be obtained. Such a rating curve is shown in Fig. 4.26.

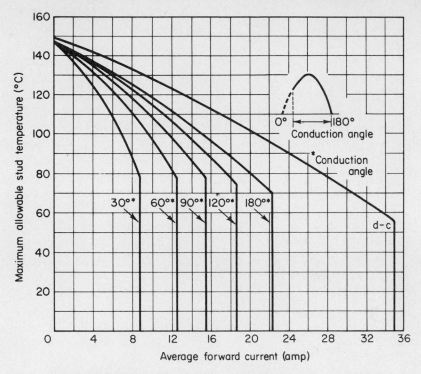

Fig. 4.26 Maximum allowable stud temperature for sinusoidal current wave form for a typical SCR having a junction area of 0.02 in.^{2} (vertical portions of the curves indicate maximum rms capability of device package).

REFERENCES

1. D. K. Bisson and R. Dyer, "A Silicon Controlled Rectifier—I," *A.I.E.E. Trans.*, Vol. **42**, Part I (May, 1959), pp. 102–6.

2. D. K. Bisson and R. Dyer, "A Silicon Controlled Rectifier—Its Characteristics and Ratings—II," A.I.E.E. Paper CP 60-67.

3. F. W. Gutzwiller, et al., *Silicon Controlled Rectifier Manual*, 2nd ed. Auburn, N. Y.: General Electric Co. Inc., 1961.

4. R. N. Hall, "Remote Base Power Transistor," *Proc. of Electronics Components Conference*, Los Angeles, Calif., May, 1955.

5. D. R. Muss and C. Goldberg, "Switching Mechanisms in *n-p-n-p* Silicon Controlled Rectifier," *I.E.E.E. Trans. on Electron Devices*, Vol. **ED-10** (May, 1963), pp. 113–20.

6. D. E. Crees and C. A. Hogarth, "Current Gain in *p-n-p-n* Silicon Controlled Rectifiers," *Jour. of Electronics and Control*, Vol. **14** (May, 1963), pp. 482–98.

7. W. Fulop, "Three Terminal Measurements of Current Amplification Factors of Controlled Rectifiers," *I.E.E.E. Trans. on Electron Devices*, Vol. **ED-10** (May, 1963), pp. 120–33.

8. C. W. Muller and J. Hildebrand, "The 'Thyristor'—A New High-Speed Switching Transistor," *I.R.E. Trans. on Electron Devices*, Vol. 5 (January, 1958), pp. 2–5.

9. J. Philips and H. C. Chang, "Germanium Power Switching Devices," *I.R.E. Trans. on Electron Devices*, Vol. 5 (January, 1958), pp. 13–18.

10. I. A. Lesk, "Germanium PNPN Switches," A.I.E.E. Conference Paper 58-1378.

11. R. F. Dyer and G. K. Houghton, "Turn-Off Time Characterization and Measurement of Silicon Controlled Rectifiers," A.I.E.E. Conference Paper CP-61-301.

12. F. W. Gutzwiller, et al., *SCR Manual*, 3rd ed. Auburn, N. Y.: General Electric Co. Inc., 1964.

13. N. Mapham, "The Rating of SCR's When Switching into High Currents," I.E.E.E. Conference Paper CP 63-498.

14. K. Aaland, "Pulse Current Limits of Silicon Controlled Rectifiers," I.E.E.E. Conference Paper 63-1236.

15. B. T. Howard and G. A. Dodson, "A Method for Rapid Evaluation of Semiconductor Device Reliability," Electron Devices Meeting, Washington, D.C., 1960.

16. D. S. Peck, "Semiconductor Reliability Predictions From Life Distribution Data," in *Semiconductor Reliability*, J. E. Shwop and H. J. Sullivan, eds. Elizabeth, N.J.: Engineering Publishers, 1961.

17. W. R. Comstock and B. W. Jalbert, "Effect of Operating Stress on Silicon Rectifier Reliability," A.I.E.E. Conference Paper 62-340, Winter General Meeting, New York, N.Y., January 20, 1962.

18. C. Zierdt, "Comparison of Operating Life Tests and Storage Tests," in *Semiconductor Reliability*, J. E. Shwop and H. J. Sullivan, eds. Elizabeth, N.J.: Engineering Publishers, 1961.

19. F. E. Gentry and R. L. Davies, "Control of Electric Fields at the Surface of *P-N* Junctions," *I.E.E.E. Transactions on Electron Devices*, Vol. **ED-8**, No. 7 (July, 1964), pp. 313–23.

20. L. F. Coffin, Jr., "Cyclic Straining and Fatigue," in *Internal Stresses and Fatigue in Metals*, G. M. Rassweiler and W. L. Grube, eds., Princeton, N.J.: Elsevier Publishing Co., 1959.

21. W. B. Green, "A Fatigue-Free Silicon Device Structure," *A.I.E.E. Trans.*, Vol. **54**, Part I (May, 1961), pp. 186–91.

22. H. W. Henkels, "The Fused Silicon Rectifier," *A.I.E.E. Trans.*, Vol. **75**, Part I (1956), pp. 733–46.

23. F. E. Gentry, "Forward Current Surge Failure in Semiconductor Rectifiers," *A.I.E.E. Trans.*, Vol. **77**, Part I (November, 1958), pp. 746–50.

24. F. A. Leith, "Study of the Effects of Fast Neutrons on Silicon Controlled Rectifiers," Electron Device Conference, Washington, D.C., October 25–27, 1962.

25. J. W. Easley, "Comparison of Neutron Damage in Germanium and Silicon Transistors," *I.R.E. Wescon Convention Record*, Part 3 (August, 1958), pp. 148–56.

26. G. C. Messenger and J. P. Spratt, "The Effect of Neutron Irradiation on Germanium and Silicon," *Proc. I.R.E.*, Vol. **46** (June, 1958), pp. 1038–44.

27. W. Shockley, "Problems Related to *p-n* Junctions in Silicon," *Solid-State Electronics*, Vol. **2** (1961), pp. 35–67.

28. K. Hubner, M. Melehy, and R. Biesele, "Uniform Turn-on in Four Layer Diodes," *I.R.E. Trans. on Electron Devices*, Vol. **ED-8**, No. 6 (November, 1961), pp. 461–64.

29. R. N. Hall, "An Analysis of the Performance of Thermoelectric Devices Made from Long Lifetime Semiconductors," *Solid-State Electronics*, Vol. **2** (1961), pp. 115–22.

30. W. M. Bullis, "Minority Carrier Thermoelectric Cooling," *Jour. Appl. Phys.*, Vol. **34** (June, 1963), pp. 1648–49.

31. J. Reese, W. W. Grannemann, and J. R. Durant, "An Electric Analog of Heat Flow in Power Transistors," *A.I.E.E. Trans.*, Vol. **45**, Part I (November, 1959), pp. 640–43.

32. F. W. Gutzwiller and P. Sylvan, "Semiconductor Ratings Under Transient Loads," *A.I.E.E. Trans.*, Vol. **79**, Part I (January, 1961), pp. 699–706.

33. E. J. Diebold and W. Luft, "Transient Thermal Impedance of Semiconductor Devices," *A.I.E.E. Trans.*, Vol. **79**, Part I (January, 1961), pp. 719–26.

34. S. Goldman, *Transformation Calculus and Electrical Transients*. Englewood Cliffs, N.J.: Prentice-Hall Inc., 1949.

35. H. C. Lin and R. E. Crosby, "A Determination of Thermal Resistance of Silicon Junction Devices," *I.R.E. National Convention Record*, Part 3, March 18–21, 1957, pp. 22–25.

36. D. K. Bisson, "The Rating and Application of a Silicon Power Rectifier," *Rectifiers in Industry*, A.I.E.E. Publication T-93, June, 1957.

37. C. D. Mohler, "Digital Computer Calculation of Rectifier and Silicon Controlled Rectifier Ratings," A.I.E.E. Conference Paper 62-433.

CHAPTER 5

TRIGGER CHARACTERISTICS AND CIRCUITS

5.1 Basic Trigger Modes

As shown in Sec. 2.3 the *p-n-p-n* and related structures can be switched from a forward blocking state to a forward conducting state by increased temperature, carrier injection into the gate, irradiation of the emitter junction, and increased electric field across the base region. In this chapter we will be concerned with basic trigger characteristics and methods.

5.1.1 TEMPERATURE TURN-ON

Temperature is usually not considered a satisfactory triggering means in conventional applications, since it is desirable to maintain the junction temperature at or below its maximum rated value. The maximum rated junction temperature is generally well below the point of self-triggering by temperature. When operated in this manner, the SCR or related semiconductor device will be least sensitive to spurious triggering by circuit transients. Circuit reliability is greatly enhanced when the SCR is either in a very stable OFF state or in a very stable ON state. Switching of the device from the ON state to the OFF state by a suitable triggering means should be of a positive nature with as much drive as possible within the device's ratings.

5.1.2 GATE-TRIGGERING

Gate-triggering is the usual means of turn-on specified for conventional SCR's. It allows stable off-biasing of the SCR for greatest circuit reliability. It provides very large turn-on gain: ratios of anode current to trigger current in the order of many thousands. Gate-triggering thus leads the circuit designer to very flexible and low-power-level control circuitry. In power control and conversion circuits this mode of triggering allows the utmost utility from the SCR.

5.1.3 LIGHT-TRIGGERING

Light-sensitive turn-on action is obtained by irradiating the emitter junction and the underlying adjacent base region of the SCR. This action may be the sole triggering means, or it may be used supplementary to gate trigger action. This means of triggering extends the usefulness of the SCR, with its sizable current and voltage capabilities, to the many application areas requiring response to light or electrical isolation between trigger signal and load. It often allows light-sensitive operation at power levels above the capability of conventional photoresistive or photovoltaic devices. However, it must be borne in mind that load-circuit action is, as with all SCR's, of a latching nature. The light-sensitive SCR is, therefore, not a direct replacement

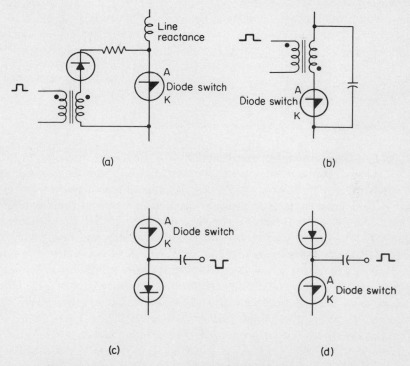

Fig. 5.1 Basic means of triggering four-layer diode: (a) shunt injection, (b) series injection, (c) alternative cathode series injection, and (d) alternative anode series injection.

for light-sensitive linear transducers. It can, however, find application as a transducer where linear action is not required. Its unique capabilities are best utilized in power circuits in a static switching or in a phase-control mode.

5.1.4 ANODE-TRIGGERING

Anode-triggering is accomplished by increasing the forward anode voltage, often in conjunction with the dv/dt or rate effect, until the device has switched into a low-impedance forward conduction state. This mode of triggering is of limited usefulness with multilayer devices having an external gate connection, such as SCR's. It might be considered, however, for cases in which the turn-on time of the SCR must be reduced below the turn-on time achieved solely with gate-triggering. However, not all SCR's lend themselves to anode-triggering, particularly at high voltage, because of dielectric and junction limitations.

Multilayer semiconductor diode switches must be anode-triggered. Figure 5.1 shows four basic arrangements for anode-triggering a unilateral semi-conductor diode switch. In Fig. 5.1(a) the trigger signal is applied in shunt across the device. In Fig. 5.1(b) the signal is applied to the device in series with the external load. Figures 5.1(c) and (d) show alternative series-injection schemes. Except for unusual applications, these means of triggering are of relatively little interest when triode switches are used with their external control, or gate, lead.

5.2 Gate-trigger Characteristics and Ratings

The conventional three-terminal SCR is triggered by causing current to flow between the gate and cathode of the device. Therefore, the trigger characteristics of the SCR can be described in terms of its forward gate-cathode electrical characteristics under specified temperature and anode-bias conditions. In order to make the device useful to the circuit designer, appropriate values of gate current to trigger (I_{GT}) and gate voltage (V_{GT}) to produce this trigger current must be specified. Also of importance is the specification of values at which the SCR will not trigger. Maximum ratings are assigned to the gate by the manufacturer which will ensure reliable service and not limit the useful output rating of the device. These are basically given in terms of maximum allowable forward and reverse gate power dissipation. Typical values of I_{GT} run in the range from microamperes to several hundred milliamperes, depending on the size of the SCR. V_{GT} is usually of the order of one volt. Because quite large currents from high-voltage sources can be triggered by the low power levels mentioned, the SCR possesses very large power turn-on gain, in the order of 10^5 to 10^6.

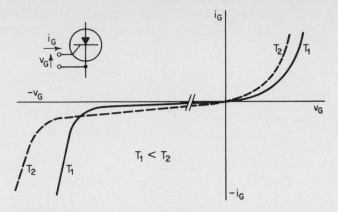

Fig. 5.2 SCR static gate-cathode E-I characteristic (zero anode bias).

5.2.1 THE FORWARD E-I CHARACTERISTICS OF THE EMITTER JUNCTION

The gate-cathode section in the SCR is essentially a diode p-n junction serving as an emitter. The SCR will trigger when this junction is sufficiently forward-biased in the presence of positive anode voltage. Conventional p-n-p-n SCR's have their gate terminals connected to the lower p-region, as shown in Fig. 2.2. This connection is known as a p-gate. Complementary n-p-n-p SCR's have their gate connected to the upper n-region. This is known as an n-gate, in which case the gate signal is applied between gate and anode.

Figure 5.2 illustrates the static forward and reverse gate-cathode characteristic of a typical p-gate SCR for two different temperature conditions and zero anode bias. The first quadrant shows positive voltage and current for forward bias of the p-n junction; the third quadrant shows a typical reverse characteristic at high levels. The voltage behavior of the characteristic follows the normal negative temperature coefficient of p-n junction voltage in the forward direction and positive temperature coefficient in the reverse direction.

Figure 5.3 illustrates in terms of equivalent circuits the behavior of the forward gate characteristic as anode-bias conditions are changed. The reverse characteristic essentially maintains its blocking characteristic as anode bias is applied. The behavior of the reverse gate characteristic is discussed more fully in Sec. 4.2, particularly for small SCR's.

When the anode of the SCR is biased positive with respect to the cathode, a small internal generator voltage E_G' will effectively appear gate-to-cathode, as indicated in Fig. 5.3(b). This voltage is a function of the applied anode voltage, internal bulk parameters, and device geometry. Depending on device-design parameters and temperature, the SCR may trigger under this condition unless an external path is provided for the current E_G'/R, where R represents the static nonlinear forward gate characteristic. For this reason, in practice small-area SCR's generally require external stabilizing bias resistors (see Sec.

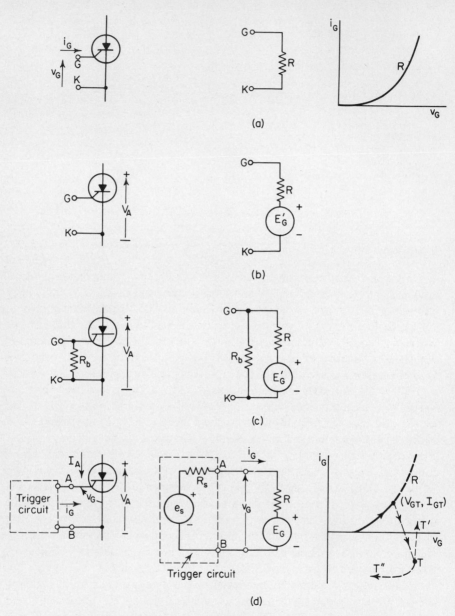

Fig. 5.3 Behavior of forward gate characteristic for various bias conditions: (a) Static forward characteristic: nonlinear resistance R; (b) Positive anode bias applied: gate acts as generator; (c) effect of gate generator neutralized by means of external bias resistor; (d) trigger circuit drives SCR into conduction of anode current.

5.4.4), whereas larger-area devices are often characterized as stable with their gate open at full rated anode voltage and maximum rated junction temperature. Figure 5.3(c) shows the addition of a stabilizing bias resistor R_b.

Once the SCR is stable, either intrinsically or by external means, the trigger circuit sees a positive resistance, requiring application of positive gate voltage v_G and positive current i_G in order to drive the gate to the point of triggering the SCR. This point is indicated in Fig. 5.3(d) as (V_{GT}, I_{GT}) on the forward gate characteristic. The point of triggering is a device characteristic dependent on temperature and anode bias. When observed at the gate terminal of the SCR in a circuit equivalent to that shown in Fig. 5.3(d), triggering will occur where the instantaneous trigger-circuit characteristic (load line) intersects the forward gate characteristic (see Sec. 5.4.1). If the anode bias is zero [as in Fig. 5.3(a)], the forward gate characteristic can be plotted as indicated in Fig. 5.3(d) by the dashed line beyond the point of triggering (V_{GT}, I_{GT}). With positive anode bias, however, the device triggers, and immediately after triggering a point T will be observed when one looks into the gate with a circuit equivalent to that shown. Point T will vary depending on E_G and the instantaneous trigger circuit characteristic (e_s and e_s/R_s). E_G is the internal gate generator voltage owing to the flow of anode current I_A. It is a function of anode current and, like E_G', it also depends on the device geometry and internal bulk parameters. During the turn-on interval of the SCR, the equivalent internal gate generator voltage E_G increases rapidly as a function of anode current I_A. For a typical 0.02 in.^{2} active-area SCR considered here, it may go from $E_G' = 0.05$ v before triggering to $E_G = 0.7$ v at an active-area current density of 400 amp/in.^{2}—a value well within the device's ratings.

If, after having triggered, the applied trigger signal voltage $e_s = 0$, a voltage $v_G = E_G - i_G R$ and a current $i_G = -E_G/(R + R_s)$ will be observed. If the trigger drive is increased ($e_s \gg 0$) beyond the value at which the trigger point (V_{GT}, I_{GT}) is attained, the point T will be observed to go toward the first quadrant and some point T'. When its characteristic crosses the abscissa ($i_G = 0$), $e_s = E_G$. If the trigger drive is made negative ($e_s \ll 0$) while the SCR is conducting anode current, the point T will go toward a point T'' in the fourth quadrant. Section 5.2.5 discusses this type of operation. For small-area devices, particularly those optimized for gate turn-off, the point T'' may go into the third quadrant. This type of operation is indicated in Fig. 4.7 and discussed in conjunction with equation (4.2) in Sec. 4.2.

5.2.2 Gate Current to Trigger

The gate current required to trigger I_{GT} and its corresponding voltage V_{GT} are given by a point on the forward gate-cathode characteristic. The location of this point is determined by the prevailing anode voltage and temperature for a given device.

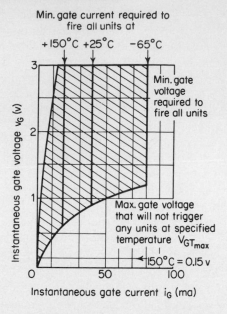

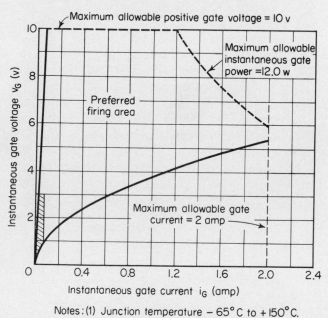

Fig. 5.4 Typical static gate trigger characteristic [courtesy General Electric Company].

The point of triggering (I_{GT}, V_{GT}) at a given anode bias and temperature for any given SCR is a stable and repeatable point. Depending on the nature of the manufacturing process, a certain spread of characteristics is likely to be found between individual SCR's of the same type. The manufacturer indicates this by giving the locus of all possible individual points of triggering which apply to a given SCR type.

Figure 5.4 shows the commercially specified gate-trigger characteristics of a typical 0.02 in.² active-area SCR rated for 16 amp continuous anode current. It will be noted that the co-ordinate axes are interchanged with respect to Figs. 5.3(a) and (d). The shaded area includes all possible points of triggering, or firing, over the indicated temperature range. Depending on the design of the device, anode voltage may also be shown as a parameter. In the case of Fig. 5.4 the manufacturer states that the data are valid for all anode voltages above 6 v.

As the gate drive under forward (positive) anode bias approaches the point of triggering, the forward blocking capability of the SCR decreases until the device switches into its forward conducting anode characteristic. The

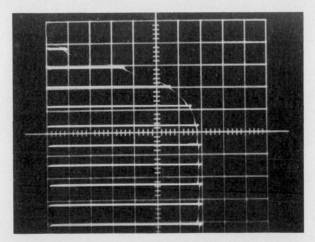

Fig. 5.5 SCR forward voltage-blocking capability versus gate drive (horizontal 50/div; vertical, 2 ma gate current per step).

oscillogram of Fig. 5.5 shows this behavior for a typical SCR of 0.02 in.² active area. Noting the horizontal sensitivity, we can see that the SCR initially blocked 350 v. The first change toward reduced forward voltage-blocking ability is seen to occur after six steps of gate current or at 12 ma. The SCR switches completely into the ON state somewhere between 20 and 22 ma of gate current.

If, during this turn-on interval, anode current is limited to a value less than the latching current for the particular load, or if the gate drive is insufficient, partial switching may occur. This condition is also discussed in Sec. 4.2. It is a condition that should be avoided in practice, because SCR's are not rated or characterized in this high-dissipation region of high forward ON voltage (voltage drop). It is usually desirable to design the trigger circuit for a rapid rate of rise of gate current. Values of several amperes per microsecond help to minimize the delay-time portion of the anode current turn-on characteristic. The reader is referred to Sec. 2.6.3 for a more detailed discussion of this.

5.2.3 TIME-DEPENDENCE OF GATE DRIVE

The characteristic of Fig. 5.4 is more accurately known as the static gate-trigger characteristic. This indicates that the co-ordinates (I_{GT}, V_{GT}) represent stationary, or d-c values. In order to be a complete specification, the minimum duration, or minimum pulse width, of I_{GT} must be given. Below this minimum pulse width it is necessary to increase the gate drive in order to trigger the SCR. Figure 5.6 shows the time-dependence of the required gate drive for a typical 0.02 in.² active-area SCR for two different temperature conditions. It is seen that, particularly at low temperatures, more trigger voltage must be supplied for very short gate-trigger pulses. In the example of Fig. 5.6 we see that the static trigger characteristic applies for trigger pulse widths greater than about 10 μsec. For shorter pulse widths the drive must be increased as shown.

5.2.4 GATE RATINGS

In addition to knowing the gate current, voltage, their time duration required to trigger the SCR, and the maximum gate signal that will not trigger the SCR, the circuit designer must also know the maximum voltage and power ratings applicable to the device he is considering.

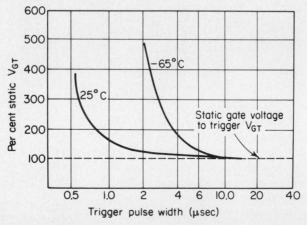

Fig. 5.6 Gate drive required versus pulse width for a typical SCR.

The peak reverse gate voltage (V_{GRM}) is the maximum instantaneous reverse bias (gate negative with respect to cathode) to which the emitter junction may be subjected without danger of damage. In other words, it is a rating analogous to the peak reverse voltage rating of a p-n junction diode. It is in the order of 5 to 20 v for most conventional SCR's.

Depending on the SCR type, reverse power ratings may be assigned to the gate. In this case reverse voltage may be applied until the junction is in reverse avalanche breakdown. Then it is necessary to limit the reverse power available from the trigger circuit to a value within the allowable gate dissipation rating.

Gate-power ratings for positive gate bias establish the maximum gate overdrive for which the device is rated and with which it can be operated. As mentioned earlier, it is generally desirable to drive the gate as hard as possible during triggering. However, the amount of permissible overdrive is limited by the mechanical and thermal construction of the gate on one hand; on the other hand, it is limited by the anode-current and junction-temperature ratings assigned to the device. Usually gate-power ratings are sufficient to allow good design flexibility. Maximum average gate-dissipation ratings run in the order of a few hundredths of a watt average gate power for a small SCR to several watts for larger devices. Corresponding *peak* gate-power ratings vary from a few tenths of a watt to about ten watts.

5.2.5 NEGATIVE GATE BIAS WITH POSITIVE ANODE VOLTAGE

In the preceding two sections, triggering requirements in terms of the gate characteristics of the conventional (p-gate) SCR were discussed. When reverse gate voltage (negative for the conventional p-gate SCR) is applied to the gate of the SCR with respect to the cathode, the emitter junction is biased OFF. This type of bias is often very useful in maintaining the device in a stable OFF state in the presence of conditions that would tend to turn it on, e.g., high temperatures, gate-circuit noise, and positive anode voltage transients effective both in magnitude and by virtue of their rate of rise (dv/dt or rate effect). Forward voltage-blocking ability and dv/dt withstand capability at a given temperature tend to increase with negative gate bias. Also, the device turn-off time (see Sec. 6.3), particularly important in higher-frequency applications, will tend to be decreased in proportion to negative gate bias. Depending on the geometry, internal design parameters, and manufacturing process of the device, the effect of negative gate bias is more or less pronounced. With point geometry gate structures, of either a center or side gate configuration, the larger the device becomes, the less will be the stabilizing influence of negative gate bias. This is due to the larger base spreading resistance of the larger device and its relatively limited gate-contact size (see Sec. 4.2 for a more detailed discussion of this). Typically, small SCR's have their peak forward blocking voltage V_{FXM} specified only for a maximum value of external gate-to-cathode resistance, which provides the necessary stabilizing bias condition. Larger SCR's are generally not specified in this manner, because gate-to-cathode resistance is less effective.

A very practical situation in which reverse gate bias is applied to an SCR is to effect turn-off action. Although all SCR's tend to some extent to turn off with negative gate current at low anode currents, some types can be optimized for efficient gate turn-off. This leads to the very useful gate turn-off switch (GTO, Trigistor, Transwitch). The reader is referred to Sec. 6.5 for a more complete discussion of this device and its characteristics.

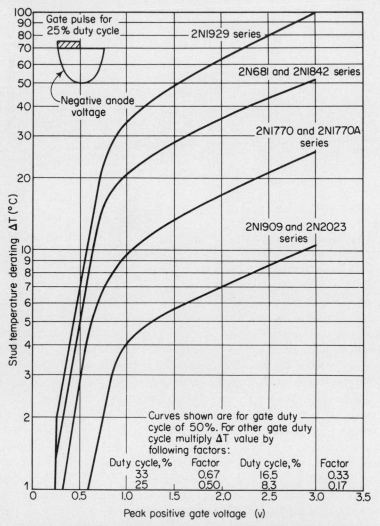

Fig. 5.7 Temperature derating to compensate for transistor action in SCR [courtesy General Electric Company].

5.2.6 POSITIVE GATE DRIVE WITH REVERSE ANODE VOLTAGE

Generally it is undesirable to apply positive gate drive to the SCR while its anode is reverse-biased (negative with respect to cathode). With reference to Fig. 2.2, junction J_1 (the SCR reverse blocking junction) is reverse-biased under this condition and can serve as a collector junction. Positive gate drive I_g makes junction J_3 serve as an emitter (as in normal SCR operation) injecting electrons into region p_2. These diffuse across p_2 to be collected at junction J_2. Upon being collected by J_2 they act as base drive for the p_2-n_1-p_1 transistor, causing p_2 to inject holes into n_1 so that operation is essentially that of a remote base transistor.[1] As a result, SCR reverse blocking current increases as positive gate drive is increased. This transistor action in the SCR leads to an additional and unnecessary component of power dissipation which must be offset by increased heatsinking or a derating of forward current. Figure 5.7 shows such a typical derating curve for three types of commercial SCR's as a function of gate voltage. This undesirable condition for SCR operation can be avoided by clamping the gate trigger circuit for positive voltage when the anode is negative. Alternatively, a diode can be inserted in series with the anode to suppress SCR reverse blocking current.

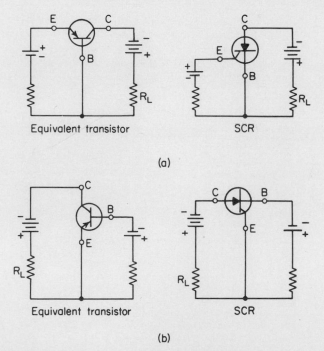

Fig. 5.8 Transistor connections of SCR: (a) common base connection and (b) common emitter connection.

The foregoing notwithstanding, transistor mode of operation of small SCR's may be desirable in certain special applications. Of some practical significance is the inherent higher voltage-blocking capability of SCR's. Figure 5.8 shows the SCR connected as a *p-n-p* remote base transistor in which the lower *n*-region of the device is used as the base connection. The common base connection is shown in Fig. 5.8(a); the common emitter connection is shown in Fig. 5.8(b). The anode, cathode, and gate of the SCR are connected as collector, base, and emitter, respectively.

Figure 5.9 shows an oscillogram of the collector characteristics for the connections of Fig. 5.8, in the third quadrant of the SCR *E-I* characteristic

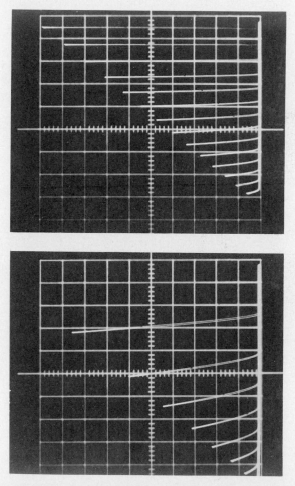

Fig. 5.9 Collector characteristics of SCR operated as transistor (horizontal, 20/div; vertical, 5 ma/div; 5 ma/step base drive): (a) common base connection and (b) common emitter connection.

(see also Fig. 4.5). A small SCR in a TO-5 package of 0.003 in.^{2} active area was used to obtain the data of Fig. 5.9. Collector current (negative anode current) is shown on the vertical scale; collector-emitter voltage (negative anode voltage) is shown on the horizontal axis. In the common-base connection [Fig. 5.9(a)] the gain is seen to be $\alpha < 1$, although linearity is moderately good. In the common-emitter connection [Fig. 5.9(b)] the gain is seen to be $\beta = 2.4$ at $I_C = -12$ ma. For increasing collector current β is seen to fall off rapidly.

5.3 Light-sensitive Trigger Action

It was mentioned in Sec. 5.1.3 that the SCR can be triggered into conduction by suitably irradiating the region near and underlying the emitter junction. Section 2.3.2 discusses the physical mechanism in detail. Certain types of p-n-p-n structures are specifically designed and specified for light-triggering. In these devices provision must be made so that the emitter junction can be irradiated from the outside. For maximum sensitivity the package must transmit a maximum of the incident radiation, and the semiconductor pellet must be oriented relative to the radiation source in such manner that the junctions receive the radiation at right angles to the surface specified by the manufacturer. The spectral sensitivity of the silicon p-n-p-n device is governed by the absorption properties of silicon, as shown in Fig. 2.13. The peak of the spectral response of a silicon p-n-p-n device depends principally on the amount of the incident trigger radiation absorbed within a diffusion length of the blocking junction. It is thus a function of device geometry and the incidence angle and location on the pellet of the radiation. The spectral response for a typical silicon p-n-p-n light-triggered switch and a comparative eye curve are shown in Fig. 2.15. It is seen that the spectral response of the silicon device lies largely outside of the visible spectrum in the near infrared region.

In order to characterize a p-n-p-n device for triggering, the total incident radiation must be taken into account. In order to do this accurately, radiometric units are used and these are weighed according to the response curve of the device.[2] This is the "effective irradiance," H_e, which is expressed in terms of flux density (watts per square centimeter). Figure 5.10 compares the radiometric with the photometric system for reference purposes. In considering the suitability of light sources for triggering, it is useful to evaluate the particular source in terms of its effective radiant emittance W_e. This quantity is obtained from the relationship between the spectral distribution of energy from the source and the spectral response of a typical silicon light-sensitive p-n-p-n structure. The effectiveness ratio W_e/W is based on typical values of emitted flux density W for various types of light sources shown in Fig. 5.11. It will be noted that the effectiveness ratio W_e/W is highest for the neon lamp.

	Radiometric (physical)	Photometric (visual)
Total flux	P = watts	F = lumen (optically effective)
Emitted flux density by a source surface	W = w/cm^2 radiant emittance	L = lumen/ft^2 = ftlambert lumen/cm^2 = lambert luminous emittance
Incident flux density upon a receiver surface	H = w/cm^2 irradiance	E = lumen/m^2 = lux lumen/ft^2 = ftcandle lumen/cm^2 = phot illuminance, illumination
Source intensity (point sources)	I_r = w/steradian radiant intensity	I_L = lumen/steradian = candle† luminous intensity
Elementary source intensity (area source)	B_r = w/cm^2/steradian radiance	B_L = candle/cm^2 = lumen/cm^2/steradian candle/st^2 = lumen/ft^2/steradian luminance (brightness)
		† Sometimes called "candlepower," or cp

Figure 5.10 Radiometric versus photometric system [from Ref. 2, by permission].

	Emitted flux density		Effectiveness
Source	W (mw/cm^2)	W_e $\left(\begin{array}{c}\text{effective}\\ \text{mw/cm}^2\end{array}\right)$	W_e/W
Candle flame	10^4	7×10^2	0.07
Sun	4.5×10^6	2.8×10^6	0.62
Tungsten lamps			
miniature (evacuated)	6×10^4	1.3×10^4	0.22
standard (gas-filled)	1.3×10^5	3.8×10^4	0.29
standard (frosted 100 w)	2.6×10^3	7.5×10^2	0.29
photo	2.5×10^5	9×10^4	0.35
Neon (NE-2 at 1 ma)	8×10^{-2}	6×10^{-2}	0.75
Fluorescent (daylight 40 w)†	30	12	0.4
Xenon flash (450 v, 10 ws)†	1.2×10^7	6×10^6	0.5
† Approximate values			

Figure 5.11 Effectiveness of various light sources for triggering typical light-sensitive SCR's (Adapted from Ref. 2, by permission).

However, its emittance is so low under rated operating conditions that, depending on device sensitivity and geometry of the source-device system, it may have to be overdriven in order to obtain sufficient energy to trigger the silicon device. Tungsten lamps provide useful trigger sources at derated voltage operating conditions in the interest of longer life and increased reliability. The xenon flash lamp provides the greatest effective radiant emittance for silicon devices because of its high power density and concentration of energy around the response band of silicon. A more recent and very promising light source is the injection luminescent gallium arsenide diode.

From the emittance characteristics of the source, its geometry, the sensitivity of the *p-n-p-n* device, and its geometry, the design of the total source-device system can be made by following the concepts and methods of basic optics. The reader is directed to Refs. 2 and 3 for a more complete treatment of this subject.

5.4 Trigger-circuit Design Considerations for Conventional SCR's

It was mentioned earlier with reference to Fig. 5.4 that for reliable operation the area of gate trigger-circuit operation should lie between the maximum allowable gate power-dissipation curve and the shaded area containing the locus of all possible trigger points (I_{GT}, V_{GT}). The basic problem in the design of the trigger circuit is to place the operating characteristic, or load line, in this specified region and to provide for sufficient duration (Sec. 5.2.3) and rise time (Sec. 2.6.3) of the trigger signal.

5.4.1 GATE CIRCUIT LOAD LINE

Consider a basic trigger circuit consisting of a source voltage e_s and a source impedance R_s driving the gate of an SCR having a typical nonlinear characteristic $i_G = f(v_G, T_J, V_A)$ in the region where $i_G < I_{GT}$, as shown in Fig. 5.3(d).

Summing the voltages, we obtain

$$e_s = v_G + i_G R_s, \tag{5.1}$$

or

$$i_G = \frac{e_s - v_G}{R_s}, \tag{5.2}$$

where

i_G = instantaneous positive gate current.
v_G = instantaneous positive gate voltage.
e_s = instantaneous open-circuit trigger source voltage.
R_s = internal trigger source resistance.

From the SCR characteristic,

$$i_G = f(v_G, T_J, V_A). \tag{5.3}$$

Since the trigger circuit is in series with the SCR gate, i_G in equations (5.2) and (5.3) must be equal; thus,

$$f(v_G, T_J, V_A) = \frac{e_s - v_G}{R_s}. \tag{5.4}$$

Since the function of $i_G = f(v_G, T_J, V_A)$ is given graphically on most specification sheets, it is convenient to solve equation (5.4) by plotting the trigger-circuit characteristic line, equation (5.2), on the same graph with the gate characteristic, equation (5.3). The trigger-circuit characteristic line, as expressed in equation (5.2), is a straight line on a linear plot, is very general, and is valid at any instant for time-varying variables. As the trigger source voltage e_s increases from zero as a function of time, the trigger-circuit characteristic line sweeps across the lightly shaded area in Fig. 5.12, as indicated by the arrow. Each successive line represents the trigger-circuit characteristic line at a later increment of time.

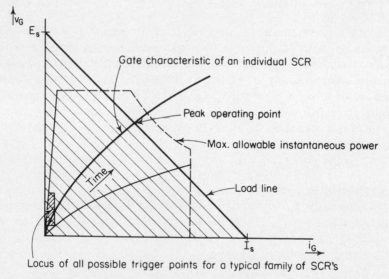

Fig. 5.12 Construction of gate circuit load line.

The maximum or peak excursion of the trigger-circuit characteristic line is popularly referred to as the load line—a term taken over from the similar technique used in vacuum-tube circuit analysis. It is, strictly speaking, a misnomer in the context presented here. However, the term is so familiar to the electronic-circuit designer that its continued use serves a useful purpose.

The load line, or peak trigger-circuit characteristic line, is most conveniently drawn, as in Fig. 5.12, by determining the maximum trigger-circuit open-circuit voltage E_s (for the ordinate) and maximum trigger-circuit short-circuit current $I_s = E_s/R_s$ (for the abscissa). For a given trigger circuit these quantities can be measured at points A-B in Fig. 5.3(d) with the load (the SCR gate) disconnected.

In the interest of minimizing turn-on time (see Sec. 2.6.3) and jitter, the load line should sweep across the gate characteristic of the SCR as rapidly as possible. Gate-current rates of rise of the order of several amperes per microsecond are desirable particularly when one is switching the SCR on in circuits exhibiting very large initial rates of rise of anode current. By the same token, the gate should be driven as hard as possible within the devices' ratings. This is accomplished by placing the peak trigger-circuit characteristic line as close to the maximum allowable power-dissipation line as practical. This is indicated in Fig. 5.12 by the load line drawn close to the maximum allowable gate-power curve.

5.4.2 PULSE-TRIGGERING

The SCR gate current to trigger (I_{GT}) and its associated gate voltage to trigger (V_{GT}) are usually given on manufacturers' specification sheets as static, or d-c, values. Figure 5.4 is such a static gate-trigger characteristic. It was pointed out in Sec. 5.2.3 that for conventional SCR's, static values are valid down to very short pulse durations. The manufacturer will usually specify the minimum pulse duration for which the static values apply. For shorter pulse durations the gate drive for typical SCR's may be increased as shown in Fig. 5.6.

It is apparent that the SCR can be triggered by signals of merely a few microseconds' duration. Hence, it lends itself very well to pulse-triggering. In view of the inherent large turn-on gain very low-power-level trigger circuitry can be used for reliable turn-on of SCR's. Typically, a trigger circuit using half-watt resistors, low-value capacitors, and a small, switching-type transistor can turn on an SCR controlling in the order of 100 kw in its anode circuit. Turn-on power gain for a typical 400 v/50 amp SCR at room temperature is of the order of 10^5. Other SCR types may offer somewhat less gain when used in a manner to optimize other characteristics, such as dv/dt withstand capability. From the point of view of circuit design a balance must be made between the turn-on gain that can be utilized in practice and the sensitivity of the circuit to spurious noise signals that might lead to false triggering of the SCR.

5.4.3 MAINTAINED TRIGGERING

Many applications require that the gate of the SCR be driven for a longer period of time than that normally supplied by a pulse trigger circuit. These types of applications generally fall into the two categories illustrated in Fig. 5.13. One is a device consideration, the other a steady-state circuit consideration.

In Fig. 5.13(a) the load is highly inductive with very small distributed capacitance. Gate drive must be maintained long enough to give the anode current time to reach latching current. If the gate is not driven for at least the length of time to reach latching current, which includes the delay time (see Sec. 2.6), the SCR will turn off again when the gate pulse terminates.

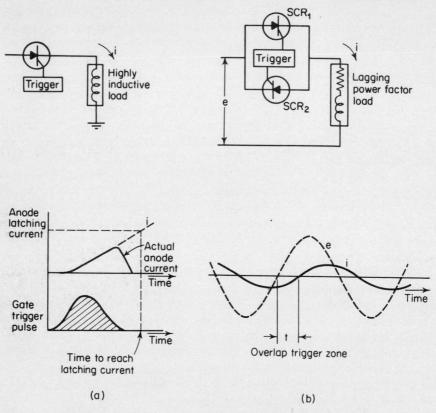

(a)

(b)

Fig. 5.13 Need for maintained trigger signals: (a) highly inductive load: trigger signal terminated before anode latching current attained; (b) lagging power factor load with parallel-inverse circuit.

In Fig. 5.13(b) steady-state line voltage and current at the SCR are out of phase. The lagging displacement power factor is one that can easily occur in a-c power-control applications like the parallel-inverse circuit illustrated. Although positive anode voltage would normally be available to SCR_1, during the time t the parallel-inverse connected SCR_2 is still conducting current i. Hence, SCR_1 cannot be triggered, since its anode voltage is negative (the conducting drop of SCR_2). If the trigger signal for SCR_1 appears and ceases in the overlap trigger zone t, the positive half-cycle of current shown in a heavy line will not be carried by SCR_1, and the circuit will have failed to perform its function. This type of circuit failure, which subjects an a-c load to a d-c voltage component, is particularly dangerous when the load is subject to magnetic-core flux saturation, as with transformers or a-c motors. The solution is either to retrigger with a pulse at the end of the time t or to use maintained triggering. This problem also arises in three-phase bridge rectifier circuits in which all elements or legs of the bridge contain SCR's (see Chart 8.1, Item 13). Certain inverter circuits when inductively loaded also require retriggering or, alternately, maintained trigger sources.

Precautions to be observed, as far as the SCR is concerned, when maintained triggering is being used, are not to exceed rated gate dissipation and to watch for negative anode voltage while the gate is still being driven positively (see Sec. 5.2.6). This latter condition can easily arise in certain types of a-c phase-shift trigger circuits in which an a-c signal derived from the a-c supply line is applied to the gate of the SCR. This type of circuit is discussed more fully in Sec. 5.5.3.

5.4.4 STABILIZING GATE-BIAS CIRCUITS

In Sec. 5.2.5 it was pointed out that negative gate bias desensitizes the SCR against turn-on. As such, its use as an "insurance policy" against spurious SCR triggering resulting from circuit noise is very useful from the point of view of achieving increased circuit reliability. With some SCR's, particularly the smaller ones, negative gate-biasing may be an integral part of the device's minimum forward blocking-voltage characterization. Some stabilization against transients, particularly anode dv/dt and positive gate voltage transients, may be obtained with a capacitor connected between gate and cathode. A value of 0.05 μf or less will usually suffice. However, it acts to limit the rate of rise of the gate signal. An approach suited to the suppression of gate circuit noise is the insertion of an RF choke in series with the gate. However, it also limits the rate of gate-current rise.

Figure 5.14 illustrates some basic approaches for obtaining gate-bias stabilization. A simple resistor connected gate-to-cathode, as shown in Fig. 5.14(a), can provide stabilizing gate bias. It serves to reduce the forward bias on the SCR emitter junction by providing a diversion path for the collector current of the upper equivalent p-n-p transistor around the lower emitter (see Fig. 2.4). This current is the SCR forward blocking current in the OFF state I_{FXM} with the gate under specified bias conditions. The shunt resistor R_b, in conjunction with the internal trigger-circuit impedance R_s, diverts a portion δI_{FXM} of this current, which in turn proportionately reduces the forward bias on the emitter of the lower equivalent n-p-n transistor. The value of δ and its effectiveness depend on the value of internal SCR cross-base-spreading resistance and the external gate-cathode impedance. For junction diameters

greater than about 100 mils, however, this type of stabilizing bias loses its
effectiveness because of the generally large base-spreading resistance of the
larger structures.

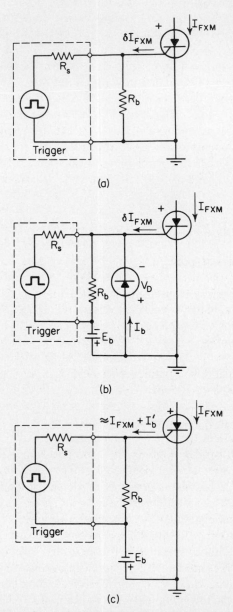

Fig. 5.14 Basic stabilizing bias circuits: (a) stabilizing bias
resistor, (b) voltage bias, and (c) current bias.

The value of the gate stabilizing resistor R_b may be a part of the SCR minimum forward blocking-voltage specification. As such, a value of 1000 ohms is commonly used. Lower values provide additional stabilizing bias. However, from a circuit point of view its minimum value is determined by the trigger-circuit source impedance. The lower the value of the resistor, the more will be the additional shunt current through it. This shunt current must be available from the trigger source above and beyond the value I_{GT} of gate current required to trigger the SCR.

When the utmost in stabilizing bias is required, the gate may be suitably taken to a voltage source E_b which is negative with respect to the cathode. Figures 5.14(b) and (c) illustrate this approach. In these cases δ becomes quite large, and most of the off-state forward blocking current I_{FXM} is diverted in small devices. In Fig. 5.14(b) the bias resistor R_b is taken directly to the negative voltage E_b. Diode CR_1 establishes a bias current $I_b = (E_b - V_D)/R_b$, which is large compared to the (negative) gate current being diverted δI_{FXM}. In this manner a fixed and stiff negative gate bias voltage V_D is established by virtue of diode CR_1's being connected gate-to-cathode. The bias-voltage source E_b need not be a battery. It can often be conveniently obtained from some other d-c point in the circuit. In a-c circuits a capacitor-resistor-diode combination power-supply circuit can be added very simply. The circuit shown dotted in Fig. 5.41 is an example.

In Fig. 5.14(c) the voltage E_b drives the gate-to-cathode junction of the SCR into avalanche and establishes a negative current bias $I_b' = (E_b - V_{GA})/R_b \| R_s$, where V_{GA} is the reverse avalanche voltage of the gate junction. If $I_b' \gg I_{FXM}$, essentially all of the forward blocking current will be extracted from the gate. Since this current bias is established against the voltage V_{GA}, there is a possibility of high reverse gate power dissipation. For this reason the application of negative current bias is generally restricted to SCR's with well-specified reverse gate characteristics and ratings.

5.5 Trigger Circuits for SCR's

The purpose of this section is to show the basic approaches to the selection of the type of trigger circuit required on a performance-versus-complexity, i.e., cost, basis. Fundamental to this are the considerations discussed in Sec. 5.4. The basic turn-on requirements (I_{GT} and V_{GT}) for the device must be met regardless of the function it is to perform in the circuit. However, the source of the trigger signal and the manner in which it is applied to the SCR gate will vary depending on the particular application requirements.

Some applications may require triggering at the earliest possible time after the anode voltage has become positive. This is the case for on-off a-c static switching, or for the 100 per cent output setting in a-c phase control. Triggering that is delayed after the anode voltage has become positive is required in a-c phase-controlled systems for settings calling for less than 100 per cent output. Triggering in a-c circuits generally requires synchronization of the trigger signal to the line frequency. In inverter circuits the signal is generally initiated by a reference frequency oscillator. In inverter and high-power a-c control, large rates of rise of gate current are generally required.

5.5.1 Resistance Trigger Circuits

Perhaps the simplest means of triggering an SCR is to supply the required gate current to trigger (I_{GT}) directly from the anode through a suitable current-limiting resistor. Figure 5.15 illustrates this basic arrangement of triggering

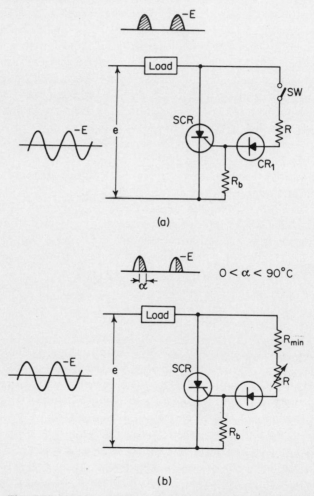

(a)

(b)

Fig. 5.15 Simple resistance "anode triggered" SCR circuits: (a) half-wave static switch and (b) limited range half-wave phase control.

from the anode. Figure 5.15(a) shows fixed resistor triggering applied to a half-wave circuit resulting in a basic a-c static switch with the a-c waveform at the load as indicated. The mode of triggering shown in Fig. 5.15(a) can, of course, also be used in d-c circuits. However, to arrive at a functionally useful d-c switch circuit, a separate means of turn-off must be employed (see Secs. 7.4 and 7.5). The functional switch or control device indicated as SW may be any type of mechanical switch (push-button, reed switch, etc.) initiated by manual control, or by heat, light, pressure, etc. transducers.

For proper operation within the ratings of the SCR, current-limiting resistor R should be selected as follows. In order not to exceed the peak rated SCR gate current I_{GFM}, for the worst case of closing switch SW at the peak of the supply voltage E, we select

$$R \geq \frac{E}{I_{GFM}} \quad \text{(ohms)}. \tag{5.5}$$

If a stabilizing bias resistor R_b is required (Sec. 5.4.4), we must also observe that the maximum voltage developed across R_b is less than the peak rated SCR forward gate voltage V_{GFM}. By considering the simple voltage divider action of resistors R and R_b, we may write

$$R \geq \frac{(E - V_{GFM})}{V_{GFM}} R_b \quad \text{(ohms)}. \tag{5.6}$$

The SCR will trigger when the instantaneous anode voltage e is

$$e = I_{GT}R + V_{GT} + D, \tag{5.7}$$

where

I_{GT} = gate current to trigger SCR at prevailing junction temperature and instantaneous anode voltage in amperes.

V_{GT} = gate voltage to trigger SCR (in volts) corresponding to I_{GT}.

D = voltage drop of diode CR_1.

If a variable resistor R is selected as a control device, limited-range half-wave phase-control operation results. This is illustrated in Fig. 5.15(b). When $R = 0$ the SCR will trigger in accordance with equation (5.7), in which $R = R_{min}$. R_{min} is determined from equation (5.5). As the resistance R is increased, the SCR will be triggered at greater values of delay angle α (in electrical degrees) until $e = E$. In an a-c circuit this occurs at the peak of the a-c voltage wave. Since the SCR will trigger and latch into conduction the first time I_{GT} is reached, its conduction cannot be delayed beyond 90 electrical degrees with so simple a trigger circuit. The circuit of Fig. 5.15(b), therefore, provides continuously variable control for the SCR from full ON (100 per cent of half-wave output) to half ON (50 per cent of half-wave output). The principles and applications of phase control when one is operating from an a-c source are discussed in detail in Chap. 8.

It is apparent that the performance of the type of circuit which depends on I_{GT} of the SCR for its triggering level will be temperature-dependent. For example, a typical low-current SCR may have a maximum $I_{GT} = 15$ ma at a junction temperature of $T_J = 25°C$; at $T_J = 125°C$, I_{GT} may decrease almost 50 per cent to 8 ma. The temperature coefficient of the gate current to trigger in this range is thus about -0.5 per cent/$°C$. This large change in gate sensitivity with varying temperature can, in circuits of the type illustrated in Fig. 5.15, cause as much as a 40 per cent change in output voltage. Trigger circuits of the type shown in Fig. 5.15 are generally well-suited for static-switching applications. However, for variable output control they suffer from a limited range of control, great sensitivity to temperature, and variation in performance between individual SCR's.

5.5.2 *RC* TRIGGER CIRCUITS

The limited range of control of the circuit of Fig. 5.15(b) can be overcome if the gate circuit is supplied by a voltage that is shifted in its phase relationship to the anode voltage in such a manner that positive gate current sufficient to trigger the SCR can be delayed beyond the peak of the anode voltage wave. The *RC* gate circuit shown in Fig. 5.16 will accomplish this. Its mode of

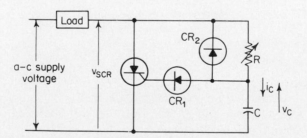

Fig. 5.16 *RC* full range half-wave phase control.

operation may be seen with the aid of Fig. 5.17. When the SCR anode voltage swings positive for $\omega t > 0$, capacitor C will charge from the peak of the negative line $-E$ (due to diode CR_2) toward positive values of anode voltage through variable resistor R. The voltage across the capacitor v_C will be the time integral of the current i_C admitted to it by variable resistor R. After the supply voltage swings positive, capacitor C is in shunt with a nonlinear equivalent resistance R_{eq} consisting of the forward characteristics of CR_1 and the SCR gate. In view of the relatively large spread of the gate characteristics of many commercially available SCR's (see the shaded area in Fig. 5.4) an analytic solution for values of trigger-delay angle $\alpha = f(\omega RC)$ is not practical. However, for a typical SCR, and in the range of power frequencies, it may

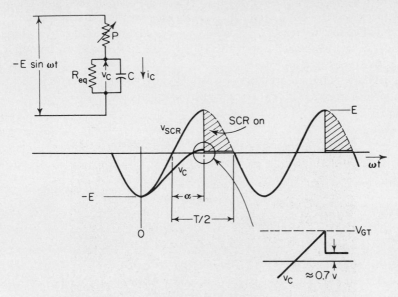

Fig. 5.17 Operation of *RC* trigger circuit.

be empirically shown that the value of *RC* (for zero output) must be chosen so that

$$RC \geq 1.3\frac{T}{2} \approx \frac{4}{\omega}, \tag{5.8}$$

where

$T = \dfrac{1}{f}$ = period of a-c line frequency in seconds.

$\omega = 2\pi f$ = angular line frequency in radians per second.

When the capacitor voltage $v_C = V_{GT} + D$, where D is the voltage drop of diode CR_1, the SCR will trigger, provided gate current I_{GT} is available. Since the voltage v_C across capacitor C can be considered essentially constant at the instant of triggering, the current I_{GT} must be instantaneously supplied by resistor R. Therefore, the maximum value of R is given by

$$e \geq I_{GT}R + v_C = I_{GT}R + V_{GT} + D,$$

or

$$R \leq \frac{e - D - V_{GT}}{I_{GT}}, \tag{5.9}$$

where

e = instantaneous supply voltage at which SCR will trigger.

D = voltage drop across diode CR_1.

Diode CR_1 protects the gate from reverse voltage when the anode of the SCR is negative. It must be rated to support at least the peak of the supply voltage E. Diode CR_2 resets capacitor C to the peak of the negative supply voltage $-E$. It must be rated to withstand at least $2E$ if there is a possibility of resistor R opening.

Figure 5.18 shows an oscillogram of the voltage waveforms of the circuit of Fig. 5.16 for three different trigger-delay angles.

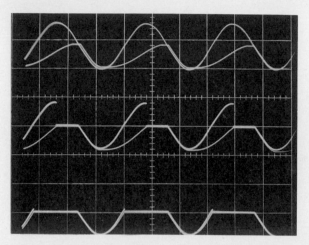

Fig. 5.18 Oscillogram of voltage waveform in the circuit of Fig. 5.16. Upper trace SCR voltage; lower trace capacitor voltage (horizontal, 5 msec/div; vertical, 200 v/div): (a) SCR held OFF; (b) SCR triggered at $\alpha = 90°$; (c) SCR triggered FULL ON.

The output of a given SCR with an RC trigger circuit is generally less sensitive to temperature variations than the simple resistance-triggered circuit discussed in Sec. 5.6.1. This is due to the action of the capacitor in parallel with the SCR gate. However, a trigger circuit which, in its operation, is strongly affected by the changing SCR gate characteristics with temperature is inherently limited in performance. This is the case for both the R and RC circuits, since the forward diode characteristic of the gate is an integral part of the circuit. Also, it has been observed that generally for alloy-type gates, the less sensitive the SCR, the greater is its negative temperature coefficient of I_{GT} and V_{GT}. Figure 5.19 illustrates the variation in the point of triggering for two SCR's having different sensitivities and temperature coefficients of V_{GF}.

There are many possible variations of the RC trigger circuit, all operating on the same basic principle. A simple circuit giving a full wave output is shown in Fig. 5.20 with actual circuit values for 120 v a-c/60 cps operation. It is the familiar "SCR in bridge" circuit with an RC network to trigger the

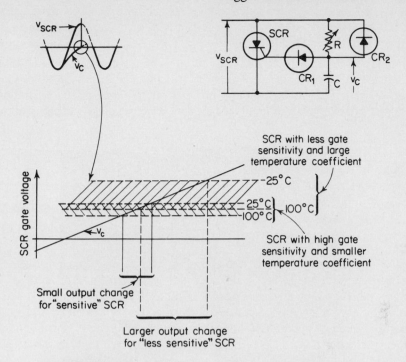

Fig. 5.19 Change in SCR output as gate sensitivity changes with temperature.

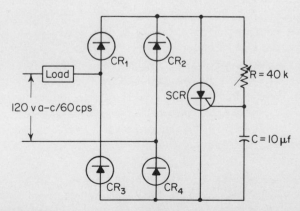

Fig. 5.20 *RC* trigger circuit applied to full wave "SCR in bridge" circuit.

SCR. In this circuit there is no diode (CR_2 in Fig. 5.16) to reset the capacitor voltage to $-E$. The initial voltage from which the capacitor C charges is essentially zero (slightly positive). Capacitor C is reset to this voltage by the clamping action of the SCR gate. For this reason, the charging time constant RC must be chosen longer here than in the circuit of Fig. 5.16 in order to delay triggering an equal amount for a given a-c half-cycle of charging voltage. For zero output, and under the same conditions applying to equation (5.8),

$$RC \geq 50 \frac{T}{2} \approx \frac{157}{\omega}. \qquad (5.10)$$

The maximum value of R is, by the considerations discussed in connection with equation (5.9),

$$R \leq \frac{e - V_{GT}}{I_{GT}}. \qquad (5.11)$$

The initial voltage prior to the charging interval is $-E$ in the circuit of Fig. 5.16 and essentially zero in the circuit of Fig. 5.20. For a given charging voltage e and charging time constant RC, the delay angle α becomes a function of the initial voltage on the capacitor. In a full-wave circuit, if the initial capacitor voltage is made a function of the amount of conduction in the power circuit on the previous (negative) half-cycle, slaving circuit action is obtained.

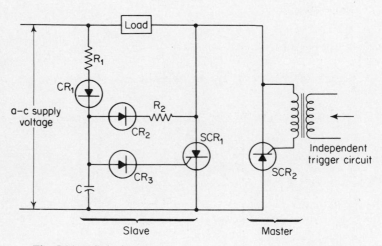

Fig. 5.21 *RC* slaving circuit.

Figure 5.21 shows a slaving circuit. SCR_1 will trigger at essentially the same delay angle α at which SCR_2 is triggered by its independent trigger circuit. Figure 5.22 illustrates the action of this circuit. The voltage across capacitor C is small compared to the a-c supply voltage e. Hence, it may be

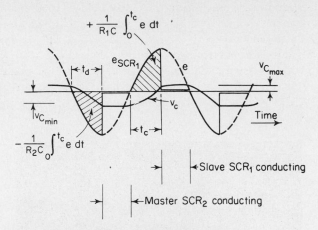

(Note: e and v_C have different scales.)

Fig. 5.22 Action of *RC* slaving circuit.

assumed that the capacitor charging current i_c delivered by resistor R_1 is $i_C = e/R_1$. Since $v_C = (1/C) \int i_C \, dt$, we may write for the (positive) capacitor voltage at the end of the charging integral

$$v_{C_{\max}} = v_{C_{\min}} + \frac{1}{R_1 C} \int_0^{t_c} e \, dt, \tag{5.12}$$

where

$v_{C_{\min}}$ = initial (negative) voltage across capacitor C prior to the charging interval.

t_c = time of charging after line voltage e has swung positive on anode of SCR.

At the end of the discharge interval (anode of SCR_1 negative), the capacitor voltage will be given by

$$v_{C_{\min}} = v_{C_{\max}} + \frac{1}{R_2 C} \int_0^{t_d} e \, dt, \tag{5.13}$$

where

$v_{C_{\max}}$ = initial (positive) voltage across capacitor C prior to discharging interval.

t_d = time of discharging after line voltage e has swung negative on anode of SCR_1.

In equation (5.13) it must be remembered that the line voltage is negative $(-e)$ for $0 < t < t_d$ while SCR_2 is not conducting, and that it is assumed that $e_{\text{SCR}_1} = e$ during this interval. This is valid if the load resistance is much smaller than R_2. This is the usual case in a power circuit.

For all practical purposes, capacitor C will hold its small positive voltage $v_{C_{max}}$ (top plate positive in Fig. 5.21) during the time that SCR_1 is conducting. The internal gate generator voltage with anode current flowing E_G (Sec. 5.2.2) initially provides sufficient voltage to reverse bias diode CR_3. Only as E_G decreases with decreasing anode current does some of the charge leave the capacitor. This can be seen by the oscillogram taken of the capacitor voltage v_C in Fig. 5.23. Capacitor C will essentially hold its negative voltage $v_{C_{min}}$

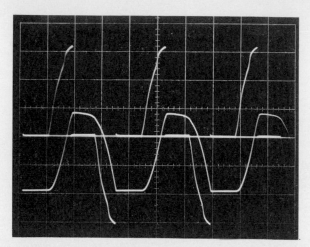

Fig. 5.23 Oscillogram of waveforms in circuit of Fig. 5.21 for delayed triggering at $\alpha = 90°$C. Anode voltage (upper trace), 50 v/div; capacitor voltage (lower trace), 2 v/div; horizontal, 5 msec/div.

while SCR_2 is conducting, because its discharge path toward the small voltage $v_{C_{min}}$ through diode drops SCR_2 and CR_1 is via the relatively long time constant R_1C. The oscillogram of Fig. 5.23 shows how $v_{C_{min}}$ remains essentially constant during the time SCR_2 is conducting. At time $t = t_c$ the capacitor voltage is $v_C|_{t=t_c} = v_{C_{max}}$. SCR_1 will trigger at time $t = t_c$ if

$$v_C|_{t=t_c} = v_{C_{max}} = V_{GT} + V_3, \qquad (5.14)$$

where

V_{GT} = SCR gate voltage to trigger.
V_3 = voltage drop across diode CR_3.

Substituting equations (5.14) and (5.13) into equation (5.12), we obtain

$$V_{GT} + V_3 = V_{GT} + V_3 + \frac{1}{R_2C}\int_0^{t_d} e\, dt + \frac{1}{R_1C}\int_0^{t_c} e\, dt. \qquad (5.15)$$

Setting $R_1 = R_2 = R$, and remembering that the line voltage e is negative for $0 < t < t_d$, we find that equation (5.15) is satisfied if $t_c = t_d$. Hence,

SCR_1 will trigger at essentially the same time $t = t_c$ as master SCR_2 was triggered at time $t = t_d$.

For design purposes, it may be shown empirically for typical low- and medium-current SCR's, that

$$R_1 C \geq 9 \frac{T}{2} \approx \frac{28}{\omega}. \tag{5.16}$$

The maximum value of R_1, in analogy to equation (5.9), is

$$R_1 \leq \frac{e - 2D - V_{GT}}{I_{GT}}, \tag{5.17}$$

where

$e =$ instantaneous supply voltage at which SCR will trigger.
$D =$ voltage drop of one diode.

Figure 5.23 shows an oscillogram of the waveforms of SCR_1 anode voltage and voltage across capacitor C for triggering at a delay angle of $\alpha \approx 90$ deg.

5.5.3 A-C Phase-shift Thyratron Trigger Circuits

This particular class of trigger circuits refers to the many circuits developed in the 1940's and early '50's for phase-shift grid control of gaseous thyratron tubes. Essentially all of these circuits lend themselves to triggering SCR's in such a fashion that a continuously variable phase-shifted output may be obtained for the load in the anode circuit. For a comprehensive treatment of this subject the reader is directed to Ref. 4. The SCR gate basically requires a current source driving a low impedance, whereas the gaseous thyratron grid basically requires a voltage source driving a high impedance. In addition to this, semiconductor technology has developed many types of trigger devices inherently better suited to the triggering of SCR's. These factors have resulted in relatively little direct application of these older circuits to the triggering of SCR's, particularly when it has been desired to keep the size of components within reasonable limits. Also, except where the peaking transformer approach may be employed with a clipped output, adaptations of the "variable d-c," the "phase-shifted a-c," and the "a-c plus variable d-c"[4] circuits often give insufficient rates of rise of gate current for optimum SCR performance, particularly when driving high-power resistive or leading power factor loads.

An adaptation of the "phase-shifted a-c" circuit for SCR triggering is shown in Fig. 5.24. The secondary of transformer T_1 provides an a-c voltage e_T across a variable RC or RL network. The voltage between the centertap of the T_1 secondary and the center point of the RC (or RL) network is indicated in Fig. 5.24(b) by V_{G-C}. Modified by resistor R_s, it is the applied gate-cathode voltage v_{G-C} indicated in Fig. 5.24(c). The design of a circuit such as that shown in Fig. 5.24 and the size of the components required depends on the SCR gate-trigger requirements and line frequency. The more sensitive the SCR, or the greater the line frequency, the smaller the components become.

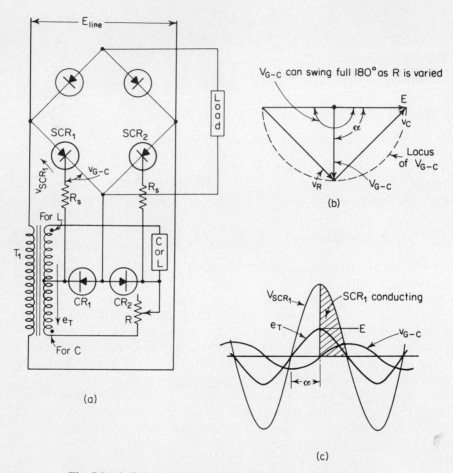

Fig. 5.24 A-C thyratron-type phase shift circuit applied to SCR's: (a) *RC* or *RL* phase shift trigger circuit, (b) voltage relationships on *RC* phase shift circuit for trigger delay of $\alpha = 90°$, and (c) voltage relationships for SCR$_1$.

For conventional SCR's requiring values of I_{GT} in the range of 10 to 100 ma and V_{GT} up to three volts the relation given by equation (5.18) may be used. That is,

$$E > 25 \text{ v}, \tag{5.18a}$$

$$\frac{1}{\omega C} \quad \text{or} \quad \omega L \leq \frac{E}{2} - 9, \tag{5.18b}$$

where

C = phase-shift circuit capacitance in farads.

L = phase-shift circuit inductance in henries.

E = peak end-to-end secondary voltage of transformer T_1 in volts.

$\omega = 2\pi f$, where f = frequency of a-c supply line.

$$R_S = \frac{E - 20}{0.2}, \qquad (5.18c)$$

where

R_S = gate series current-limiting resistance.

$$R \geq \frac{10}{\omega C} \quad \text{or} \quad 10\omega L. \qquad (5.18d)$$

It should be noted that in circuits of this nature it is easy to get the condition of positive gate bias when the anode is negative. The resulting undesirable transistor action is discussed in Sec. 5.2.6.

5.5.4 SATURABLE-REACTOR TRIGGER CIRCUITS

The switching properties of a reactor with a core material with a square B-H loop characteristic can be used to advantage in SCR trigger circuits for operation on a-c. Figure 5.25 illustrates two approaches for the use of a

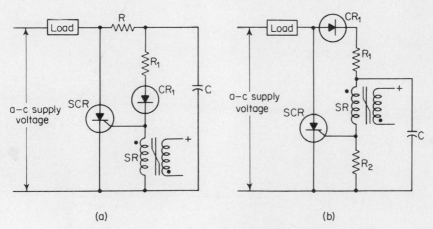

(a)   (b)

Fig. 5.25 ON-OFF saturable core magnetic trigger circuits: (a) shunt saturable reactor and (b) series saturable reactor.

saturable reactor SR in the gate circuit of an SCR for on-off operation. When SR saturates, it can divert gate current to hold the SCR OFF [Fig. 5.25(a)], or it can act as a switch for admitting gate current to the SCR [Fig. 5.25(b)].

In Fig. 5.25(a) the SCR cannot be triggered after the saturable reactor SR has once been brought into magnetic saturation. On each positive half-cycle of SCR anode voltage, insufficient voltage is developed across the saturated impedance of SR to trigger the SCR. On the negative half-cycle diode CR_1 prevents the core of SR from resetting. If, however, during the negative half-cycle a positive signal $(+)$ is applied to the control winding of SR, the core flux will be reset. On the next positive half-cycle SR will sustain voltage sufficiently long to trigger the SCR. The network RC provides a filter for line transients. Resistor R_1 in conjunction with R is selected to limit current to SR when it is in the saturated state.

In Fig. 5.25(b) the SCR is also not triggered when SR is saturated. If $R_1 \gg R_2$, most of the supply voltage E will appear across R_1 even with SR saturated. The voltage across R_2 in this state is insufficient to trigger the SCR. If, on the negative half-cycle, a positive signal $(+)$ is applied to the control winding of SR, the core flux will be reset. On the next positive half-cycle SR will initially sustain voltage for the first few electrical degrees permitting capacitor C to charge. When SR saturates, capacitor C discharges into the gate of SCR, triggering it into conduction. R_2 is selected to divert SR leakage current from the SCR gate while it is unsaturated and the SCR is to be held off.

The saturable reactors in the circuits of Fig. 5.25 for ON-OFF operation need be designed for absorbing the gate voltage signal only for a small initial portion of the half-cycle of supply voltage. When it is desired to delay the triggering selectively over the complete cycle, the saturable reactor must be

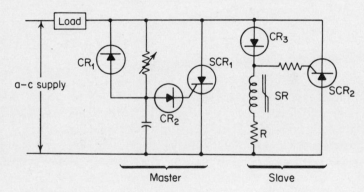

Fig. 5.26 Saturable reactor slave circuit.

designed to absorb at least the volt-seconds of a full half-cycle of line frequency without saturating. For the proper design procedure of saturable reactors, the reader is referred to the literature.[5,6,7] A practical design procedure using small tape-wound cores is also given in Ref. 8.

Figure 5.26 shows a saturable-reactor slave circuit. It illustrates the use of a saturable reactor for delaying the trigger signal for its associated SCR for an interval equal to the trigger delay of the "master" SCR. The circuit of Fig. 5.26 uses the RC phase-shift trigger circuit of Fig. 5.16 as a "master." If slave reactor SR is assumed to be initially in negative saturation, it will absorb positive volt-seconds (anode of SCR_1 positive) until SCR_1 is triggered. At that point the flux in SR will have been set to some value proportional to the amount of delay in the triggering of SCR_1. On the negative half-cycle (anode of SCR_2 positive) SR will be reset to negative saturation by the same number of (negative) volt-seconds. When saturation occurs, SCR_2 will be triggered from its anode. Resistor R is selected to limit the gate current in conjunction with the resistance of the saturated winding of SR.

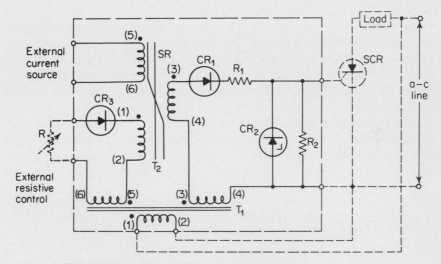

Fig. 5.27 Magnetic amplifier-type trigger circuit.

The saturable reactor is well adapted to continuously variable magnetic-amplifier-type SCR trigger circuits. Figure 5.27 illustrates a typical half-wave magnetic-amplifier trigger circuit. Because of its isolated windings, it can be readily extended to full wave and polyphase operation. Referring to Fig. 5.27, we notice that the gate signal is obtained from winding 3-4 of supply transformer T_1. With saturable-reactor core T_2 unsaturated, this voltage will be absorbed by winding 3-4 on T_2. During the next (negative) half-cycle of supply voltage, diode CR_1 will block the voltage from T_1, leaving the core flux at the level to which it was brought on the preceding positive half-cycle. However, the control windings 1-2 and 5-6 on SR allow resetting of the flux during the negative half-cycle. Depending on the amount of reset, a variable number of positive volt-seconds will be absorbed by the core T_2 before it saturates on the following positive half-cycle and applies the signal from winding 3-4 of T_1 to the SCR gate. In this manner the SCR(s) can be triggered at different delay angles, and continuously variable output control can be achieved. Zener diode CR_2 clips the supply voltage. This allows the use of a higher-voltage secondary on winding 3-4 of transformer T_1 in order to obtain a steep rate of rise of initial gate voltage at the beginning of the half-cycle of supply voltage.

Zener diode CR_2 then holds the voltage at a level within the ratings of the SCR gate for the remainder of the positive a-c supply wave. Resistor R_1 acts as a current limit, while R_2 diverts the saturable-reactor leakage current from the SCR gate for improved stability before triggering.

Two types of control are illustrated in the typical circuit of Fig. 5.27. The upper control winding 5-6 derives its signal from a variable low-level external current source. The control current delivered by this source, in conjunction with the number of turns of the control winding 5-6, impresses an mmf on the core of T_2. For a given reluctance of the magnetic path, the reset core flux will be directly proportional to the impressed mmf. For this reason, this type of control is often referred to as "mmf control" of the magnetic amplifier. The lower control winding 1-2 illustrates the so-called "reset" mode of operation. On the negative half-cycle of supply voltage, the setting of the external variable resistor R determines the amount of core reset. This mode of operation requires no external power source and provides very simple control over the continuously variable output.

5.5.5 Two-terminal Trigger Devices with Negative-resistance Switching Region

Devices exhibiting negative-resistance switching characteristics can be very useful in triggering SCR's. Two basically different but practical devices of this nature are discussed below: the neon glow lamp and the multilayer semiconductor switch; the latter includes the unilateral and bilateral switching diodes and unilateral four-layer, or Shockley, diode. The Zener, or, more properly, the avalanche diode, is not considered in this category of switching devices. Its characteristic is not that of a switch, since its avalanche-voltage reverse breakdown characteristic exhibits positive incremental resistance in its normal operating range. It is, however, a very useful and stable reference device in trigger circuits and should be used where such a function is required. This may be as a voltage regulator in furnishing the trigger circuit with a well-regulated supply voltage (as an example of this application, see Sec. 5.5.7) or as a trigger reference in the control portion of the circuit preceding the actual SCR trigger circuit.

Basic Function of Switch in Trigger Circuit: In the RC phase-controlled trigger circuits discussed in Sec. 5.5.2, the capacitor provides a means by which to obtain the required degree of gate-voltage phase shift. The resistive element of the trigger circuit provides the necessary gate current to trigger I_{GT} at the instant of triggering. Hence, the circuit requires a relatively low value of resistance and a large value of capacitance for a given time delay. A superior circuit from the point of view of efficiency, size, and performance results if the SCR is triggered by the charge stored on the capacitor rather than by the current drawn instantaneously from the supply through a resistor. In this manner, much higher values of charging resistance may be used, since the resistance must supply only the smaller peak trigger current of the trigger device rather than that of the SCR. The "switch" for dumping the charge of the capacitor into the SCR gate must be capable of blocking the trigger voltage until triggering is desired at some particular delay angle. It should require a minimum amount of current to trigger in the interest of maintaining high values of charging resistance (and small values of capacitance) and thus lower stand-by trigger-circuit power dissipation for a given time constant and supply voltage. In the ON state the trigger switch should have a low forward drop, so that during switching a maximum amount of charge is transferred to the SCR. Another desirable requirement for the trigger device is that it block reverse voltage. Many trigger circuits require that full peak reverse line voltage be blocked in the SCR gate circuit. In other circuits, peak reverse gate-blocking-voltage requirements are low, in the order of 6 to 10 v.

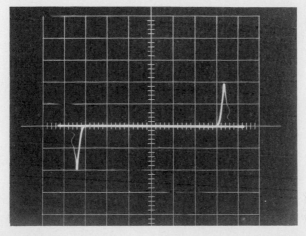

Fig. 5.28 Neon lamp *E-I* characteristic (horizontal, 20 v/div; vertical, 5 ma/div).

Neon-lamp Circuits: Figure 5.28 shows an oscillogram of the bilateral *E-I* characteristic of a typical neon lamp (NE-83). The zero voltage and current point is at the center of the graticule. Voltage is on the abscissa and current on the ordinate for both "positive" and "negative" directions. The particular device shown reaches its ignition voltage and switches symmetrically in either direction at 86 v under the prevailing temperature and ambient light conditions. At a peak current of 10 ma it has "switched down" by 18 v. Switching action is seen to be very rapid by the light trace in the switching region.

The circuit shown in Fig. 5.29 illustrates a practical application of this switching action in discharging capacitor C into the primary of a pulse transformer. Depending on the design of the transformer and the selection of its turns ratio, a small amount of resistance R' may be required in order to improve the waveform of the pulse. The charging resistance $(R + R_{min})$ can be quite large in a circuit of this type. This leads to a low-dissipation trigger circuit, one that lends itself to control of the capacitor C charging rate, and thus the delay angle of triggering the SCR, by suitable transducers responsive to light, heat, pressure, etc. One basic limitation in a simple neon-lamp circuit of the type shown in Fig. 5.29 is the relatively high ignition (trigger) voltage of the neon lamp. It is usually in the order of 60 to 100 v. Since the supply voltage must first reach this voltage before the neon lamp can trigger the SCR, there will be a certain amount of inherent "front-end loss" of the a-c

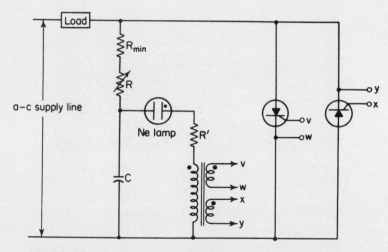

Fig. 5.29 Simple neon lamp transformer-coupled SCR trigger circuit.

supply voltage wave that is available for application to the load. The importance of this loss, of course, depends on the peak value of the supply voltage. Often it is insignificant. For example, in a 120 v a-c circuit a typical "front-end loss" is 60 electrical deg, which amounts to about a 10 per cent loss of rms output voltage. This situation can be improved, however, with prebiasing techniques at the expense of slightly more circuit complication. Available neon lamps are limited in the amount of current they can deliver. For this reason, the neon-lamp trigger circuit is limited to SCR's with relatively sensitive gates.

Multilayer semiconductor trigger device circuits: It is possible to build a variety of small multilayer (alternate p-type and n-type material) semiconductor switches as two-terminal devices or with suitable control leads added.

The SCR itself belongs in this class of devices. Of particular usefulness in SCR trigger circuits are two such devices which distinguish themselves by the degree to which they switch and by the presence or absence of a bilateral switching characteristic. The latter characteristic is very useful, because a single small trigger device can be used to trigger two SCR's or a single triode switch (Secs. 5.6 and 7.3) in a full-wave a-c control circuit. This principle is illustrated in the neon-lamp circuit of Fig. 5.29, where one bilateral device triggers the SCR's, each in its respective half-cycle of positive anode voltage.

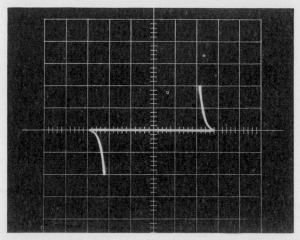

Fig. 5.30 *E-I* characteristic of a bilateral *n-p-n* trigger diode (horizontal, 10 v/div; vertical, 5 ma/div).

Figure 5.30 shows the bilateral (forward and reverse) *E-I* characteristic of a small glass-packaged three-layer semiconductor trigger device. It can be seen that at the prevailing temperature condition it has a switching voltage of 28 v in the "forward" direction and 29 v in the "reverse" direction. The negative voltage swing for this device is about six volts either way up to 10 ma of current. Temperature stability of the switching voltage is quite important in a trigger device if trigger-circuit design is to be optimized. It is desirable to limit the temperature coefficient of switching voltage to a value below about 0.05 per cent/°C in the interest of output stability over a temperature range. The device whose characteristic is shown in Fig. 5.30 satisfies this requirement. Values greatly in excess of 0.15 per cent/°C limit satisfactory performance over a range of temperature when output stability and repeatability of a control setting are important. However, over-all performance, even at this level of temperature coefficient, is better than that of the *R* and *RC* circuits described in Secs. 5.5.1 and 5.5.2.

The circuit of Fig. 5.31 shows the application of the device with the characteristic of Fig. 5.30 in a simple full-wave a-c phase-control circuit.

Capacitor C_1 is charged with alternate polarities on every half-cycle of the supply voltage. The bilateral action of the trigger diode will alternately discharge capacitor C_1, providing positive gate current to each of the SCR's when their respective anodes are positive. Gate current to SCR_2 is a-c coupled through capacitor C_2. Capacitor C_3 provides a return path for the gate pulse.

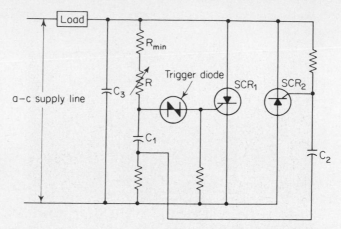

Fig. 5.31 Simple bilateral trigger diode a-c coupled SCR trigger circuit.

This means of coupling is an alternative to the transformer coupling shown for the neon-lamp circuit in Fig. 5.29. However, this type of coupling is limited in its usefulness because of its susceptibility to spurious triggering of the SCR by line transients coupled into the gate of SCR_2 by capacitor C_2. The circuits of Figs. 5.29 and 5.31 are very similar in their principle of operation. However, the lower switching current of the semiconductor device, in the order of 100 μa and two orders of magnitude less than the neon lamp, allows the use of a much larger value of charging resistance $(R_{min} + R)$ in the circuit of Fig. 5.31.

The conventional unilateral four-layer *p-n-p-n* diode can also be used to trigger SCR's. Figure 5.32 shows an oscillogram of its *E-I* characteristic. It is similar to that of an SCR. However, switching is initiated by raising the forward voltage of the device to its breakover level. Switching is extremely rapid. This diode has the advantage of "switching down" to a voltage drop of the order of a volt. It is thus inherently capable of transferring more of a given charge stored on a capacitor to an SCR gate. Bilateral trigger devices with this characteristic are also possible by means of semiconductor structures similar to those discussed in Sec. 3.8.

The circuit of Fig. 5.33[9] shows the unilateral *p-n-p-n* diode applied to the triggering of an SCR in the full-wave "SCR in bridge" circuit. It is the same basic circuit as that of Fig. 5.20. However, the addition of the *p-n-p-n* diode

CR_1 allows the use of much larger values of charging resistance and smaller capacitance, as can be seen from the actual component values given for operation from a 120 v a-c line.

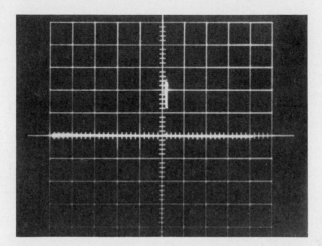

Fig. 5.32 *E-I* characteristic of a 20 v unilateral *p-n-p-n* diode (horizontal, 5 v/div; vertical, 10 ma/div).

5.5.6 TRANSISTORS IN SCR TRIGGER CIRCUITS

The transistor as a control element can find a multitude of applications in control circuitry preceding the actual SCR trigger state. As an amplifier, phase inverter, and logic element, the transistor is almost inseparable from any large SCR control system. It is particularly useful as an active element in converting various transducer output signals (a-c, d-c pulse) at different

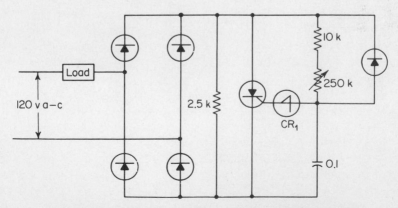

Fig. 5.33 Unilateral *p-n-p-n* diode applied to triggering SCR in simple "SCR in bridge" circuit.

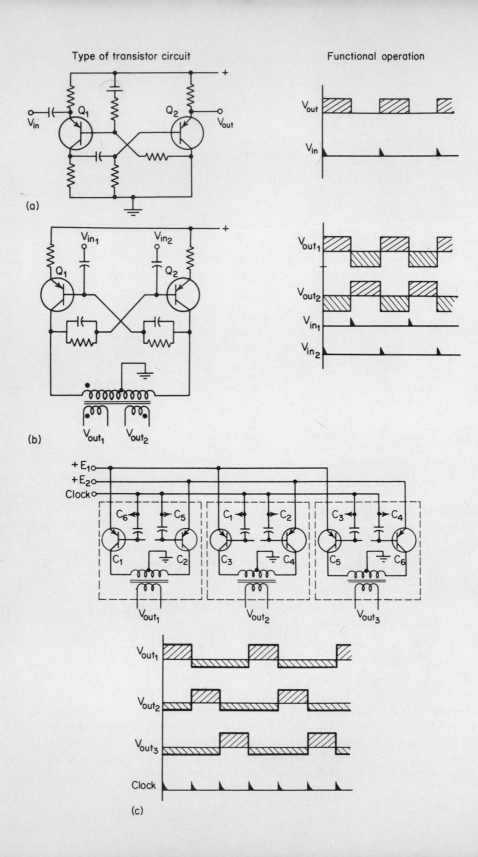

Type of transistor circuit

Functional operation

(a)

(b)

(c)

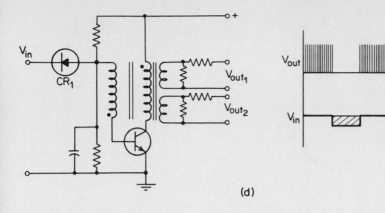

(d)

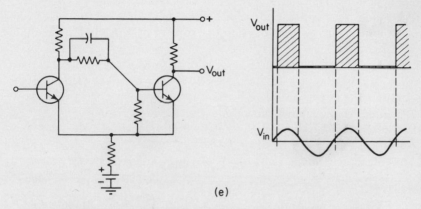

(e)

Fig. 5.34 Types of transistor circuits and waveforms useful for triggering SCR's: (a) monostable multivibrator (one shot), (b) bistable multivibrator, (c) cascaded unsymmetrical bistable multivibrator, (d) astable or free-running blocking oscillator, and (e) Schmitt trigger.

impedance levels to the required SCR trigger signals. As a trigger element for SCR's, the transistor is most useful when operated in a switching mode to apply a trigger signal to the SCR gate. With the availability of special semi-conductor devices optimized and characterized to trigger SCR's with pulses, one of the principal roles of the transistor in SCR trigger circuits lies in the generation of maintained trigger signals. Hence, in many high-power a-c control, a-c to d-c controlled rectification, and d-c-to-a-c inversion applications, transistor-driven SCR trigger circuits are considered.

The subject of transistor-circuit design is well covered in the literature.[10,11,12] Rather than to treat the design of specific transistor circuits suitable for triggering SCR's, this section will indicate the possibilities inherent in the use of transistors in SCR trigger-circuit design with respect to some of the application requirements arising in the use of SCR's in power circuitry. The small input required to the transistor trigger circuit will normally be derived from a sensing or command circuit in open-loop systems or an error amplifier in closed-loop systems. Generally, in a-c systems the input signal must be synchronized to the line frequency. In inverters operating from a d-c supply, a stabilized clock frequency must usually be provided. In many cases a unijunction oscillator will serve this purpose (see Sec. 5.5.7). Figure 5.34 illustrates some useful trigger waveforms for SCR's. Indicated also is the type of transistor circuit capable of generating the particular waveform shown. Each of the types of circuits indicated has many variations beyond the scope of this discussion. Where p-n-p transistors are indicated, circuits may readily be designed for utilizing complementary n-p-n transistors. This may be of particular importance where it is desirable to use silicon transistors in critical high-temperature applications.

The monostable multivibrator, or "one-shot," indicated in Fig. 5.34(a) is a very useful circuit building block for amplifying and stretching an available small signal pulse. The output pulse width is readily adjustable by proper selection of the circuit time constants to provide a maintained-type trigger signal required in some applications (see Sec. 5.4.3). The circuit resets itself and removes the gate drive from the SCR in preparation for the next input pulse.

When the cross-coupling networks between base and collector of the two transistors are made symmetrical, the multivibrator has two stable states: Q_1 ON and Q_2 OFF, or Q_1 OFF and Q_2 ON. This results in the bistable multivibrator illustrated in Fig. 5.34(b). Alternate positive input signals at V_{in_1} and V_{in_2}, or signals of alternate polarity at one of the inputs will switch the state of the circuit. The output of the circuit is useful, for example, when two SCR's are being triggered in a single-phase center-tap, in a bridge circuit, or in a two-element parallel-inverter circuit. In the latter case a unijunction transistor relaxation oscillator (see Sec. 5.5.7) may be used to generate the input clock pulses. The transformer-coupled circuit output waveform has the desirable feature of providing negative gate bias during the SCR OFF time (see Sec. 5.4.4).

The bistable multivabrator may be cascaded in the manner of a ring counter to give a number of outputs suitably phase-displaced for triggering SCR's in polyphase a-c or inverter circuits. When multiple secondary transformer output windings are employed, additional output-signal flexibility may be obtained by proper vector addition of outputs. Figure 5.34(c) suggests a particular version of an SCR trigger waveform which may be obtained by a cascaded bistable multivibrator which has an unsymmetrical output. This waveform is particularly well-suited for providing SCR trigger signals to a controlled three-phase bridge a-c rectifier circuit. Phase shift may be obtained by controlling the phasing of the clock pulses in response to the input signal with respect to an oscillator synchronized to the supply-line frequency. During the SCR OFF time a negative bias is applied to the SCR gate. Since the SCR duty cycle is one-third of the supply voltage period in a three-phase circuit, the voltages E_1 and E_2 to the appropriate transistors are selected to give zero net volt-seconds across the individual multivibrator output transformers. Appropriate cross coupling, lock-out, and starting circuits are required for this type of circuit.

The blocking oscillator in its monostable or in its astable mode is also a useful SCR trigger element. In its monostable mode it can function basically as an externally triggered pulse amplifier which is suitable for an SCR trigger circuit when pulse-triggering is permissible. Output pulse width in practical designs is in the area of 10 to 50 μsec. Thus, this circuit is a pulse trigger occupying an intermediate position between the unijunction transistor trigger (of roughly two to five μsec effective pulse width) and the maintained type of SCR trigger circuits. The principle of the blocking oscillator circuit's operation depends on regenerative coupling between the input and output circuits of the transistor similar to the familiar underlying principle used in a large variety of oscillator circuits. Owing to the regenerative principle, output pulse rise time can be very rapid, a particular advantage in obtaining fast turn-on action in the SCR. Figure 5.34(d) illustrates how the astable, or free-running, blocking oscillator may be used functionally to supply a maintained trigger signal to an SCR in the form of a burst of pulses from a very low-level input circuit. A small signal that reverse-biases diode CR_1 releases the circuit into its free-running mode at a frequency that is very high compared to the desired SCR triggering repetition rate. Typically, the blocking oscillator may run at several kilocycles per second for an SCR repetition rate of 60 cps. The oscillator transformer may also have multiple output windings for simultaneous triggering of SCR's whose cathodes are at different potentials.

Another of many transistor circuits useful in triggering SCR's is the Schmitt trigger indicated in Fig. 5.34(e). Its output is independent of the input waveform, since it triggers at a preset voltage level determined by the bias conditions established in the circuit. It is similar to the bistable multivibrator, except that one of the cross-coupling networks is replaced by a common emitter resistor which, owing to its regenerative action, provides a very fast rise-time output pulse. The Schmitt trigger may, therefore, be employed to supply fast rise-time pulses from transducer or inputs having waveforms unsuitable for triggering SCR's.

5.5.7 Unijunction Transistor Pulse-trigger Circuits

The unijunction transistor (UJT) is a unique device available in several types well-suited to supplying trigger pulses to SCR's. The UJT is functionally

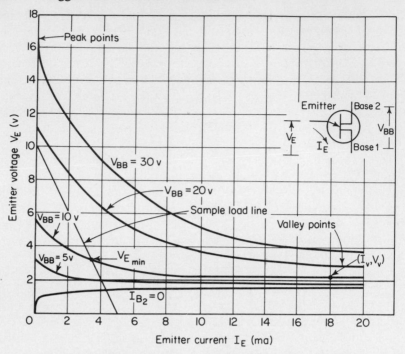

Fig. 5.35 Typical unijunction transistor static emitter characteristics [courtesy General Electric Company].

a unilateral voltage-ratio activated device. The static emitter input characteristic of a typical UJT is shown in Fig. 5.35. When the emitter (E) to base 1 (B_1) voltage V_E exceeds a specified fraction η (called intrinsic standoff ratio) of the interbase voltage V_{BB} between base 2 (B_2) and base 1 (B_1), the previously blocking emitter-base 1 junction switches into a low dynamic impedance state of the order of 5 to 20 ohms. The emitter voltage and current at which this takes place are $V_E = V_p$ and $I_E = I_p$, the peak-point voltage V_p and peak-point current I_p, respectively. The peak points are shown in Fig. 5.35. We see that their respective values V_p are a function of the interbase voltage V_{BB} such that $V_p \approx \eta V_{BB}$. The negative resistance regions between the peak points and the valley points indicated in Fig. 5.35 give the UJT the switching characteristic so useful in SCR trigger circuits.

When the UJT is placed into the basic trigger circuit shown in Fig. 5.36, it functions basically as a relaxation oscillator. Capacitor C_1 is charged from the supply V_1 through resistor R_1. Capacitor C_1 discharges through load resistor R_{B_1}, producing the pulse output V_{OB_1} when

$$V_E = V_p = \eta V_{BB} + V_D, \tag{5.19}$$

where

V_D = equivalent emitter diode voltage (between 0.4 and 0.7 v at 25°C).

Figure 5.36 also indicates the waveform of a typical UJT output pulse. It is a function of the circuit and UJT parameters. For a more complete treatment of the UJT, the reader is directed to Refs. 13 and 14. When the emitter voltage $V_E = V_{E_{min}}$ at the intersection of the emitter load line with the static emitter characteristic curve of interest, as illustrated in Fig. 5.34 for the case of

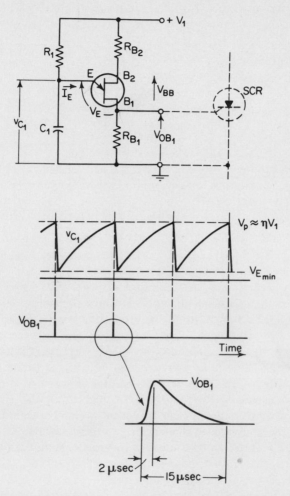

Fig. 5.36 Basic UJT relaxation oscillator SCR trigger circuit and waveforms.

$V_{BB} = 10$ v, the emitter ceases to conduct, the capacitor may be recharged, and the cycle can be repeated. The pulse of amplitude V_{OB_1} may be directly, capacitively, or transformer coupled to the SCR gate. In the latter case, the primary of a pulse transformer may be substituted for R_{B_1}. Making $R_{B_1} = 0$

and placing the pulse transformer primary in series with capacitor C_1 eliminates the small d-c component of current in its primary. This component is otherwise given by

$$I_{\text{d-c}} \approx \frac{V_1}{R_{B_2} + R_{BB} + R_{Xfmr}}, \tag{5.20}$$

where

R_{BB} = minimum specified interbase resistance of UJT.
R_{Xfmr} = equivalent d-c resistance of transformer.

When V_{OB_1} is directly coupled to the SCR gate, care must be taken that $I_{\text{d-c}}$ does not prebias the SCR gate to turn on. This can be avoided if R_{B_1} is selected on the basis of voltage dividing action so that

$$R_{B_1} < \frac{R_{BB_{\min}} + R_{B_2}}{\dfrac{V_1}{V_{GT_{\max}}} - 1}, \tag{5.21}$$

where

R_{BB} = minimum specified UJT interbase resistance.
$V_{GT_{\max}}$ = maximum gate voltage at specified temperature at which SCR will not trigger.
V_1 = UJT supply voltage (see Fig. 5.36).

The equivalent emitter diode voltage V_D has a negative temperature coefficient. On the other hand, the interbase resistance R_{BB}, and hence the interbase voltage V_{BB}, has a small positive temperature coefficient. Referring to equation (5.19), we see that the point of triggering, when $V_E = V_p$, will thus be relatively little affected by temperature variations. When extremely close temperature compensation is required, however, a resistor R_{B_2} may be specially selected. This method has made operation of the circuit of Fig. 5.36 as a secondary frequency standard practical. Selection of specific values of R_{B_2} depends on the type of UJT used. For additional information on temperature compensation, the reader is directed to Ref. 14. A minimum value of $R_{B_2} \geq 100$ ohms should always be present in order to limit the UJT's peak power dissipation during its switching action when conductivity modulation of the interbase resistance causes a pulse of interbase current.

The period T of the desired output-pulse repetition rate can be determined from[13]

$$T \approx R_1 C_1 \ln\left(\frac{1}{1 - \eta}\right) = 2.3 R_1 C_1 \log_{10}\left(\frac{1}{1 - \eta}\right). \tag{5.22}$$

Capacitor C_1 must store sufficient charge to trigger the SCR. Typical values are between 0.01 and 0.5 μf. The selection of charging resistor R_1 must meet two requirements. It must be small enough to admit the required peak-point current I_p from the source voltage V_1, or approximately

$$R_1 < \frac{V_1 - V_p}{I_p}, \tag{5.23}$$

if the emitter diode drop V_D and load resistance R_{B_1} are neglected. On the other hand, it must be large enough so that the load line formed by R_1 and V_1 intersects the appropriate static UJT emitter characteristic curve to the left of the valley point, or $V_{E_{min}} > V_V$ (see Fig. 5.35). This condition for oscillation of the circuit of Fig. 5.36 is met if

$$R_1 > \frac{V_1 - V_V}{I_V}, \tag{5.24}$$

where

V_V = valley voltage for particular interbase voltage V_{BB}.

I_V = valley current corresponding to V_V.

The sample load line in Fig. 5.35, drawn for $V_1 = 10$ v and $R_1 = 2$ k ohms, shows $V_{E_{min}} > V_V$ and to the left of the valley point. If the load line intersects the static emitter characteristic to the right of the valley point, the UJT emitter will not recover its blocking state, and thus cease to oscillate, because of the stable operating point formed by the intersection of the load line with the positive emitter resistance.

The choice of supply voltage V_1 is determined on the low end by the acceptable value of pulse output V_{OB_1} and on the high end by the maximum allowable UJT interbase voltage V_{BB} in addition to the consideration expressed by equation (5.21). Values of V_1 between 10 and 35 v are typical. In practice the UJT supply voltage V_1 may come from a Zener-diode-regulated d-c power supply or be taken through a dropping resistor directly from the a-c supply line. The former approach is applicable to triggering SCR's in a wide variety of a-c and d-c circuits. The circuit shown in Fig. 8.12 shows this type of UJT circuit applied to the triggering of an SCR in a half-wave a-c phase-controlled circuit. Section 8.12 deals with the control transfer characteristics of UJT trigger circuits for SCR's.

Base 2 rather than the emitter may be also used to control the UJT. If, in the circuit of Fig. 5.36, the interbase voltage V_{BB} suddenly decreases, the peak-point voltage V_p will also decrease in accordance with equation (5.19). For a given voltage on capacitor C_1 at that time, the UJT will trigger when $v_{C_1} > V_p \approx \eta V_1$. This mode of UJT control makes supply-line synchronization a simple matter in a-c circuits. If, for example, the voltage V_1 is derived from the unfiltered output of a Zener-diode-clipped full-wave rectified a-c supply-line voltage, V_1 will dip when $e < V_Z$, where e is the instantaneous line voltage and V_Z is the Zener voltage. The UJT will subsequently trigger when $\eta e \gtrless v_{C_1 min}$, where $v_{C_1 min}$ is the voltage on capacitor C_1 toward the end of the supply-voltage half-cycle. Also, if V_1 is taken from a similar supply but not clipped, the UJT will likewise trigger at the end of the half-cycle and reset. In either case, by causing the UJT to trigger at the end of the supply half-cycle, capacitor C_1 will be discharged to essentially zero volts when the supply voltage goes through zero. Accordingly, the timing capacitor C_1 begins to charge consistently immediately following voltage zero on every (positive) half-cycle of the supply-line voltage. Synchronization of the UJT oscillator trigger circuit with the supply line is thus assured in this simple manner.

When the UJT supply voltage V_1 is a function of time, the peak-point voltage V_p will vary as a time function according to $V_p(t) \approx \eta V_1(t)$. If, furthermore, the capacitor C_1 in Fig. 5.36 is charged from the same supply $V_1(t)$, the

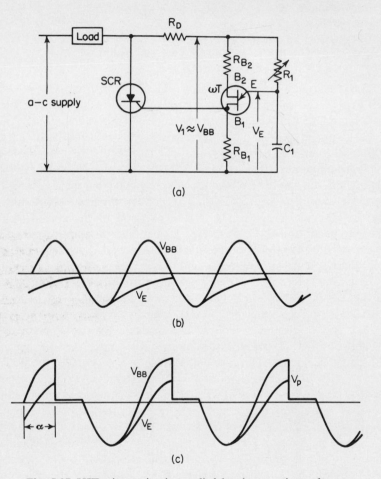

Fig. 5.37 UJT trigger circuit supplied by time-varying voltage: (a) simple half-wave SCR phase-controlled circuit with UJT trigger, (b) waveforms with SCR in OFF state, and (c) waveforms with SCR triggered at a delay angle of $\alpha = 90°$.

simple half-wave SCR phase-controlled circuit of Fig. 5.37 results. Resistor R_D drops the a-c supply voltage E_{a-c} to such a value that the rated peak interbase voltage of the UJT is not exceeded. Since the UJT interbase resistance R_{BB} is usually very much larger than either R_{B_1} or R_{B_2}, the UJT interbase voltage V_{BB} in practice equals the peak of the instantaneous line voltage E_{a-c} dropped by R_D. Also, the UJT emitter-base 1 resistance in its blocking state is very large compared to R_{B_1} so that the capacitor voltage $v_{C_1} \approx V_E$.

Figure 5.37(b) illustrates the phase delay of the emitter voltage V_E introduced by the capacitor C_1 and its associated charging resistor R_1. The action of this part of the circuit in the OFF state is identical to that of the simple RC trigger circuit of Fig. 5.16 and in particular to its capacitor voltage waveform shown in Fig. 5.17 or Fig. 5.18(a). For maintenance of the OFF condition for the circuit of Fig. 5.37, it can be empirically shown that

$$R_1 C_1 \geq 0.64 \frac{T}{2} \approx \frac{2}{\omega}, \tag{5.25}$$

where

T = period of line frequency = $1/f$.
$\omega = 2\pi f$ = angular supply frequency.

As the time constant $R_1 C_1$ is reduced, the capacitor C_1 charges more rapidly. When $V_E \approx \eta V_{BB}$ the UJT will trigger. This is indicated in Fig. 5.37(c) for a delay angle of $\alpha = 90$ electrical deg. The sketch indicates a value of $\eta = 0.5$ for the UJT.

The application of this type of UJT trigger-circuit operation is shown for two cases of full-wave SCR phase control in Figs. 5.38 and 5.39. Figure 5.38

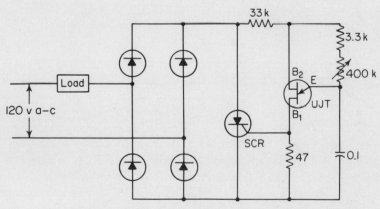

Fig. 5.38 Simple UJT trigger applied to "SCR in bridge" circuit.

shows the "SCR in bridge" full-wave phase-controlled circuit with a UJT trigger circuit operating from a 120 v a-c supply line. Its principle of operation is very similar to the RC circuit shown in Fig. 5.20. Instead of triggering the SCR, however, a much higher-impedance RC network triggers the UJT, which in turn triggers the SCR.

Figure 5.39 shows the application of the UJT trigger circuit operating from the supply line to a parallel-inverse SCR power circuit for full-wave a-c phase control. Each SCR has its associated RC-UJT trigger circuit. The single potentiometer R exercises full symmetrical control over both halves of the circuit by varying the impedance of the cross-coupling network between the two UJT emitters.

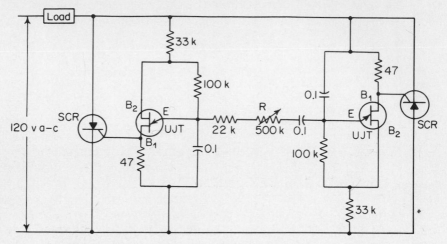

Fig. 5.39 Simple UJT crosscoupled trigger circuit for parallel-inverse connected SCR's.

5.5.8 SCR's IN SCR TRIGGER CIRCUITS

Some of the characteristics of the SCR make it, in turn, a useful device for triggering other SCR's. Acting as a fast-triggered latching switch for high voltage and with high gain, it may be used where other devices, notably transistors, are not an economical solution. However, means must be provided to turn off the SCR. In a-c circuits such means are readily available. In d-c circuits auxiliary turn-off circuitry must be used, as discussed in Chap. 6. When an SCR is used as a pilot device, a larger SCR can be triggered from the anode or "anode-fired." This technique, found very useful with earlier mercury arc devices, is also practical with SCR's. Figure 5.40 shows a practical application. Gate current for the power SCR is derived from its anode a-c power supply through the pilot SCR. Phase control is obtained by triggering the pilot SCR with the proper timing and synchronization. Regardless of the size of the power SCR, the pilot device need handle only the relatively small gate current required to trigger the larger SCR. Resistor R_1 limits the current, and resistor R_2 acts as a load for the pilot SCR across which the triggering signal is developed. Diode CR_1 blocks negative anode voltage from the pilot SCR in the event that its gate should be positive at the time the anode is

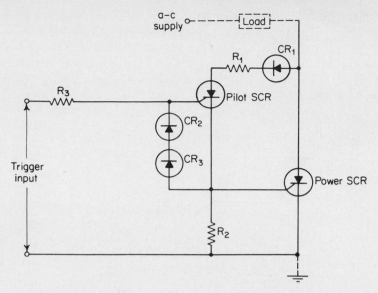

Fig. 5.40 Pilot SCR used to "anode trigger" power SCR.

negative (see Sec. 5.2.6). A positive trigger input forward-biases the gate-cathode emitter junction of the pilot SCR. Depending on the choice of pilot SCR, its gate sensitivity, and resistor R_3, the trigger input impedance of the circuit of Fig. 5.40 may be made very large. On this basis the input character-istic of a gaseous thyratron tube may be simulated.[15] Diodes CR_2 and CR_3 provide stabilizing gate bias for the pilot SCR when the trigger input is negative with respect to ground (see Sec. 5.4.4). If the gate-to-cathode junction of the SCR has a specified reverse avalanche voltage characteristic, the gate may be reverse biased directly, and diodes CR_2 and CR_3 may be eliminated.

In contrast to the "anode-fired" application of Fig. 5.40, an auxiliary SCR is shown as a gate amplifier in a "driven-gate" type of trigger circuit in Fig. 5.41. A small control transformer T_1 supplies a-c power to the gate-cathode circuit of the power SCR. When the anode of the power SCR is positive, the auxiliary SCR may be triggered from its trigger input source. The a-c half-cycle waveform passed by the auxiliary SCR is current-limited by R_1 and clipped by avalanche (Zener) diode CR_1. Network R_2C_1 ensures a large initial gate signal while limiting gate dissipation in the power SCR's after they have triggered. The circuit also acts as a pulse stretcher for cases where a maintained trigger signal is required (see Sec. 5.4.3). The auxiliary SCR may be triggered from a very low-level pulse source. Resistors R_3 and R_4 may also be required for bias purposes on the auxiliary SCR. Diode CR_2 clamps the gate for any negative trigger input voltage. The components shown dotted provide a negative gate bias network for the power SCR. During the negative anode half-cycle the capacitor is charged to the polarity

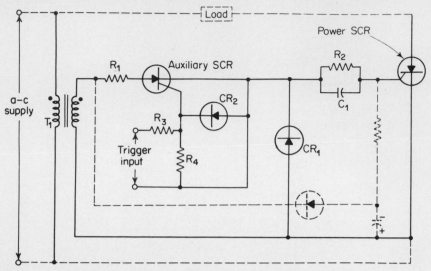

Fig. 5.41 Auxiliary SCR used to drive gate of power SCR.

indicated. When the anode swings positive, the gate is negatively biased. The circuit illustrated in Fig. 5.41 allows driving the gate of the power SCR directly from the supply rather than from the instantaneous anode voltage waveform. This type of drive is required when driving a-c inductive loads in single or polyphase circuits. This is discussed further in Chap. 8.

Of considerable interest in some cases is the use of light-triggered SCR's or switches for triggering SCR's. They can, for example, provide very simple isolation between various control and power circuits. Direct optical readout of information stored on cards or tape can actuate power circuits by the use of a small light-triggered diode switch in conjunction with a larger SCR similar to the circuit of Fig. 5.40. Where reliable, fast-rise-time light sources, such as junction luminescent diodes, are available, light-triggered diodes may serve individually to trigger a long string of series-connected SCR's. In high-voltage, high-current applications this method eliminates the need for difficult pulse-transformer designs.

5.6 Triggering Semiconductor Bilateral Triode Switches

The basic considerations and circuitry discussed in the preceding section for the triggering of conventional p-gate SCR's also apply to other types of semiconductor switches which are triggered by virtue of an externally applied forward bias to a p-n (or n-p) emitter junction. The bilateral switch serves to illustrate this point. Figure 5.42 shows a full-wave continuously variable

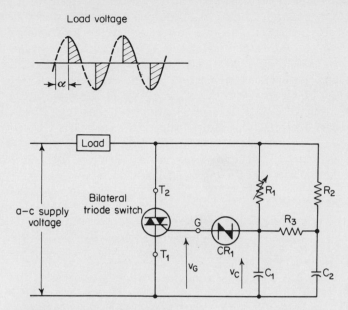

Fig. 5.42 Bilateral triode switch trigger circuit for continuously variable phase control.

phase-controlled circuit which supplies an a-c load. It uses only a single power semiconductor—the bilateral triode switch or Triac. Functionally, the circuit performs identically to the parallel-inverse and the "SCR in bridge" circuits shown in previous sections and in Chap. 8. However, in the conventional circuits at least two (parallel-inverse) to five ("SCR in bridge") power semiconductors are required.

From the trigger-circuit point of view, the bilateral triode in Fig. 5.42 switches into conduction in the first quadrant (see Fig. 2.1) like a conventional p-gate SCR when, if T_2 is positive with respect to T_1, the gate G is driven positive with respect to T_1. On the supply voltage half-cycle of opposite polarity (T_2 negative with respect to T_1) a negative gate signal with respect to T_1 will trigger the device in the third quadrant analogous to a complementary n-gate SCR. Some bilateral trigger triodes also have a secondary trigger mode; i.e., they trigger on a negative signal in the first quadrant and a positive signal in the third quadrant, although usually at different sensitivities.

The trigger circuit shown in Fig. 5.42 is basically an RC phase-shift circuit of the type discussed previously (Secs. 5.5.2 and 5.5.5). For improved performance for large values of triggering delay angle α, a second phase-shift network $R_2 C_2$ is cascaded with the main timing network $R_1 C_1$. Resistor R_3 is selected to minimize the loading effect on $R_1 C_1$. Diode CR_1 is a bilateral trigger diode of the type discussed in Sec. 5.5.5. A neon lamp of the type discussed in the same section can also be used. The bilateral trigger diode serves three important functions. First, it provides the desirable switching action discussed earlier. Second, as a result of having a switching device as a trigger element, the trigger circuit can be designed for low stand-by power dissipation (Sec. 5.5.5). Third, the bilateral trigger diode serves to discriminate between the primary and secondary trigger modes of the bilateral triode switch. For example, in the case of the simple RC network of Fig. 5.42, the capacitor voltage v_C lags the supply voltage by a variable phase shift α. For stable phase-controlled operation, triggering is desired in the first quadrant only when $v_C > 0$, in the third quadrant only when $v_C < 0$. In the absence of trigger diode CR_1 this condition is not assured if the bilateral switch exhibits both primary and secondary trigger modes.

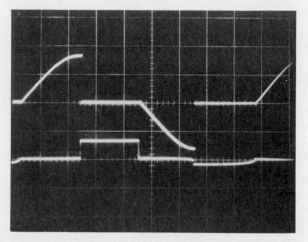

Fig. 5.43 Oscillogram of forward voltage (upper trace) and gate voltage (lower trace) of bilateral triode switch in circuit of Fig. 5.42 [horizontal, 2 ms/div; vertical (upper), 100 v/div; vertical (lower), 1 v/div].

Figure 5.43 shows an oscillogram of the forward voltage across the bilateral triode switch (T_2 positive with respect to T_1) and gate voltage v_G (G positive with respect to T_1) in the circuit of Fig. 5.42 supplied by a 120 v a-c line. The internal gate generator voltage E_G [see Fig. 5.3(d)] is seen to differ, depending on the direction of conduction. However, by inspection of the forward voltage trace, we see that the triggering on the positive and the negative half-cycles has very good symmetry.

REFERENCES

1. R. N. Hall, "Remote Base Power Transistor," *Sixth Annual Electronics Components Proc.* (May, 1955), pp. 1–3.

2. E. K. Howell and D. R. Grafham, "The Light Activated Switch," Application Note 200.29, General Electric Co., Auburn, N.Y., 1963.

3. F. W. Sears, *Optics*. Reading, Mass.: Addison-Wesley, 1958.

4. P. H. Chin and E. E. Moyer, a series of articles in *Electrical Manufacturing* (now *Electro-Technology*): "Practical Circuits for Grid Control of Thyratrons" (January, 1956); "Phase Shift Grid Control of Thyratrons" (February, 1956); "AC Plus DC Grid Control of Thyratrons" (March, 1956); "Effects of Circuit Parameters on Thyratron Performance" (April, 1956); "Peaking and Interphase Transformers for Thyratron Control" (May, 1956).

5. *Magnetic Circuits and Transformers*, Staff of Department of Electrical Engineering, Massachusetts Institute of Technology. New York: John Wiley and Sons, Inc., 1947.

6. H. F. Storm, et al., *Magnetic Amplifiers*. New York: John Wiley and Sons, Inc., 1955.

7. R. C. Barker, "Nonlinear Magnetics," *Electro-Technology* (March, 1963).

8. *Design Manual TWC*-300, Magnetics, Inc., Butler, Pa., 1962.

9. Preliminary Data C, Clevite-Shockley Transistor, a division of the Clevite Corp., Palo Alto, Calif., January, 1962.

10. R. F. Shea, et al., *Principles of Transistor Circuits*. New York: John Wiley and Sons, Inc., 1953.

11. J. G. Linvill and J. F. Gibbons, *Transistors and Active Circuits*. New York: McGraw-Hill Book Company, 1961.

12. D. DeWitt and A. L. Rossoff, Transistor Electronics. New York: McGraw-Hill Book Company, 1957.

13. T. P. Sylvan, "Notes on the Application of the Silicon Unijunction Transistor," General Electric Co., Syracuse, N.Y., 1961.

14. *Transistor Manual*, 7th ed., General Electric Co., Syracuse, N.Y., 1964.

15. R. R. Rottier, "A Packaged SCR Circuit for Direct Thyratron Replacement," A.I.E.E. DP 62-1013, May, 1962.

CHAPTER 6

TURN-OFF CHARACTERISTICS AND METHODS

The SCR is a latching device and, once triggered into conduction, it will remain in its low-impedance forward conducting state as long as anode current is maintained above the holding current. Unlike a transistor, where removal of the base drive will bring collector current to zero, removal of the SCR gate drive will not reduce its anode current. In other words, the control, or gate, lead no longer has control over the conventional SCR once the device has been triggered. Exceptions to this are the gate turn-off devices discussed in Sec. 6.5.

6.1 SCR Turn-off Criteria

In connection with the two-transistor analogue discussed in Sec. 2.2 it is shown that the SCR or related-structure semiconductor device is in the ON state, or latched into conduction, when the loop gain of the system equals or exceeds unity. By the same analogue the SCR is in the OFF, or blocking, state if the loop gain, or the sum of the respective α's of the upper p-n-p and the lower n-p-n equivalent transistors, is less than unity. Accordingly, the basic SCR turn-off problem is properly to establish the necessary conditions to reduce and maintain the equivalent loop gain below unity.

Current gain α of the equivalent transistors is a function of junction temperature T_J, gate drive v_G, anode current I_A, and anode-cathode voltage V_A. Figure 6.1 gives a qualitative illustration of these relationships.

With increasing junction temperature [Fig. 6.1(a)] the SCR is easier to turn on and more difficult to turn off.

With increasing gate drive [Fig. 6.1(b)] the SCR turns on; negative gate drive tends to turn it off. Reverse gate-biasing is effective in obtaining turn-off action only for SCR's with low base-spreading resistance, as discussed in Sec. 4.2. Negative gate bias tends to reduce the α's in even the larger conventional SCR's and is, therefore, effective as stabilizing bias as discussed in Sec. 5.2.5. Some types of SCR's, usually in lower power ratings, are specifically designed and characterized for gate turn-off action.

As anode current is reduced [Fig. 6.1(c)], α drops off. If the junction-temperature and gate-drive contributions to α are kept small, the SCR will turn off when the anode current drops below the holding current. Under dynamic conditions time becomes an important parameter, as is discussed further below.

With increasing anode-to-cathode voltage V_A, current gain α increases until the SCR turns on at its static value of forward breakover voltage with open gate, $V_{(BR)FO}$. Conversely, if, during the process of SCR turn-off, positive anode voltage V_A is applied prematurely or at too great a rate, the SCR may revert to the ON state and thus not turn off. This aspect of dependence of α on rate of change of anode voltage is particularly important under conditions of dynamic turn-off. This is discussed further in Sec. 6.3.

Turn-off action for SCR's is effected by suitable reduction of anode current for a sufficient period of time. For this reason, all practical SCR power circuits must incorporate provisions to effect anode turn-off by means of auxiliary circuit interruption, circuit reversal of current, reverse-biasing of the anode for a sufficient period of time, or by diverting anode current.

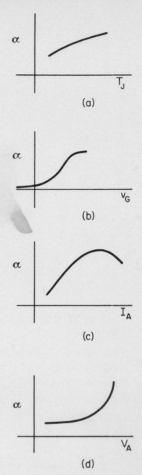

Fig. 6.1 Dependence of equivalent transistor gain α on SCR operating parameters: (a) junction temperature, (b) gate voltage, (c) anode current, and (d) anode voltage.

6.2 Significance of Circuit Turn-off Interval

The significance of the turn-off interval to dynamic circuit operation is illustrated in Fig. 6.2. Also included for the sake of completeness is the important turn-on interval discussed in Sec. 2.6. The SCR is shown in a simple capacitor turn-off (see Sec. 6.4.2) chopper test circuit. The test circuit turns the SCR on and off and delivers the output waveform indicated in Fig. 6.2(b). When SCR_1 is ON, an output voltage appears across R_L. The turn-off

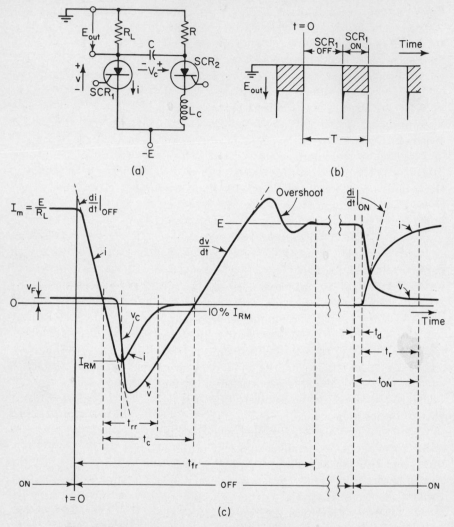

Fig. 6.2 SCR turn-off and turn-on intervals: (a) general circuit, (b) output waveform, and (c) detail of switching intervals.

t_{rr}	Reverse recovery time	t_d	Delay time of SCR
t_c	Circuit turn-off time (Time SCR is reverse-biased by circuit)	t_r	Rise time of SCR
		t_{on}	Turn-on time of SCR
I_m	Peak forward anode current at time of initiation of turn-off at $t = 0$	T	Period of output waveform
		t_{fr}	Circuit forward recovery time
v_F	SCR ON voltage (forward voltage drop)	dv/dt	Initial rate of application of forward blocking voltage
E	Forward blocking voltage applied to SCR by circuit		

circuit portion of the circuit consists of capacitor C, charging source resistor R, SCR_2, and inductance L_C. When SCR_2 is triggered, it applies the capacitor voltage V_C across SCR_1 sufficiently long to effect turn-off action. Illustrated are the waveforms of voltage v and current i for SCR_1.

At $t = 0$, SCR_2 is triggered and turn-off is initiated by applying the turn-off voltage V_C across SCR_1. Initially, V_C appears across the turn-off circuit inductance L_C. This forces the current $I_m = E/R_L$ through SCR_1 to zero at an initial rate $di/dt|_{\text{off}} = -V_C/L_C$. In the test circuit of Fig. 6.2(a) inductance L_C simulates the inductance effective in the circuit during the early part of the reverse recovery interval. For example, in a-c power rectifier circuits, L_C is the so-called commutating inductance seen on looking back toward the source from the rectifier (or SCR) cell undergoing commutation. In d-c circuits, such as the test circuit of Fig. 6.2(a), it is the effective circuit inductance in the presence of which the commutating voltage V_C must force the load current to zero.

The anode current through SCR_1 continues through zero and reverses owing to the fact that time is required for the SCR to regain its reverse voltage-blocking ability. With reference to Fig. 2.2, both junctions J_1 and J_3 become reverse-biased when the anode is biased negative with respect to the cathode. However, in most practical cases the reverse blocking capability of the gate-cathode emitter junction J_3 is negligible. Therefore, in practice it is realistic to consider only the behavior of junction J_1 during the reverse recovery time t_{rr}. The waveforms shown in Fig. 6.2(c) illustrate, from a circuit point of view, only the recovery of the J_1 junction. The reverse recovery time t_{rr} and the reverse current and voltage waveforms are generally determined by both device and circuit parameters. The physical reverse recovery process in the device is discussed in Sec. 2.6. From a circuit point of view, it is useful to take the reverse recovery time t_{rr} from where $i = 0$ to where the reverse current through the device has decayed to 10 per cent of the peak reverse current I_{RM}. In practice with conventional SCR's and low-reverse-impedance circuits, the reverse recovery time is a small part of the total cell forward recovery time required for the SCR to regain its forward blocking capability.

During the initial part of the reverse recovery time, the SCR anode voltage v_F remains positive until the J_1 junction has recovered. Up to that time, the current is determined primarily by the external circuit. Following junction recovery, the reverse blocking junction rapidly assumes voltage until the full applied turn-off voltage V_C is blocked when $i = I_{RM}$, the peak reverse recovery current. Since at that point $di/dt = 0$ and the J_1 junction has recovered, the only voltage in the equivalent turn-off circuit is V_C, which appears across the SCR at that time. (It is assumed that V_C has not decreased significantly, owing to the flow of current up to this time). Beyond that point the reverse voltage across the SCR is determined by the circuit inductance and the rate at which the magnitude of the reverse current decreases from I_{RM} toward normal reverse blocking current. Depending on circuit and device parameters, the device may snap off—that is, suddenly cease to conduct high reverse current. This can lead to dangerously high induced reverse voltages in the circuit.[1] On the other hand, reverse voltage may merely overshoot slightly before assuming and blocking the applied reverse circuit voltage.

In the test circuit of Fig. 6.2(a), the voltage v across SCR_1 immediately swings toward a positive value following the reverse recovery interval by virtue of capacitor C charging its left-hand plate through R_L. Full forward recovery of the SCR must be achieved at time $t = t_{fr}$, the circuit forward recovery time. By that time the SCR has switched from conduction of forward current I_m to blocking of the full forward voltage E. The portion of this time that the SCR is reverse-biased is called the circuit turn-off time t_c. The total circuit OFF and ON times are indicated in both Figs. 6.2(b) and (c). They are, of course, determined in a d-c circuit by the frequency at which the SCR's are triggered and the delay introduced between the triggering of SCR_2 relative to SCR_1.

When it is desired to minimize t_{fr} for higher-frequency operation, the critical SCR parameters become device turn-off time t_{OFF}, and dv/dt withstand capability. The minimum allowable value of circuit turn-off time t_c is then determined by the minimum turn-off time capability of the SCR t_{OFF}. Maximum operating frequency of an SCR circuit at a given power level also depends on the basic circuit used and its transient characteristics. For example, $di/dt|_{ON}$ during the turn-on interval, and dv/dt of transient voltages generated in the circuit (for example, circuit ringing and overshoot) may affect the forward blocking capability of the SCR, the former because of possible high heating of the J_2 junction (Fig. 2.2) if high current is attained before the full junction area is turned on (di/dt effect), the latter because of the dv/dt, or rate, effect. However, an estimate of maximum operating frequency may be obtained for a-c circuits by considering the following steady-state circuit conditions.

A circuit turn-off ratio, which gives the fraction of time that each SCR (or diode) in a circuit is reverse-biased, may be defined as

$$R_0 = \frac{t_c}{T}, \tag{6.1}$$

where

t_c = circuit turn-off time.
T = period of output waveform.

Typical circuit turn-off ratios in a-c systems are illustrated in Fig. 6.3. The ratio R_0 is a constant for conventional rectifier circuits, where the period $T = 1/f$ is given by the supply frequency f, and t_c is given by the circuit configuration, the load, and circuit reactance.

The maximum operating frequency of an SCR circuit $f_m = 1/T_m$ is approached when the maximum required device turn-off time of the SCR

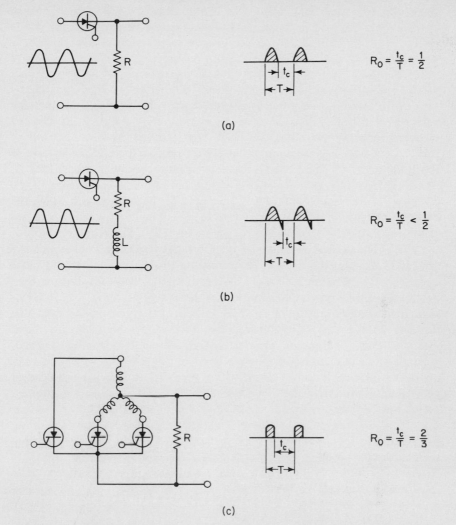

(a)

(b)

(c)

Fig. 6.3 Typical per cell circuit turn-off ratios: (a) half-wave rectifier (resistive load), (b) half-wave rectifier (inductive load), and (c) three-phase half-wave rectifier (resistive load).

equals the circuit turn-off time, or $t_{OFF} = t_c$. This condition assumes that the dv/dt capability of the SCR is not limiting, and it neglects the time to reach zero current $t = \dfrac{I_m}{di/dt|_{OFF}}$. Substituting $t_c = t_{OFF}$ and $T = T_m = \dfrac{1}{f_m}$ in equation (6.1), and solving for the maximum theoretical operating frequency, we have

$$f_m = \frac{1}{t_{OFF}} R_0, \tag{6.2}$$

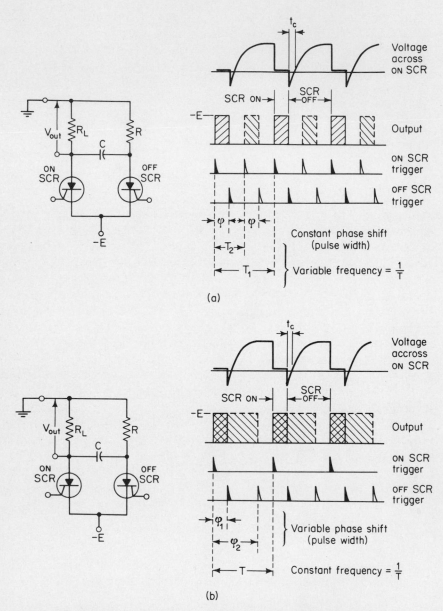

Fig. 6.4 (a) Time-ratio power modulation; (b) pulse-width power modulation.

where

t_{OFF} = SCR device turn-off time under specified conditions.

In practice the dv/dt capability of an SCR at its operating junction temperature may be frequency-limiting. In a-c circuits with a sinusoidal driving voltage and a resistive load, the maximum theoretical operating frequency is limited by both equation (6.2) and the following relation:

$$f_m \leq \frac{1}{2\pi E_m} \frac{dv}{dt}, \tag{6.3}$$

where

E = peak voltage of the sinusoidal supply.

dv/dt = maximum initial rate of reapplication of SCR forward blocking voltage of a sinusoidal waveform which SCR can block under specified test conditions.

With inductive loads and large overlap angles (see Sec. 8.7) an SCR may be subjected to very large values of dv/dt in the forward direction at the time the current reaches zero. Although not a frequency limitation as such, it is a circuit condition that must be provided for by suitable SCR specifications or filtering.

In d-c circuits the maximum theoretical operating frequency is likewise limited by the maximum SCR device turn-off time t_{OFF} and the dv/dt withstand capability of the SCR. In the cases of time-ratio modulation and pulse-width modulation, illustrated in Figs. 6.4(a) and 6.4(b) respectively, the limit condition of maximum operating frequency is approached when $t_c = t_{OFF} \to$ OFF time. The circuit turn-off time t_c in d-c circuits is a design variable determined by the time constants or periods of oscillation of the circuit. This is discussed in greater detail in Sec. 6.4.2. In practice, as in a-c circuits, the operating frequency may be further limited by the dv/dt of circuit transients or the reduction of SCR minimum forward blocking voltage $V_{(BR)FX}$ by large turn-on switching dissipation (di/dt effect).

An example may serve to illustrate the theoretical frequency limitation in a d-c circuit. Consider the chopper circuit of Fig. 6.2(a). Assume the following circuit parameters:

$$E = 400 \text{ v.}$$

$$R_L = 8 \text{ ohms.}$$

$$I_m = \frac{E}{R_L} = \frac{400}{8} = 50 \text{ amp.}$$

$$di/dt|_{OFF} = 25 \text{ amp}/\mu\text{sec.}$$

The total circuit forward recovery time t_{fr} is, with reference to Fig. 6.2(c),

$$t_{fr} = \frac{I_m}{di/dt|_{OFF}} + t_c + \frac{E}{dE/dt}.$$

Assume that the SCR is specified at its operating junction temperature for $t_{\text{OFF}} = 20$ μsec and an initial $dv/dt = 20$ v/μsec. If the maximum SCR capability is to be limiting, we may substitute limiting-device parameters for operating-circuit parameters by taking $t_c = t_{\text{OFF}}$ and $dE/dt = dv/dt$, or

$$t_{fr_{\min}} = \tfrac{50}{25} + 20 + \tfrac{400}{20} = 2 + 20 + 20 = 42 \ \mu\text{sec}.$$

Hence, the minimum allowable circuit OFF time in this example is $t_{fr_{\min}} = 42$ μsec. If a duty cycle of $\dfrac{\text{ON}}{\text{ON} + \text{OFF}} = 50$ per cent is required, and if the total circuit OFF time is consumed by the minimum forward recovery time of the SCR $t_{fr_{\min}}$, the maximum theoretical circuit operating frequency, if it is assumed that neither dv/dt nor di/dt effects are limiting, is

$$f_m = \frac{1}{2t_{fr_{\min}}} = \frac{10^6}{2(42)} = 11.9 \ \text{kc/sec}.$$

6.3 SCR Turn-off Parameters

It was shown in Sec. 6.2 that SCR device turn-off time t_{OFF} and dv/dt capability are vital in determining the maximum circuit frequency response of which a given SCR is capable. Hence, the specification of these parameters and the variables on which they depend is of great importance in the design of higher-frequency SCR circuits. At commercial power frequencies up to 400 cps, however, t_{OFF} and dv/dt are usually not limiting. In view of the strong dependence of SCR turn-off and turn-on performance on the operating conditions illustrated in Fig. 6.2, as well as the superposed transient conditions in practical circuits (peak reverse current, dv/dt of oscillations, etc.), a test

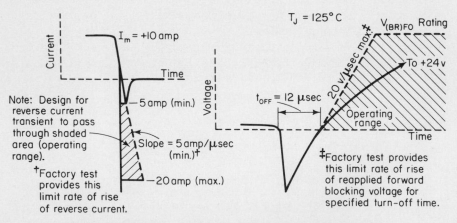

Fig. 6.5 Parameters measured in typical SCR turn-off specification [from Ref. 2, by permission].

and specification for SCR turn-off time must take all these conditions into account simultaneously. It is not meaningful to speak of SCR device turn-off time unless the test conditions are specified completely.

Figure 6.5 illustrates the test conditions in a typical commercial 25 amp SCR turn-off time specification. Junction temperature T_J, initial forward current I_m, reverse test circuit impedance, and gate bias conditions are the independent variables in the specifications under which the maximum SCR device turn-off time t_{OFF} and its maximum dv/dt capability are determined. Usually the independent variables are arbitrarily set in accordance with the operating conditions under which turn-off time and dv/dt are to be specified. For example, the 25 amp SCR, to which the specification shown in Fig. 6.5 applies, is capable of controlling more than merely 10 amp forward current. However, at a higher initial current I_m the turn-off time would typically increase for a given device. Conversely, from a production-lot point of view, the yield to a given turn-off time would decrease at a higher level of initial forward current I_m.

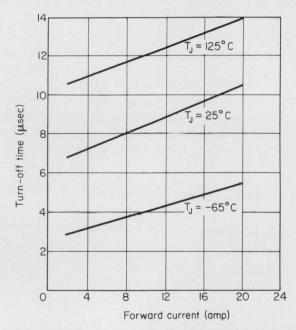

Fig. 6.6 Effect of forward current on turn-off time [from Ref. 2, by permission].

For a typical medium-current SCR, Dyer and Houghton[2] show in Figs. 6.6, 6.7, and 6.8 the dependence of SCR turn-off time t_{OFF} on initial forward current I_m, rate of rise of reapplied forward voltage dv/dt, and gate bias, respectively. These authors also show in Fig. 6.9 the yield distribution of

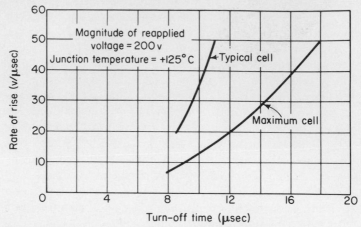

Fig. 6.7 Effect of rate of rise of reapplied forward blocking voltage on turn-off time [from Ref. 2, by permission].

turn-off time to the specification conditions illustrated in Fig. 6.5 for a typical medium-current SCR.

The turn-off time test circuit can be similar to the one illustrated in Fig. 6.2(a) if an exponential rate of rise of reapplied forward blocking voltage is allowable. A modified circuit allows the reapplication of a linear rate of rise of reapplied forward blocking voltage, as indicated by the dashed outline in Fig. 6.5.[2] This specification is more stringent and of more general applicability to those types of turn-off circuits which subject the SCR to an approximately linear rate of rise of reapplied forward blocking voltage.

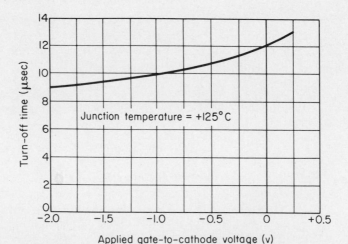

Fig. 6.8 Effect of gate bias on turn-off time [from Ref. 2, by permission].

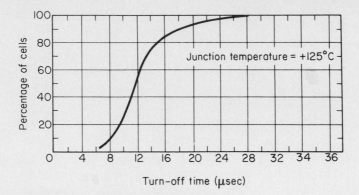

Fig. 6.9 Turn-off time distribution for a typical production lot [from Ref. 2, by permission].

6.4 Anode Turn-off Methods

It was shown earlier that in practice all but the smallest SCR's and the gate turn-off devices must be turned off, or commutated, by the anode circuit rather than the SCR gate. Practical SCR circuit operation can be conveniently classified by the following two basic types of turn-off circuitry. In either case the function of the turn-off circuit is to reverse-bias the SCR momentarily.

In one case the supply voltage reverses and thus forces reverse bias on the SCR to turn it off. This condition is met in a-c circuits supplied by a stiff source. This is referred to as a-c supply source or line commutation.

In the other case the supply-voltage source does not reverse, and auxiliary-circuit means must be employed to bring the SCR anode current to zero and to maintain a reverse-bias condition sufficiently long to turn the SCR off. This is referred to as external or forced commutation.

6.4.1 A-C Supply or Line Commutation

In an a-c power circuit the SCR turns off shortly after its anode current has been brought to zero by the action of the circuit. At usual power frequencies the circuit turn-off time t_c, or the time that the SCR is reverse-biased, is very large compared to the maximum SCR device turn-off time t_{OFF} (see Sec. 6.2). This results in highly efficient power-frequency operation and makes the SCR, in conjunction with its low forward ON voltage (voltage drop), a most practical active control device for applications in controlled a-c and controlled rectification circuits. This type of operation is discussed more fully in Chap. 8.

6.4.2 TURN-OFF IN D-C CIRCUITS

It was mentioned earlier that SCR turn-off, or commutation of load current, in a circuit supplied by a d-c source requires that the anode current be brought to zero and that a zero or reverse bias be maintained sufficiently long. The means of bringing this condition about under the circuit operating conditions of the prevailing current, voltage, and operating frequency provide the basis for the various classes of SCR chopper, inverter, and d-c static switching circuits. SCR turn-off methods in d-c circuits can be classified as follows.

Starvation mode: When SCR anode current is reduced below its holding current, forward anode voltage may be reapplied after internal recombination of carriers has restored its forward blocking capability. This mode of turn-off is illustrated in Fig. 6.10. Figure 6.10(a) shows manual switch interruption of

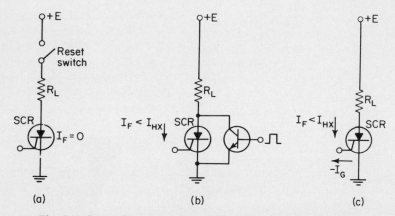

(a)   (b)   (c)

Fig. 6.10 Starvation mode of turn-off: (a) reset switch, (b) diversion of anode current, and (c) increase of holding current.

anode current. This means of turn-off has application in alarm, crowbar, and certain low-current information-readout circuits. By this method a typical SCR must be allowed a time in the order of 100 μsec to recover before the switch may be reclosed without the SCR's reverting to the ON state, provided the dv/dt withstand capability of the SCR is not exceeded. The forward recovery time under this condition is about one order of magnitude greater than that achieved by the other methods of d-c commutation discussed in this chapter.

Figure 6.10(b) illustrates diversion of SCR anode current by means of an auxiliary device. A transistor is shown, but a mechanical contact or other transducer could accomplish the same function. The SCR will block forward voltage if its forward current I_F is held below its holding current I_{HX} sufficiently long.

Figure 6.10(c) illustrates use of negative gate drive $-I_G$ to increase the holding current I_{HX} of an SCR. For a given "null" current in a circuit, SCR turn-off may thereby be achieved by adjusting the holding current to a slightly greater value. This variation of starvation mode turn-off can be very useful in pulse-modulator or other capacitor discharge circuits when the SCR holding current can be raised above the capacitor charging current by means of negative gate drive after the discharge pulse has taken place.

Parallel-capacitor turn-off: A previously charged capacitor may be switched into the circuit so that it forces SCR anode current to zero and then maintains reverse bias for the required SCR turn-off time t_{OFF} under the prevailing SCR operating conditions. The basic chopper and its associated family of parallel-capacitor-commutated inverter circuits are based on this mode of turn-off. The application of this method of turn-off to d-c static switches is discussed in Secs. 7.4, 7.5, and 7.6, to inverters in Secs. 9.1 and 9.2, and to choppers in Sec. 9.6.

In this class of circuits the capacitor, often referred to as the commutating capacitor, is connected effectively in parallel with the load. The charge stored on the capacitor establishes the required SCR turn-off bias conditions by resistive (RC) or damped resonant (RLC) discharge during the commutation interval. The discharge of the capacitor and the attendant reverse-biasing of the SCR are transient occurrences relative to the operating circuit frequency for a square-wave output. However, the output of a circuit commutated in this manner may approach that of a sine wave if the circuit is operated at a frequency approaching the charging and discharging times of the capacitor. Charging of the capacitor may be effected either resistively or resonantly. Figure 6.11 illustrates various types of capacitor turn-off methods.[3]

In Fig. 6.11(a) the commutating capacitor C will charge to E v in the polarity shown when load SCR_1 is turned on. When auxiliary SCR_2 is triggered, the left plate of capacitor C is connected to ground. Thus SCR_1 is initially reverse-biased by essentially E v. The right-hand plate of the capacitor now reverses polarity as it charges toward the supply voltage $+E$ at a time constant $R_L C$, which must be sufficiently long to allow SCR_1 to recover. At the end of the charging time the capacitor is charged to essentially E v in a polarity reverse to that shown. When load SCR_1 is triggered, SCR_2 is turned off in the same manner. The left-hand plate of the commutating capacitor now charges to $+E$ at a time constant $R_1 C$. At the end of the charging interval, the capacitor is charged to essentially E v in the polarity shown, SCR_2 can be triggered, and the cycle can be repeated. This circuit illustrates the classic parallel-capacitor turn-off method. It will be recognized as the basic SCR flip-flop. If triggered symmetrically into a transformer primary, it is the basic parallel inverter. Section 7.4 gives design equations for this basic circuit.

Figure 6.11(b) shows resonant charging of commutating capacitor C via inductance L and diode CR when SCR_1 is triggered. It is important that the capacitor be initially charged as indicated. Resonant charging causes the

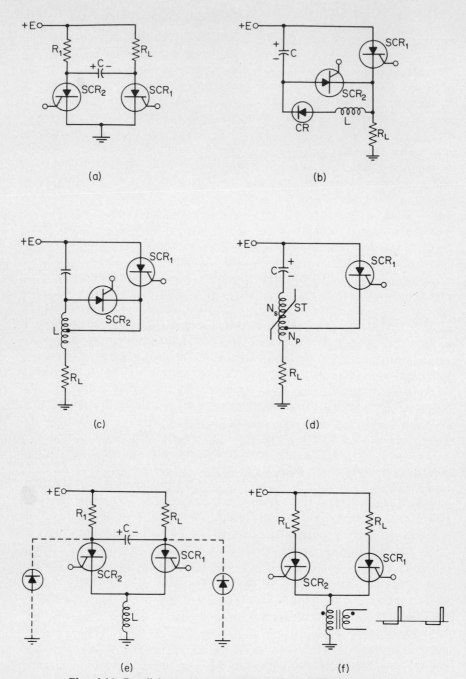

Fig. 6.11 Parallel capacitor turn-off methods: (a) classic parallel capacitor turn-off, (b) cathode pulse turn-off, (c) load-sensitive cathode pulse turn-off, (d) basic time ratio chopper circuit, (e) resonant cathode pulse turn-off, and (f) cathode pulse turn-off by series injection.

capacitor to reverse its polarity and to charge to approximately E v. Diode CR will block this charge until auxiliary turn-off SCR_2 is triggered. A cathode pulse of approximately E v with respect to its anode then reverse-biases SCR_1 and turns it off. The circuit will be recognized as basically a d-c chopper.

Figure 6.11(c) illustrates load-sensitive resonant charging of commutating capacitor C. Inductor L acts as an autotransformer which charges capacitor C to higher than E v when the load is heavy. Otherwise the circuit functions as the one in Fig. 6.11(b).

Figure 6.11(d) shows a basic time-ratio chopper, or Morgan, circuit. It uses a saturable reactor to combine the functions of the autotransformer action of the tapped inductor L and the auxiliary turn-off SCR_2 shown in the circuit of Fig. 6.11(c). Its mode of operation is described in Sec. 9.6.

An important type of parallel-capacitor turn-off is shown in Fig. 6.11(e). The configuration is recognized as the basic parallel inverter although with a common inductance on the cathode of the SCR's. The circuit functions in a manner similar to that of Fig. 6.11(a). However, capacitor C discharges resonantly through inductance L. The diodes shown dotted provide a return path for the discharge; alternatively, a low and known source impedance can be used. If half the period of the oscillatory discharge is made greater than the SCR device turn-off time, SCR_1 (or, respectively, SCR_2) will be commutated by a positive pulse on its cathode. For an analysis of this type of commutation, see Sec. 7.6.

The type of commutation shown in Fig. 6.11(e) can be extended as shown in Fig. 6.11(f).[4] Pulses suitable to effect SCR commutation are injected in series with the SCR's. This type of commutation provides isolation of power and turn-off circuitry. With suitably co-ordinated control of the trigger and turn-off circuits, regulation of the output is facilitated, since both SCR's may be in the OFF state simultaneously, unlike the method of Fig. 6.11(e). The circuit as shown assumes low source and load impedance to the commutating pulse.

Series-capacitor commutation: Unlike parallel-capacitor commutation, the commutating capacitor may be effectively connected in series with the load. If the circuit parameters are selected appropriately to give underdamped resonant operation, the SCR is basically applied in an alternating-current circuit. Under this condition of operation, commutation of the SCR is effected by reversal of circuit current in a manner similar to a-c line commutation, discussed in Sec. 6.4.1. However, the energy available for commutation is limited to that stored in the capacitor at the beginning of the turn-off interval, as in the case of parallel-capacitor commutation. Series-capacitor commutation gives rise to a number of series inverter circuits discussed in greater detail in Sec. 9.3. Figure 6.12 illustrates series-capacitor turn-off for a single element of what might be a multi-element series inverter circuit (see Sec. 9.3).[3] Two alternative positions of load resistance R_L are shown. For the case of series

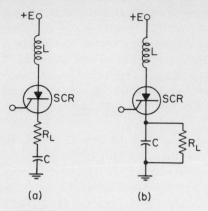

load in Fig. 6.12(a), the circuit resonant frequency is determined by the classic relation

$$f = \frac{1}{2\pi} \sqrt{\frac{1}{LC} - \frac{R_L^2}{4L^2}}. \quad (6.4)$$

When the SCR turns on, the current builds up sinusoidally. As it starts to reverse, the SCR is turned off, provided the half period of the resonant frequency is larger than the SCR device turn-off time t_{OFF}. In this case the load may be large (low value of R_L) and the condition

Fig. 6.12 Series capacitor turn-off methods: (a) series load and (b) shunt load.

$$R_L < \sqrt{\frac{4L}{C}} \quad (6.5)$$

must be satisfied for resonant operation.

Figure 6.12(b) illustrates series-capacitor commutation adapted to the case in which the load is small (large value of R_L). The circuit resonant frequency is

$$f = \frac{1}{2\pi} \sqrt{\frac{1}{LC} - \frac{1}{4R_L^2 C^2}}. \quad (6.6)$$

The theoretical criterion of underdamped operation must be met as before. It is, by classical circuit theory,

$$R_L > \sqrt{\frac{L}{4C}}. \quad (6.7)$$

The cases covered by equations (6.4) and (6.6) are, of course, equivalent. Although, strictly speaking, the commutating capacitor C in the case of Fig. 6.12(b) appears to be in parallel with the load R_L, it must be borne in mind that the capacitor will actually supply load current during the major part of the operating cycle. Hence, the capacitor is effectively in series with the load most of the time.

6.5 Gate Turn-off

It was shown earlier (see Sec. 2.7) that some p-n-p-n structures can be turned off if sufficient current is extracted from the gate to cause the loop gain of the equivalent transistors to fall below unity. Some commercially available devices are specifically designed and characterized for such gate turn-off action. Included in this line of devices are the GTO (gate turn-off switch), SCS (silicon-controlled switch), GCS (gate-controlled switch), Trigistor, and Transwitch.

The symbol used for the *p-n-p-n* gate turn-off device emphasizes its nature as basically that of a d-c switch.[5] It can be pulsed on and remain latched into conduction like an SCR by a positive gate pulse of amplitude I_{GT} and pulse width t_p. Once latched into conduction, turn-off action can be effected by a negative pulse of amplitude I_{GTO} and pulse width t_{po}. This action is illustrated in Fig. 6.13. For GTO's, or similarly characterized devices, typical pulse widths t_{po} are in the order of 5 to 50 μsec. The minimum gate turn-off current amplitude I_{GTO} required for turn-off is determined by the turn-off current gain $A_G = I_A/I_{\mathrm{GTO}}$. Generally, the turn-off gain is less than the turn-on gain I_A/I_G and, for example, is 10 at rated anode current for a typical two-ampere GTO.

From a circuit point of view the application considerations for a GTO with respect to gate-bias stability, susceptibility to the rate effect, junction temperature, etc., are the same as for conventional SCR's. The principal application limitation of the GTO lies in the fact that beyond a certain critical anode current I_{A_c} its turn-off gain A_G becomes zero. This is illustrated qualitatively in Fig. 6.14. Below the holding-current level I_{HX} where $A_G \to \infty$, the device reverts to a forward blocking state. At the critical anode current I_{A_c} no amount of negative gate current will turn the *p-n-p-n* device off; its turn-off gain is zero. This is due to the effect of the cross-base resistance discussed in Sec. 2.7. In this region attempts to turn off the GTO can lead to failure of the device.

The GTO, by the nature of its design and processing, is inherently faster than the SCR. This fact gives the GTO an operating advantage over the SCR in circuits requiring higher-frequency operation such as oscillators, pulse generators, and flip-flop circuits. If anode turn-off (Sec. 6.4) is used in addition to gate turn-off, the GTO may replace an SCR and give the circuit a higher-frequency capability. Holding the gate at a negative potential with respect to

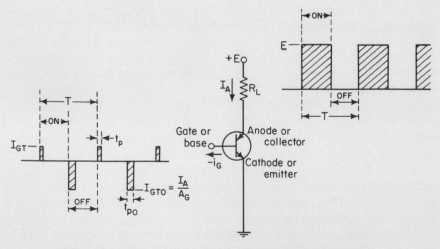

Fig. 6.13 Basic *p-n-p-n* turn-off device gating requirements: (a) symbol and functional operation and (b) detail of gate drive.

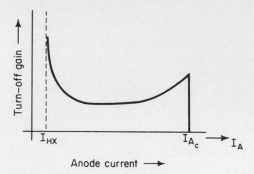

Anode current ⟶

Fig. 6.14 Turn-off gain versus anode current.

the cathode during the anode turn-off pulse allows the flow of negative gate current $-i_G$ (see Fig. 6.13). Under this condition forward blocking voltage may be reapplied to the anode-commutated GTO after the cessation of reverse recovery current flow, and the rate of reapplication of forward blocking voltage may be quite high, since, with the negatively biased gate, capacitive displacement current, which would ordinarily tend to forward-bias the emitter (gate-to-cathode) junction owing to the dv/dt or the rate effect, is diverted to the negative trigger source. Thus, the required circuit forward recovery time t_{fr} (see Fig. 6.2) is reduced by an amount $t_c - t_{rr}$ and by a time $t = \dfrac{E}{dv/dt}$, where E is the working forward blocking voltage of the circuit and dv/dt is the maximum device dv/dt capability under the given bias conditions.

From the point of view of the drive circuit, operation of the GTO in its gate-pulsed switching mode may be more efficient than operation of a linear device, such as a transistor, in its switching mode.[6] Particularly, when operating at a high duty cycle, the average power level of the GTO trigger circuit may be less than that of the drive circuit required for a transistor of an equivalent power output. However, a transistor of higher gain may easily nullify this advantage. In other words, the transistor's peak drive power taken over the full period may require less average power from the drive circuit than the peak GTO turn-on and turn-off powers averaged over their respective duty cycles. Another factor of decisive importance, when one is appraising GTO versus transistor switching efficiency, is anode switching dissipation. Often the lower collector saturation voltage of a power transistor results in lower dissipation for a given load current than with the GTO. It is possible to take advantage of the best properties of each device by using a GTO to drive a power transistor. Depending on device capabilities, a relatively simple pulse-drive circuit of very low average power level (and hence cost, size, and weight) may trigger the GTO, which, in turn, will latch on and supply base drive to a power transistor of lower saturation voltage.

REFERENCES

1. I. Somos, "Commutation and Destructive Oscillation in Diode Circuits," *A.I.E.E. Trans.* 61-89, *Communications and Electronics* (May, 1961), pp. 162–72.

2. R. F. Dyer and G. K. Houghton, "Turn Off Time Characterization and Measurement of Silicon Controlled Rectifiers," A.I.E.E. CP 61-301 (January, 1961).

3. *Silicon Controlled Rectifier Manual*, 2nd ed., General Electric Company, Auburn, N.Y., 1961.

4. G. P. Underbrink, "Activated Commutation for SCR Power Inverters," 16th Annual Power Sources Conference (May, 1962), PSC Publications Committee, P.O. Box 891, Red Bank, N.J.

5. D. R. Grafham, "Ratings and Application of a 2 Ampere Gate Turn-off Switch," I.E.E.E. CP 63-434, 1963.

6. J. W. Motto, Jr., "Characteristics of the Gate Controlled Turn-off Trinistor Controlled Rectifier," I.E.E.E. CP 63-510, 1963.

CHAPTER 7

STATIC SWITCHES

Switching semiconductors like the SCR have permitted *static* switches to make significant inroads on mechanical and electromechanical switches. This trend has been particularly marked in those applications where speed, duty cycle, size, sensitivity, long-term reliability, and resistance to such environmental conditions as shock, vibration, and explosive and corrosive atmospheres are premium requirements. In static-switching applications, the bistable characteristics of the SCR and its wide range of voltage and current capabilities make it particularly suitable among semiconductor devices for this use.

7.1 Characteristics of SCR Static Switches

Static switches using SCR's may be designed to perform any of the functions of conventional switches. In addition to straightforward ON/OFF action, SCR switches can be used as time-delay relays, latching switches, over- and under-voltage and -current relays, circuit breakers, selector switches, and stepping switches. Actuation may be initiated by electrical or mechanical means as well as by more specific triggering sources, such as current and voltage, touch, light, position, pressure, proximity, etc.

Following are some of the main characteristics of interest in static switches. Characteristics are expressed in established relay and mechanical switch terminology. Depending on their design and cost, SCR switches may have superior or inferior characteristics and features compared to their electro-mechanical counterparts.

7.1.1 A-C or D-C Operation

A specific SCR switch can be designed to operate on either an a-c or a d-c system, but not on both without considerable complication. A-C switches generally rely on the cyclical reversal of the line voltage to turn off the SCR when the gate signal is removed. Except in the case of bilateral *p-n-p-n* semiconductors (Secs. 3.8 and 7.3.1), two back-to-back SCR's or a single SCR with diode bridge are required to provide bilateral action. Maximum a-c frequency is limited by the turn-off characteristics of the SCR and is typically limited to below 50 kc. On the other hand, d-c switches require special circuit means, such as a commutating capacitor, a series reset contact, or a special gate turn-off semiconductor device, to effect interruption of the load current.

7.1.2 Voltage/Current Ratings

Practical SCR switches are limited in voltage and current only by cost considerations. Single SCR's are capable of handling currents from milliamperes to hundreds of amperes and can block voltages greater than one thousand volts. Series and parallel arrays of SCR's (Secs. 10.4 and 10.5) make possible higher currents and voltages. Transient voltage and overcurrent capabilities are generally lower than comparably rated electromechanical switches, but limitations owing to these conditions can be minimized by careful design (Chap. 10).

7.1.3 Number of Poles and Throws

A single SCR device will serve as a single contact. In some special cases, a single SCR can duplicate double-pole or double-throw action (Fig. 7.1) through control of gate phasing. Otherwise, additional SCR's are necessary to provide multiple-pole or multiple-throw action.

7.1.4 Pick-up and Drop-out Speed

When triggered, the SCR turns on (picks up) within a few microseconds. Drop-out time depends on circuitry. In a typical a-c switch the SCR turns off within one-half cycle after the gate signal is removed. Typical SCR switches on d-c service require 20 to 100 μsec to achieve their OFF state.

7.1.5 Snap Action

SCR's inherently provide snap action since they have no stable state between ON and OFF. Unless properly triggered, however, SCR's in a-c switches may produce "phase-control" action (Chap. 8), thus applying

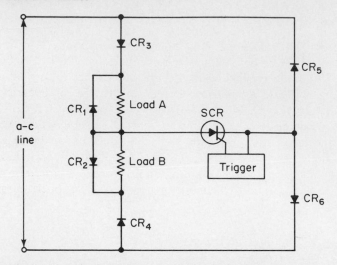

Fig. 7.1 Use of single SCR to switch two d-c loads independently. If SCR is triggered when top a-c line is positive, voltage will be applied to load A through CR_3, SCR, and CR_6. Triggering during negative half-cycle will apply power to load B. CR_1 and CR_2 serve as free-wheeling diodes for inductive loads.

reduced voltage to the load. In some cases, phase control during pick-up of the switch may provide significant functional advantages over conventional switches by limiting inrush currents to such loads as lamps and transformers.

7.1.6 ISOLATION

SCR switches are at their simplest when electrical isolation between the input signal and the individual power circuits is not required. Suitable triggering circuitry, however, makes any degree of isolation possible. Light-triggered semiconductors (Sec. 2.3) provide inherent isolation between signal and output.

7.1.7 ON AND OFF RESISTANCE

The basic SCR characteristic introduces approximately one volt drop in the power circuit when the SCR is conducting. Since this voltage drop is essentially constant with varying loads, load regulation is affected very little by the SCR. To remain in the ON state, the SCR must be continuously actuated by a gate signal, or the load current must be maintained above the holding-current level. In its open state, the SCR does not provide complete isolation between line and load in the same sense as a mechanical disconnect. Instead, a leakage current in the order of microamperes to a few milliamperes may flow, depending on the rating and characteristics of the specific SCR.

7.1.8 INPUT SENSITIVITY

Low-power SCR switches can be directly triggered by inputs of a few microwatts. Larger SCR's may require several hundred milliwatts at low voltage. In all cases, simple trigger circuitry can be used to adapt the SCR switch to practically any degree of sensitivity required.

7.1.9 INTERFERENCE

Because of their susceptibility to triggering on fast rates of rise of anode voltage, SCR switches may require some high-frequency filtering of the line voltage to prevent misfiring from the transient effects of other switches operating from the same line. Also, triggering circuits may require shielding or filtering to prevent SCR misfiring owing to pick-up on the gate (Sec. 10.8).

7.1.10 INTERRUPTING CAPACITY

Fault-current limitations of SCR's are defined by the surge and I^2t characteristics. These capabilities generally fall far short of those inherent in mechanical contacts. However, suitable turn-off circuitry permits the SCR to interrupt fault currents long *before* they build up to destructive proportions, a feature not possible with conventional switches (see Fig. 7.13). In this sense, the SCR has a potential interrupting capacity limited only by its speed and the ability of control circuitry to sense and anticipate the buildup of fault current.

7.2 The Single-phase A-C Switch

Figure 7.2 illustrates three basic SCR circuits for switching full-wave single-phase power to a load. In Fig. 7.2(a) two SCR's are connected back-to-back, or in inverse-parallel, as this connection is sometimes called. An elementary trigger using a low-power contact in the gate circuit is shown.

Figure 7.2(b) employs a single SCR to control both halves of the a-c cycle by connecting the SCR across the d-c terminals of a single-phase bridge. In this connection, care must be taken to keep inductance on the d-c side of the bridge to an absolute minimum. Otherwise, current will continue to flow through the SCR during the brief interval when the rectified a-c voltage dips to zero. This will prevent the SCR from interrupting the circuit when the trigger signal is removed.

The circuit variation in Fig. 7.2(c) allows two SCR's to be actuated from a trigger source with a common ground, because the SCR cathodes are electrically connected.

The forward blocking-voltage capability $V_{(BR)FX}$ of the SCR's in all three of the foregoing circuits must be at least equal to the peak of the a-c line voltage, that is, $\sqrt{2}$ times the rms value of this voltage. Additional safety

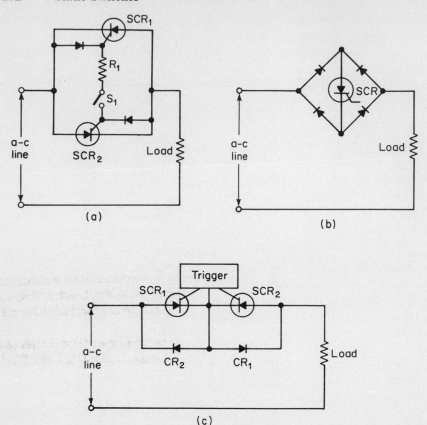

Fig. 7.2 Single-phase a-c switches using SCR's.

factors may be necessary for withstanding line-voltage transients. The SCR's in Fig. 7.2(a) must also be capable of blocking the same peak line voltage in the reverse direction. The circuits in Figs. 7.2(b) and (c), however, apply negligible reverse voltage to the SCR's.

Individual SCR's in Figs. 7.2(a) and (c) share the load current equally. The ratio between the average current, $I_{F(AV)}$, through each SCR (the current for which the SCR is rated) and the rms line current I_{rms} can be defined as follows:

$$\frac{I_{F(AV)}}{I_{rms}} = \frac{\dfrac{\displaystyle\int_0^\pi I \sin \omega t \, d(\omega t)}{\displaystyle\int_0^{2\pi} d(\omega t)}}{\sqrt{\dfrac{\displaystyle\int_0^{2\pi} (I \sin \omega t)^2 \, d(\omega t)}{\displaystyle\int_0^{2\pi} d(\omega t)}}} = 0.45.$$

Accordingly, the average SCR current in terms of the line current for the SCR's in Figs. 7.2(a) and (c) is

$$I_{F(AV)} = 0.45I_{rms}. \qquad (7.1)$$

By similar analysis, the average SCR current in the circuit of Fig. 7.2(b) is

$$I_{F(AV)} = 0.90I_{rms}. \qquad (7.2)$$

7.3 Typical Trigger Circuits for A-C Switches

One of the most straightforward triggering methods for SCR's in a-c switches uses the anode voltage as a source of gate-triggering current. An example of this is illustrated in Fig. 7.2(a) for a full-wave circuit. (A half-wave circuit of this type is discussed in Sec. 5.5.1.) If contact S_1 is closed, current

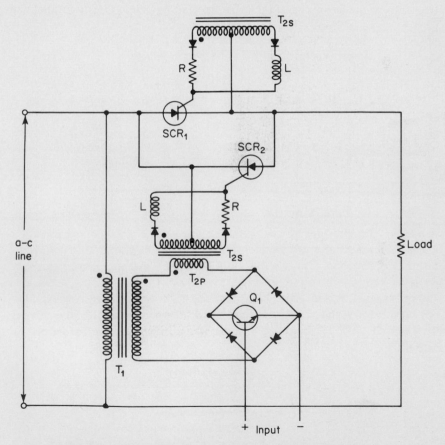

Fig. 7.3 A-C switch with separately excited gate trigger and electrically isolated control.

flows into the gate of SCR_1 whenever its anode is positive. Resistor R_1 limits current to a value within the ratings of the contacts and the gate. As soon as the SCR turns on and its anode voltage drops, gate current decreases to essentially zero. The diodes prevent reverse voltage from being applied to the gates.

This type of triggering is attractive and simple when the sensing or actuating element can be linked to a set of low-current contacts. Typical contacts include those on thermostats, pressure switches, tachometers, current-sensitive relays, and timers. A reed switch in this trigger circuit can be actuated by a low-level isolated signal applied to a winding around it or by the position of a small magnet. The latter arrangement can be used to provide limit switch action.

One of the disadvantages in driving the gate from the anode lies in the fact that the load impedance is effectively in series with the gate trigger. If the load impedance is high, it limits gate current, and will prevent the SCR from triggering at the beginning of the cycle. Instead, resistance R_1 in parallel with

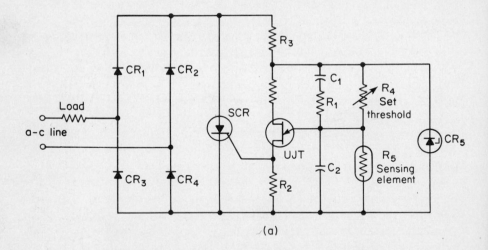

(a)

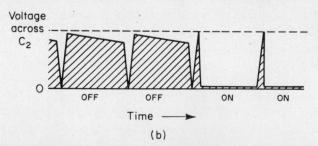

(b)

Fig. 7.4 A-C switch controlled by sensing resistor and unijunction transistor trigger.

the unfired SCR's will constitute a partially closed switch, and reduced voltage will be applied to the load.

The limitations of anode firing may be overcome by deriving the gate drive from across the line ahead of the load. An a-c switch of this type which operates satisfactorily over wide ranges of load and power factor is shown in Fig. 7.3.[1] Gate power is secured from the line through transformer T_1 and is applied to the primary of transformer T_2 whenever transistor Q_1 is driven into saturation by the electrically isolated input signal. Each of the two secondary windings of T_2 provides current to the gate of an SCR through a full-wave centertap rectifier. Through the phase-shifting action of R and L in the legs of the secondary windings of T_2, the gates of the SCR's are driven during almost the full 360 deg of each cycle that the switch is energized, and substantial gate drive is applied to the SCR at the instant when its anode voltage swings positive at the beginning of its conducting half-cycle. Thus each SCR is provided with adequate gate signal for full 180 deg conduction, regardless of load impedance or power factor.

Figure 7.4(a) illustrates an a-c switch that can be triggered into conduction by a small change in a resistive sensing element, R_5. The main power circuit composed of SCR and CR_1–CR_4 is identical to the circuit in Fig. 7.2(b). The SCR trigger circuit employs a unijunction transistor relaxation oscillator (Sec. 5.5.7) modified so that the voltage waveshape across capacitor C_2 [Fig. 7.4(b)] has a higher value at the beginning of each half-cycle than at the end. This waveshape results from the higher charging current through R_1 and C_1 at the beginning of each half-cycle owing to the voltage rise across the zener diode CR_5. As the resistance of the sensing element (thermistor, photocell, etc.) increases, the capacitor voltage rises until it reaches the peak point voltage at which UJT triggers. Since this condition occurs first at the leading edge of the cycle, UJT will trigger only at this point, thus turning on the SCR early in each cycle. When SCR is triggered, voltage is removed from the unijunction circuit, and capacitor C_1 discharges. At the beginning of the next half-cycle, the discharged condition of C_1 produces a higher charging current for C_2, thus assuring snap action into the ON condition. The sensing resistor, which has a resistance in the order of 10,000 ohms, must be reduced to a value lower than the pick-up value in order to stop triggering UJT and SCR. This differential and snap action prevents "chattering" effects. The switch can be controlled by a d-c input signal by replacing the sensing resistor with a grounded-emitter n-p-n transistor.

The properties of square-loop magnetic-core materials may also be used advantageously for triggering SCR's in a-c static switches. Figure 7.5 illustrates one type of such switch, a latching type, noteworthy for its simplicity and compactness. The reset characteristics of T_1 and T_2, which are two small tape-wound cores, determine whether or not the SCR's are triggered into the conducting state during a particular cycle. When the switch is "open," both core T_1 and T_2 are saturated by the flow of current from the main a-c supply

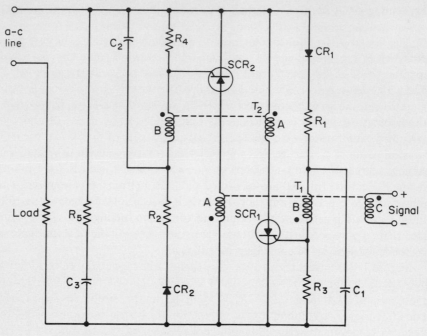

Fig. 7.5 A-C static latching relay with isolated input.

through their respective B windings during alternate halves of the cycle. This current is limited to a low value by resistors R_1 and R_2. Under these conditions, the gate voltage on the SCR's is limited to a few tenths of a volt by the voltage-dividing action of R_1 and R_3 across SCR_1 and by R_2 and R_4 across SCR_2. Neither SCR triggers, and no current flows in either of the reset windings A of the cores.

If a low-level signal is applied to the "Signal" C winding of T_1, this core resets during the half-cycle when the anode of SCR_1 is negative and CR_1 is blocking. When the anode of SCR_1 starts to swing positive on the following half-cycle, winding B on T_1 will sustain part of the supply voltage, and capacitor C_1 will charge through CR_1 and R_1. Depending on its design, core T_1 saturates after a few electrical degrees, discharging C_1 into the gate of SCR_1 and triggering it. Current flows from the line through SCR_1 to the load.

The gate-triggering circuit on SCR_2 is identical to that on SCR_1, except that no separate "Signal" winding is used. Core T_2 depends on current through its reset winding A to reset the core and thus trigger SCR_2. Thus, if SCR_1 is triggered by the foregoing sequence, anode current in SCR_1 resets T_2 and SCR_2 triggers on the following half-cycle. Full-wave voltage is thereby delivered to the load.

With reset winding A on T_1 connected in the anode circuit of SCR_2, T_1 in turn is reset by anode current through SCR_2. Hence, once conduction has been initiated in SCR_1 by a positive pulse on the "Signal" winding of T_1, the switch remains closed as long as load current flows, even though no further signal is applied to the input. The switch may be turned off by a momentary negative pulse on the "Signal" winding of T_1. This prevents winding A from resetting T_1 and interrupts further triggering of either SCR. The switch then reverts to the open state.

This circuit can duplicate the action of a nonlatching relay by eliminating the reset winding A on T_1. With this change the switch remains closed only as long as positive voltage is applied to the signal winding.

Components C_3 and R_5 serve to filter line transients from triggering the switch. They also assist in completing reset action of the cores in the latching mode if the line voltage is interrupted at a critical part of the cycle. The impedance of the switch in the open state is the parallel impedance of this filter and the trigger circuits. Besides this limitation, this circuit withholds a small initial portion of each half-cycle from the load until the SCR is triggered by the saturation of its associated magnetic core.

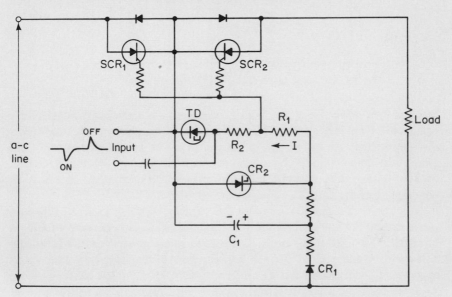

Fig. 7.6 A-C latching relay with separate excitation of gate circuit.

The latching relay shown in Fig. 7.6 overcomes these limitations. The SCR power circuit here is similar to that in Fig. 7.2(c). The gate-trigger circuit is furnished with regulated d-c by half-wave rectifier CR_1 and the filtering action of capacitor C_1 and zener diode CR_2. A tunnel diode TD, preferably one operating over a large voltage range, is connected in shunt with the gates of SCR_1 and SCR_2. The tunnel diode is supplied with a constant current I from the gate supply through R_1 and R_2. This current is set at a value below the peak current of the tunnel diode, but adequate to trigger both SCR's. With *TD* in its low-impedance state, only a few tenths of a volt are developed across it and R_2 by the current *I*. This is insufficient to trigger the SCR's and the switch remains open. If a negative pulse is applied to the input terminals as shown, *TD* switches to its high-impedance state, and current *I* now develops sufficient voltage across *TD* and R_2 to trigger both SCR's. The tunnel diode remains in its high-impedance state, and the switch remains closed until a positive pulse at the input returns the circuit to its original state.

Since continuous current is supplied to the gates in the closed state, the entire cycle of voltage is supplied to the load. Also, since the gate excitation is derived from the a-c line rather than through the load, wide load-impedance changes do not affect the operation of the switch.

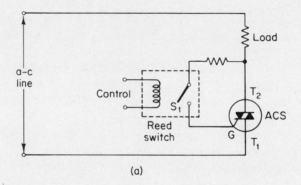

(a)

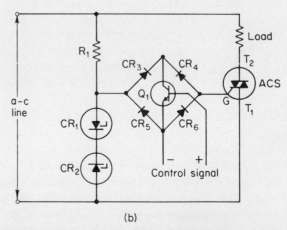

(b)

Fig. 7.7 Typical trigger circuits for a bilateral triode switch operating as an a-c switch.

7.3.1 TRIGGERING THE BILATERAL TRIODE SWITCH

The bilateral triode switch (Triac) device (Sec. 3.9.5) lends itself well to a-c switching. One of the simplest methods is illustrated in Fig. 7.7(a). Here the gate is connected through a current-limiting resistor and a small control contact such as a reed switch to terminal T_2 of the bilateral switch ACS. With the control contact open, no gate drive is supplied to ACS, and the main power circuit remains open. When the contact is closed by a signal on its control winding or by some other means, ACS receives a gate signal of proper polarity to trigger it in each direction. Once triggered, ACS shorts out the voltage supply for S_1, hence limiting the current-handling and -interrupting duty on the contacts.

The trigger circuit in Fig. 7.7(b) does not require contacts for control of the bilateral triode switch. In this circuit, the trigger power is developed across two inverse series zener diodes, CR_1 and CR_2. Transistor Q_1 is connected inside a bridge to control both directions of gate trigger current to ACS. When base drive is applied to transistor Q_1, trigger current is supplied to ACS, and the load is energized for both halves of the a-c cycle. Removal of base drive de-energizes the load.

Some types of bilateral triode switches can be triggered with the same polarity of gate signal for both halves of the cycle. These types of switches can be turned on in a-c circuits with a d-c voltage applied between the gate and terminal T_1.

7.4 The Parallel-capacitor Commutated D-C Switch

As a d-c latching switch, the SCR is nearly ideal because of its own inherent latching characteristic. For alarm and protection systems and for annunciator circuits which are manually reset, the SCR can be simply connected in series with the load and the reset contact with no additional provision except suitable means in the gate circuit to detect and trigger the SCR when the input signal exceeds a predetermined threshold.

To turn the SCR off by static means in a d-c system requires external commutating means, as discussed in Sec. 6.4. Figure 7.8(a) illustrates one of the fundamental methods of SCR turn-off that can be used as a d-c switch or static flip-flop. It makes use of a capacitor and a second SCR to turn off the load-carrying SCR.

When SCR_1 is triggered into conduction, voltage E is applied to the load R_1. With SCR_2 in the OFF state, capacitor C is connected across the load through R_2 and charges to the supply voltage with positive polarity on its left-hand plate. When SCR_2 is triggered, the right-hand, or negative, plate of C is connected to the positive d-c supply line while its positive plate is still connected to the cathode of SCR_1. This momentary reverse voltage on SCR_1

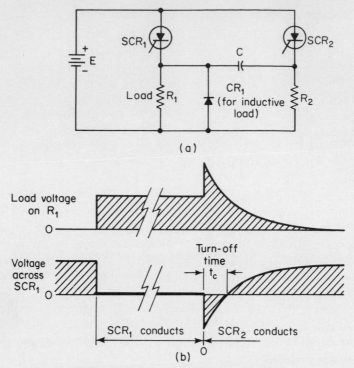

(a)

Fig. 7.8 Parallel capacitor commutated d-c switch.

turns it off, while SCR_2 continues to apply the supply voltage to its load R_2. Capacitor C now reverses its charge to positive polarity on its right-hand plate. If SCR_1 is triggered at this time, the circuit reverts to its original state. Figure 7.8(b) illustrates the voltage waveforms across SCR_1 and the load R_1 during a typical sequence of triggering. For satisfactory turn-off of SCR_1, time t_c indicated on this waveform must be longer than the maximum required turn-off time of SCR_1. Otherwise, SCR_1 will fail to turn off, and both SCR_1 and SCR_2 will conduct simultaneously.

The required size of commutating capacitor C for resistive loads can be determined by analyzing the switching interval just after SCR_2 is triggered. As in other calculations of this type, the SCR's are assumed to be perfect switches; that is, they are assumed to have infinite resistance in the OFF state and zero resistance in the ON state. Also, it is assumed that reverse recovery is instantaneous, that is, that no reverse recovery current flows.

Just before SCR_2 is triggered, capacitor C is charged to E. If SCR_2 is triggered at time $t = 0$, and we then consider the discharge current i through C and load R_1,

$$E = \frac{1}{C} \int_0^t i \, dt + iR_1.$$

The Laplace transform of the loop equation is

$$\frac{E}{s} = I(s)R_1 + \frac{I(s)}{Cs} - \frac{E}{s}.$$

Solving for i, we have

$$i = \frac{2E}{R_1} \exp -t/R_1 C. \tag{7.3}$$

The voltage v_c across capacitor C, which is also the voltage across SCR_1 when SCR_2 is conducting, is

$$v_c = -E + \frac{1}{C} \int_0^t i \, dt = -E + \frac{1}{C} \int_0^t \frac{2E}{R_1} \exp(-t/R_1 C) dt,$$

so

$$v_c = E[1 - 2 \exp(-t/R_1 C)]. \tag{7.4}$$

Turn-off time t_c is the interval between $t = 0$ and the instant when $v_c = 0$ or

$$0 = E[1 - 2 \exp(-t_c/R_1 C)].$$

Solving for t_c, we get

$$t_c = 0.69 R_1 C.$$

Since $R_1 = E/I_D$ (the maximum load current), the minimum required commutating capacitor C is

$$C \geq \frac{1.45 t_c I_D}{E} \quad \text{(resistive load).} \tag{7.5}$$

Conversely, the turn-off time is

$$t_c = \frac{CE}{1.45 I_D} \quad \text{(resistive load).} \tag{7.6}$$

If the load is inductive, a free-wheeling rectifier CR_1 should be connected across the load to discharge the inductive energy in the load when its circuit is interrupted. If the inductance of the load is assumed to be sufficiently large to maintain continuous load current during the turn-off interval, capacitor C will discharge at a constant rate; that is,

$$i_c = I_D.$$

The capacitor voltage during the turn-off interval is

$$v_c = -E + \frac{1}{C} \int I_D \, dt = -E + \frac{I_D t}{C}. \tag{7.7}$$

Again, the circuit turn-off time t_c is the interval until v_c reaches zero:

$$E = \frac{I_D t}{C}.$$

The minimum required commutating capacitor for inductive load is

$$C \geq \frac{t_c I_D}{E} \quad \text{(inductive load)},\tag{7.8}$$

or, conversely, the turn-off time as a function of circuit parameters is

$$t_c = \frac{CE}{I_D} \quad \text{(inductive load)}.\tag{7.9}$$

It is not advisable to use a capacitive or other counter-EMF load with this type of switch without series surge resistance, since destructively high currents may otherwise flow during the commutating interval.

From equations (7.6) and (7.9) it is evident that the circuit turn-off time is a direct function of the load current. The commutating capacitor C must be selected for the heaviest load that will ever be commutated consistent with the turn-off time requirements of the SCR. The waveforms in Fig. 7.8(b) indicate a momentary transient voltage of $2E$ on the load during the turn-off interval. For loads where this transient is undesirable, the circuits considered later can be used.

Variations of the parallel-capacitor commutated switch shown in Fig. 7.8, as well as the other d-c switches discussed in this chapter, can be used for d-c chopping service, ring counters, flashers, and transfer switches.

7.5 The Resonant-circuit Commutated D-C Switch

The turn-off characteristics of the d-c switch in Fig. 7.9 are less sensitive to load-current changes than the foregoing circuits.[2] Also, the load voltage varies less than two volts during the commutation interval, compared to the double voltage transient introduced by the parallel-capacitor commutated switch. Turn-off action depends on the resonant action of L and C.

With SCR_1 conducting and SCR_2 in its OFF state, voltage is applied to the load, and capacitor C charges to E (positive on left-hand plate) through L and R_2. When SCR_2 is triggered, C resonantly discharges through SCR_2, L, and either SCR_1 or CR_1. Until this resonant discharge current reaches the level of load current already flowing through R_1, the discharge current acts to reduce current flowing through SCR_1. When the sinusoidal resonant discharge current exceeds the load current, it reverse-biases SCR_1 and continues its discharge by passing through CR_1 and SCR_2.

The resonant discharge current of C through L reverses the charge on C but is prevented from further oscillation by CR_1 and SCR_1, which now blocks in the forward direction. Load current through R_1 drops to zero, except for inductive load current, which can decay through CR_3 by freewheeling action. SCR_2 now delivers power to R_2, a resistance which can be selected for low power dissipation or can act as an alternate load. In the latter case, this circuit acts as a single-pole double-throw switch. When SCR_1 is again triggered, SCR_2 is turned off by the series resonant discharge of C in the opposite direction to that previously described.

Successful turn-off of SCR_1 (or SCR_2) depends on the resonant circuit maintaining discharge current through CR_1, thus reverse-biasing SCR_1 long enough for SCR_1 to regain its forward blocking capability. Circuit turn-off time t_c is the interval that CR_1 conducts and is defined as $(t_2 - t_1)$. Expressed differently, t_c is the length of time that capacitor discharge current i_c exceeds I_D, the maximum load current through R_1. Assuming no resistive losses in the resonant discharge of C, we may express the capacitor current as

$$i_c = E\sqrt{\frac{C}{L}} \sin \frac{t}{\sqrt{LC}},$$

where $E\sqrt{C/L}$ = peak discharge current I_p through C. Equating i_c with I_D in order to find the points t_1 and t_2 when $i_c = I_D$, we get

$$I_D = E\sqrt{\frac{C}{L}} \sin \frac{t}{\sqrt{LC}},$$

$$t_1 = \sqrt{LC} \text{ arc sin} \left(\frac{I_D}{E}\sqrt{\frac{L}{C}}\right),$$

$$t_2 = \sqrt{LC} \left[\pi - \text{arc sin} \left(\frac{I_D}{E}\sqrt{\frac{L}{C}}\right)\right].$$

Since $t_c = t_2 - t_1$,

$$t_c = \sqrt{LC} \left[\pi - 2 \text{ arc sin} \left(\frac{I_D}{E}\sqrt{\frac{L}{C}}\right)\right]. \tag{7.10}$$

Let

$$k = \frac{I_p}{I_D} = \frac{E}{I_D}\sqrt{\frac{C}{L}}.$$

Then

$$\sqrt{C} = \frac{kI_D\sqrt{L}}{E}. \tag{7.11}$$

Substituting in equation (7.10) and solving for L, we obtain

$$L = \frac{Et_c}{kI_D}\left(\frac{1}{\pi - 2 \text{ arc sin} \frac{1}{k}}\right), \tag{7.12}$$

and, by substituting for L in equation (7.11),

$$C = \frac{kI_D t_c}{E}\left(\frac{1}{\pi - 2 \text{ arc sin} \frac{1}{k}}\right). \tag{7.13}$$

Circuit constants for practical switch designs can be determined from the preceding equations.

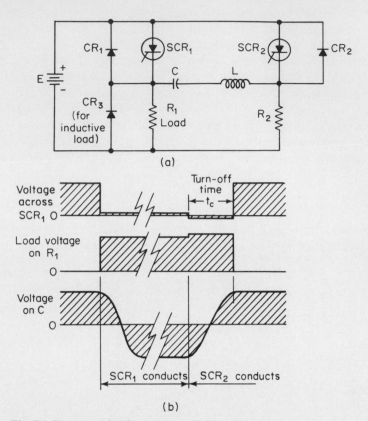

Fig. 7.9 Resonant circuit commutated d-c switch.

7.6 The Resonance Commutated D-C Switch with Inductor in Load Circuit

Although the circuit in Fig. 7.9 can be used for a wide range of loads with only minor voltage transients applied to the load, the SCR in some cases may encounter difficulty in turning off owing to the fast rate of rise (dv/dt) of positive anode voltage at the end of the commutating period. By relocating the inductor in series with the anodes of the two SCR's, as indicated in Fig. 7.10, the dv/dt applied to the SCR's can be considerably reduced while the desirable switching characteristics of Fig. 7.9 are maintained. The difference in dv/dt characteristics can be observed from the waveshapes of the respective circuits. The disadvantage of the circuit of Fig. 7.10 is the fact that a somewhat larger value of inductance is usually required in this circuit, and the inductor must be capable of carrying the load current on a steady-state basis. On the other hand, the presence of series inductance is sometimes an asset for limiting fault current when the load is short-circuited momentarily.

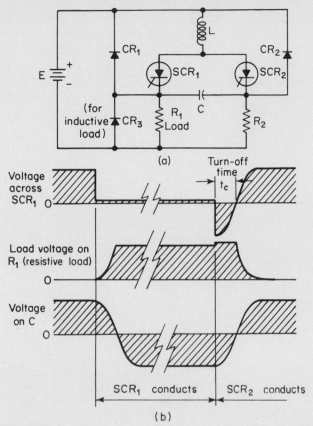

(a)

(b)

Fig. 7.10 Resonance commutated d-c switch with inductor in series with load.

In many respects this d-c switch is similar to the parallel inverter with feedback, which is discussed in Sec. 9.2, except that two loads R_1 and R_2 are used instead of the two primary windings of a transformer. When SCR_1 in Fig. 7.10 is triggered, d-c voltage is applied to load R_1 through inductor L and SCR_1. With SCR_1 conducting, the left-hand plate of capacitor C charges positive with respect to the right-hand plate through R_2. When SCR_2 is triggered to interrupt the load, the negative plate of C is connected to the anode of SCR_1, thus reverse-biasing SCR_1 and interrupting current through it. Capacitor C resonantly discharges through CR_1 and L, reversing its voltage in a manner similar to that shown in Fig. 7.9. With load

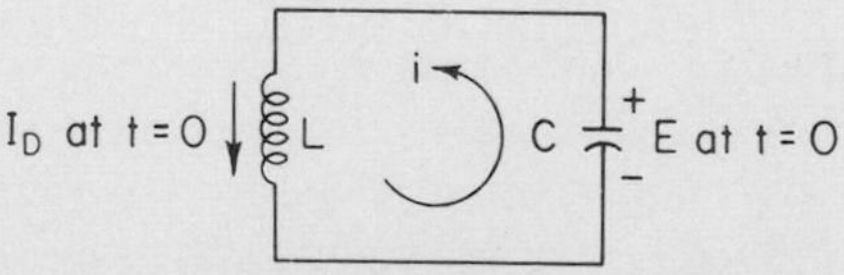

Fig. 7.11 Equivalent circuit of Fig. 7.10 during commutating interval.

voltage now applied to R_2, C charges with positive voltage on its right-hand plate. When SCR_1 is triggered, the action is reversed, so SCR_2 is turned off.

Turn-off action may be analyzed by considering the equivalent circuit in Fig. 7.11. At the instant of triggering SCR_2, I_D is flowing in L, and C is charged to voltage E as indicated. CR_1 and SCR_2 conduct and are assumed to have negligible voltage drop, and R_2 is assumed to be infinite for this interval, a valid assumption for charging resistors or inductive loads. The Laplace transform for the voltage v across L and C is as follows:

$$\frac{V(s)}{sL} + \frac{I_D}{s} = -sCV(s) + EC,$$

so

$$V(s) = \frac{E\left(s - \dfrac{I_D}{EC}\right)}{\left(s^2 + \dfrac{1}{LC}\right)},$$

$$v = E\left(\cos\frac{t}{\sqrt{LC}} - \frac{I_D}{E}\sqrt{\frac{L}{C}}\sin\frac{t}{\sqrt{LC}}\right). \tag{7.14}$$

Turn-off time t_c is the interval from $t = 0$ until v, the voltage across C, reaches zero. Solving equation (7.14) for t when $v = 0$, we get

$$t_c = \sqrt{LC}\ \text{arc}\tan\left(\frac{E}{I_D}\sqrt{\frac{C}{L}}\right) \tag{7.15}$$

for the turn-off time.

Values of L and C for design purposes may be determined by the following approximation. From equation (7.15),

$$\tan\frac{t_c}{\sqrt{LC}} = \frac{E}{I_D}\sqrt{\frac{C}{L}}. \tag{7.16}$$

For $\dfrac{t_c}{\sqrt{LC}} < 0.5$,

$$\tan\frac{t_c}{\sqrt{LC}} \cong \frac{t_c}{\sqrt{LC}}.$$

Substitution of the preceding quantity in equation (7.16) yields

$$\frac{t_c}{\sqrt{LC}} \cong \frac{E}{I_D}\sqrt{\frac{C}{L}},$$

$$C \cong \frac{t_c I_D}{E}. \tag{7.17}$$

Since turn-off time t_c is one-fourth of the natural resonant period $2\pi\sqrt{LC}$,

$$t_c = \frac{\pi\sqrt{LC}}{2},$$

$$L = \frac{4t_c^2}{\pi^2 C}.$$

Substituting for C from equation (7.17), we obtain finally

$$L = \frac{4Et_c}{\pi^2 I_D}. \tag{7.18}$$

Design calculations based on these equations should use maximum values of SCR turn-off time and load current and a value of supply voltage that is consistent with the maximum load-current value.

7.7 Typical Trigger Circuits for D-C Switches

A wide variety of trigger schemes can be used for d-c switches employing SCR's. The particular type of circuit and its complexity depends to a large extent on the functions of the switch and the nature of the initiating signal. Figure 7.12 illustrates five trigger circuits of varying complexity. For the sake of illustration, all circuits are shown with basic parallel-capacitor commutation, although other turn-off means, as discussed earlier, can be used.

Figure 7.12(a) employs a low-power single-pole double-throw (SPDT) switch to trigger the SCR and to turn it off by connecting the commutating capacitor across the SCR. When an alternate load must be energized by an SCR, a SPDT switch can be used to trigger both SCR's, as indicated in Fig. 7.12(b).

Figure 7.12(c) is analogous to a single-pole double-throw relay that is actuated by a low-level d-c signal. When no signal is present, transistor Q_1 does not conduct. The d-c supply voltage exceeds the avalanche voltage of Zener diode CR_1, triggering SCR_1 and energizing load 1. If a positive d-c signal of sufficient amplitude is applied to the input terminals, Q_1 is driven on, supplying gate trigger current to SCR_2. At the same time, the collector voltage of Q_1 drops below the avalanche voltage of CR_1, removing gate current from SCR_1. Hence, load 2 is energized while load 1 is de-energized. This circuit is useful at the relatively low d-c voltages for which transistors are available. Circuit component values must be selected so that only one SCR can be triggered at a given signal level.

Figure 7.12(d) illustrates an alternate d-c static relay which has an isolated control signal and is not limited to as low d-c voltages as the previous circuit. When a d-c signal is applied to the primary of T_1 with the polarity shown, the rise in magnetic flux couples a positive pulse to the gate of SCR_1, triggering

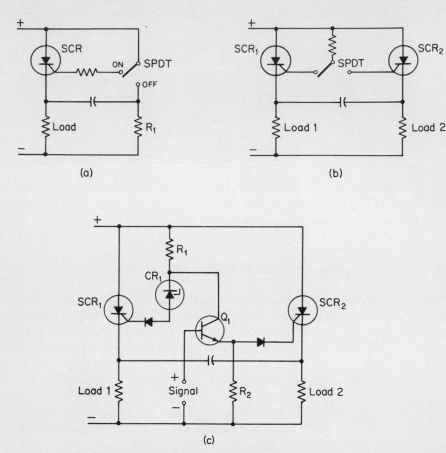

Fig. 7.12 Trigger circuits for d-c switches.

it and delivering power to load 1. When the d-c signal is removed, the collapsing flux couples a positive pulse to the gate of SCR₂. This energizes load 2 while de-energizing load 1 by conventional capacitor commutation. For proper operation, the d-c signal must be abruptly and cleanly applied and removed.

The trigger circuit in Fig. 7.12(e) provides a precise level of pick-up and drop-out while maintaining isolation between the control signal and SCR anode circuit.[3] Also, this circuit is unaffected by the rate of application of the control signal. The gates of two SCR's in one of the d-c static switches already discussed are connected to the indicated secondary windings of pulse transformers T_1 and T_2 in respective unijunction trigger circuits. Zener diode CR_1 limits the voltage on the emitter of unijunction transistor UJT₁. As a result, UJT₁ will oscillate only when the d-c control signal is less than approximately V_{CR_1}/η, where V_{CR_1} is the avalanche voltage of CR_1 and η is

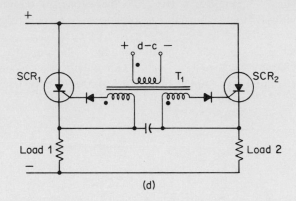

(d)

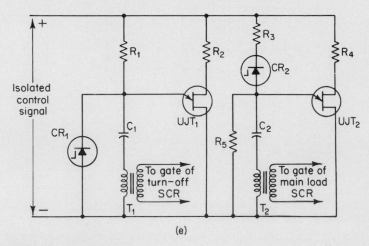

(e)

Fig. 7.12 (cont.)

the intrinsic stand-off ratio of UJT_1. Zener diode CR_2 permits UJT_2 to trigger only when the control signal is greater than approximately $V_{CR_2}/(1 - \eta)$, where V_{CR_2} is the avalanche voltage of CR_2. By proper selection of component values, UJT_1 and UJT_2 will respectively trigger their associated SCR's below and above a predetermined level. This will cause single-pole double-throw action of the d-c switch to a state that depends on whether the control signal is above or below the predetermined level.

The high speed of SCR switches can provide current-limiting action superior to the fastest fuses, which of necessity are limited by thermal time constants. The elementary diagram of such a high-speed d-c circuit breaker shown in Fig. 7.13 employs a basic parallel-capacitor commutated SCR switch. In addition to the normal ON and OFF trigger controls, the gate of SCR_2 is connected via reference diode CR_1 to a current-monitoring resistor R_1. Resistance R_1 is selected to have a negligible voltage drop at normal load currents. However, when a d-c short circuit occurs, the voltage across R_1 increases very rapidly. As soon as the voltage across R_1 exceeds the avalanche

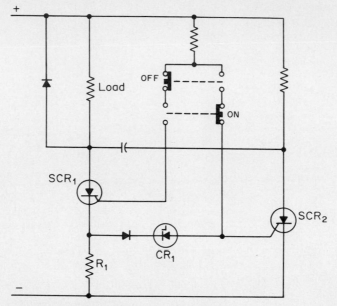

Fig. 7.13 Current-limiting circuit breaker.

voltage of CR_1, SCR_2 is triggered, turning off SCR_1 and interrupting the fault current. Since this type of switch can function in a matter of microseconds, it can interrupt a fault current long before it reaches final destructive proportions. Additional circuit details are cited in Ref. 4.

7.7.1 TIME-DELAY CIRCUITS

By combining the wide range stability and timing characteristics of the unijunction relaxation oscillator (Sec. 5.5.7) with the power-switching characteristics of the SCR, one can design simple yet accurate and versatile solid-state time-delay circuits. Figure 7.14 illustrates a circuit which applies power to the load a predetermined time after d-c voltage is applied to the circuit or after a shorting contact across C_1 is opened. Operating voltage and current affect only the selection of the SCR. Resistor R_5 and Zener CR_1 apply a stable voltage to the unijunction timing circuit.

Initially the SCR is off. The timing interval begins when voltage is applied to the circuit or when C_1 is permitted to start charging through R_1 and R_2. When the voltage across C_1 reaches the peak-point voltage of UJT_1, it fires, generating a pulse across R_4 and triggering the SCR. This applies voltage to the load. Holding current for the SCR can flow through R_5 and CR_2, thus permitting heavily inductive loads to be controlled and allowing wide variations or opening of the load circuit without affecting the timing sequence. The circuit can be reset for another timing cycle by momentarily shorting the SCR or by opening the d-c supply.

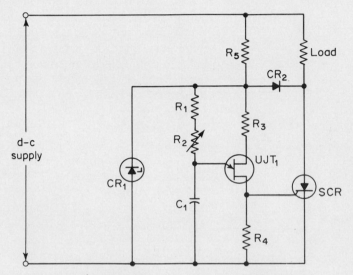

Fig. 7.14 Time-delay circuit for operation on direct current.

The time delay depends on the time constant $C_1 (R_1 + R_2)$ and can be set to any desired value by appropriate choice or adjustment of these components. The maximum limit of time delay depends on the required accuracy, the minimum peak-point current of the UJT, the leakage current of the UJT emitter and the capacitor, and the maximum ambient temperature. The upper limit of $(R_1 + R_2)$ is set by the requirement that it provide the peak-point current needed to trigger the UJT. With the use of stable, low-leakage types of high-capacitance tantalytic capacitors and of unijunction transistors with low peak-point currents, time delays of many minutes can be achieved. These delays can be extended to several hours by adding a second UJT oscillator circuit to provide negative pulses of a few tenths of a volt peak at base two of UJT_1. These pulses act to reduce the effective value of peak-point current of UJT_1 by as much as 100 times, thus permitting the use of a larger value of charging resistance $(R_1 + R_2)$.

Resistor R_3 serves as temperature compensation for the circuit. At any given temperature, the overall temperature coefficient of the time delay can be set at exactly zero by careful adjustment of R_3.

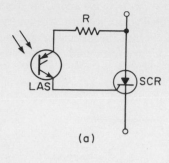

(a)

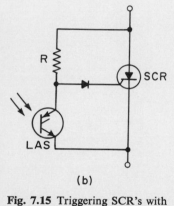

(b)

Fig. 7.15 Triggering SCR's with light-activated switches: (a) normally open configuration; (b) normally closed configuration.

7.8 The Light-activated Switch for Static Switching

Both two-lead and three-lead light-activated equivalents of the SCR (Sec. 2.3) offer unique simplicity and isolation for multiple-contact static switches. A single source of light can be used to energize many contacts in one switch, and multiple light sources can be incorporated for logic functions, interlocking, and normally closed operation. Light-activated switches can be substituted for the SCR in many of the a-c and d-c switching circuits described earlier in this chapter.

The power-handling ability of the light-activated switch (LAS) may be increased by using it as a gate amplifier to trigger a larger SCR, as shown in Fig. 7.15(a). Repositioning the LAS with respect to the driven SCR [Fig. 7.15(b)] converts the circuit into the equivalent of a normally closed contact for a-c operation. In the absence of light falling on the LAS, it remains in the nonconducting state, thus allowing current through resistor R to trigger the SCR. When light triggers the LAS into conduction, gate current no longer can flow to the SCR, and it opens on the following cycle.

The LAS lends itself to static synchronization with mechanical devices through use of moving apertures and shutters. Typical examples are automotive ignition systems, commutatorless d-c motors, and limit switches.

7.9 The Gate Turn-off Switch

SCR's that can be turned off by a negative trigger signal at the gate are particularly useful for d-c static switching (Sec. 2.7). Turn-off of anode current by a momentary negative gate current generally requires less energy and is faster acting than turn-off by reversing the anode voltage, as for conventional SCR's. As with SCR's, the gate turn-off switch is triggered on by a positive gate pulse.

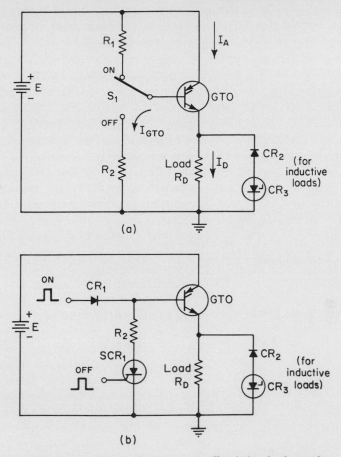

Fig. 7.16 Trigger circuits for gate turn-off switches in d-c static switch applications.

Negative trigger signals for turning off this type of static switch can be secured from any one of many sources, such as transistor flip-flops, unijunction transistors, or saturable reactors. By connecting the load on the cathode side, we can circumvent the need for a negative signal with respect to ground, as shown in Fig. 7.16. To illustrate this basic action, Fig. 7.16(a) employs an SPDT switch to close and open the gate turn-off switch. When S_1 is moved to the ON position, the positive supply voltage delivers current to the gate and through the load to turn GTO on. Once GTO latches into the conducting state, its cathode rises to essentially the positive supply voltage. If S_1 is moved to the OFF position, the gate of GTO is connected to ground through R_2. A portion of the load current then flows out of the gate to ground through R_2 and turns GTO off.

Similar action can be achieved electrically, as shown in Fig. 7.16(b). Here the ON trigger is coupled to the gate through CR_1. CR_1 prevents reverse gate current from flowing as soon as the cathode voltage builds up and hence keeps GTO latched on after the ON trigger signal is removed. To turn GTO off, a positive trigger is applied to the gate of SCR_1. As SCR_1 turns on, it draws gate current from GTO, thus turning GTO off. CR_2 allows inductive load current to decay on turn-off without building up excessive voltage across the GTO. A Zener diode CR_3 can be introduced to speed the decay of load current within tolerable limits of induced voltage.

Resistor R_2 must be selected with a sufficiently low value of resistance that reliable turn-off action will occur. If the voltage between gate and cathode to effect turn-off action is low compared to the d-c supply voltage E, the voltage across the load resistance will be essentially equal to the voltage across resistance R_2 during turn-off:

$$I_{GTO}R_2 = R_D I_D = E,$$

where I_{GTO} is the negative gate current required to turn off I_D, and

$$R_2 = \frac{E}{I_{GTO}}. \tag{7.19}$$

From Sec. 6.5, the turn-off gain A_G of the GTO is defined as

$$A_G = \frac{I_A}{I_{GTO}}.$$

Since $I_A = I_D + I_{GTO}$, we can substitute for I_A and solve for I_{GTO} as follows:

$$I_{GTO} = \frac{I_D}{A_G - 1}.$$

Substituting this for I_{GTO} in equation (7.19), we get

$$R_2 \leq \frac{E(A_G - 1)}{I_D} \tag{7.20}$$

for resistive loads, where A_G is the minimum turn-off gain specification for the device under consideration.

REFERENCES

1. R. F. Blake, "Designing Solid-State Static Power Relays," *Electronics* (May, 27, 1960), pp. 114–17.

2. R. Langfelder, "Design of Signal and Control Static Relays," *Static Relays for Electronic Circuits*. Elizabeth, N.J.: Engineering Publishers, 1961, p. 50.

3. "Static Switching Devices, Fifth Quarterly Report," November 1, 1960 to January 31, 1961; Report No. 2202-Q5; submitted by Walter Kidde and Co., Inc. to U.S. Army Signal Research and Development Laboratories, Fort Monmouth, N.J.

4. *Silicon Controlled Rectifier Manual*, 2nd ed. Rectifier Components Department, General Electric Company, pp. 96–103.

CHAPTER 8

PHASE CONTROL

In alternating-current circuits the SCR is a nearly ideal static power switch. When its anode is positive with respect to its cathode, the SCR can be triggered into the conducting state with a low-power signal on its control gate element. Thereafter the SCR will continue to conduct current in its anode circuit regardless of gate signal until the anode current is reduced to zero by the external circuit. It is this basic SCR action that lends itself so nicely to switching in a-c circuits. More specifically, the SCR can be readily used for proportional control of power in a-c circuits through the medium of *phase control*. This type of control was pioneered by the gas thyratron tube and the mercury arc rectifier, and the literature dealing with these electronic devices has many useful ideas that may be applied to SCR systems. In this chapter we shall consider basic phase-control principles as they apply specifically to SCR's.

8.1 Fundamentals of Phase Control (the Half-wave Circuit with Resistive Load)

In its simplest form, phase control can be described by considering the half-wave SCR circuit with resistive load R shown in Fig. 8.1(a). The circuit is energized by a line voltage or transformer secondary voltage, $e = E \sin \omega t$. It is assumed that the peak supply voltage never exceeds the forward and reverse blocking ratings of the SCR. During the negative half-cycle of the supply voltage, from π to 2π, the SCR blocks the flow of load current, and no voltage is applied to the load R.

Chart 8.1 CIRCUIT CONSTANTS OF SOME MAJOR PHASE CONTROLLED CIRCUITS†

Circuit		(c)	(d)	Peak reverse voltage		(g) Max. load voltage ($\alpha = 0$)
(a) Name	(b) Connections	Load voltage waveforms	Peak forward voltage on SCR	(e) On SCR	(f) On diode	E_D = average d-c value E_a = RMS a-c value
(1) Half-wave resistive load	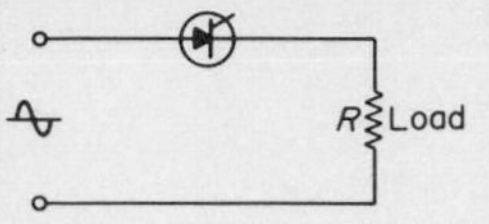	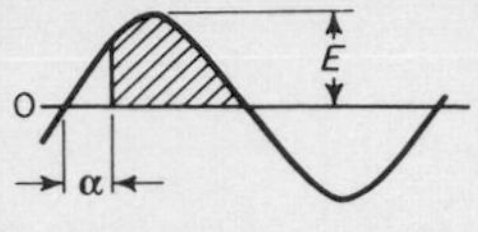	E	E	—	$E_D = \frac{E}{\pi}$ $E_a = \frac{E}{2}$
(2) Half-wave inductive load with free-wheeling rectifier	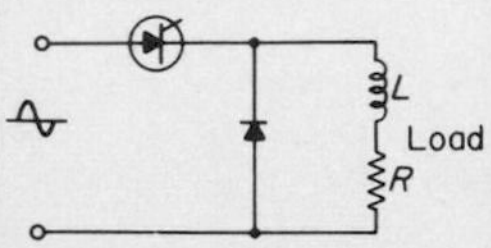	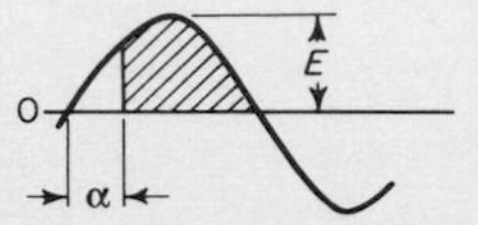	E	E	E	$E_D = \frac{E}{\pi}$
(3) Centertap with resistive load, or inductive load with free-wheeling rectifier	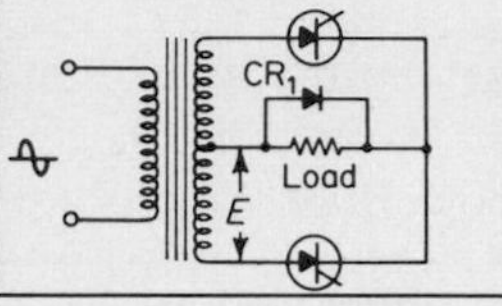	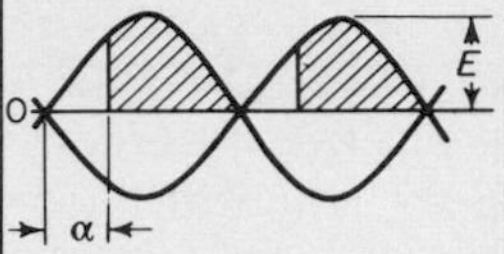	E (possibly $2E$ if load open)	$2E$	E	$E_D = \frac{2E}{\pi}$
(4) Centertap with resistive or inductive load—SCR in d-c circuit	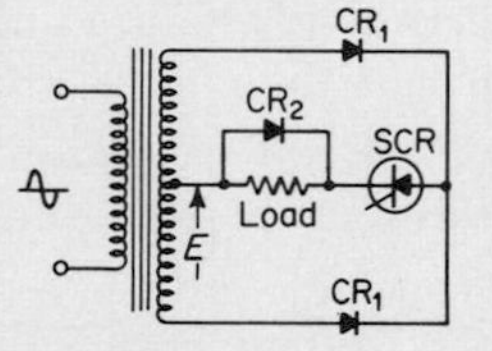	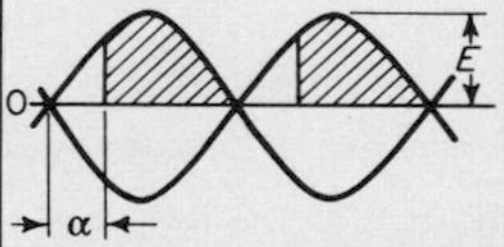	E	0	$2E$ ON CR$_1$ / E ON CR$_2$	$E_D = \frac{2E}{\pi}$
(5) Centertap with inductive load (no free-wheeling rectifier)	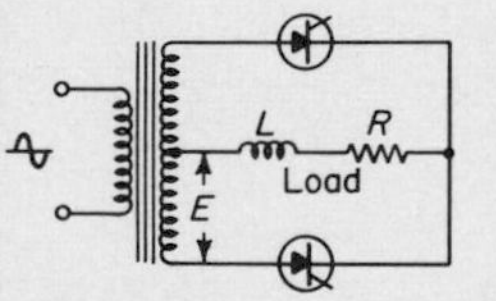	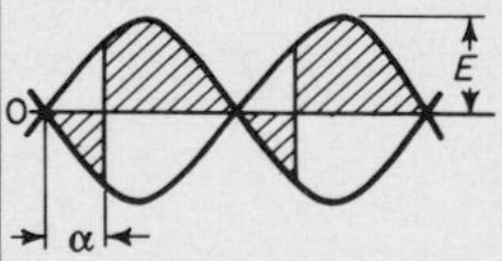	$2E$	$2E$	—	$E_D = \frac{2E}{\pi}$
(6) Single-phase bridge with 2 SCR's with common anode or cathode. Resistive load, or inductive load with free-wheeling rectifier	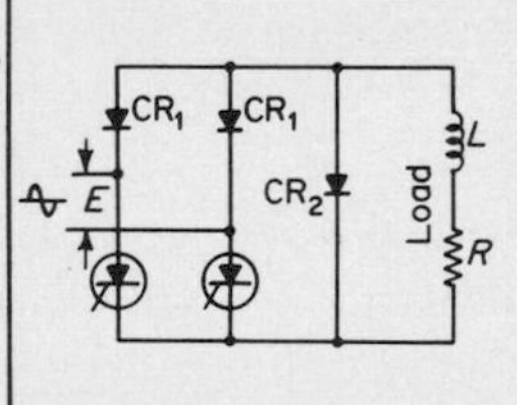	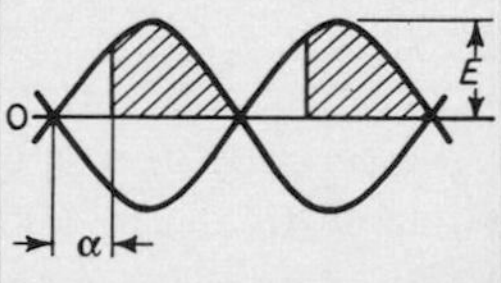	E	E	E (CR$_1$ and CR$_2$)	$E_D = \frac{2E}{\pi}$

† Assumes zero forward drop in semiconductors when conducting, and zero current when blocking; also zero a-c line and source reactance. Inductive d-c loads have pure d-c current.

Chart 8.1 (cont.)

(h) Load voltage vs trigger delay angle α	(j) Trigger angle range full ON to full OFF	Max. steady-state current in SCR		Max. steady-state current in diode rectifier		(p) Ability to pumpback inductive load energy to supply line	(q) Fundamental frequency of load voltage (f = supply frequency)	(r) Notes and comments
		(k) Average amp	(l) Cond. angle	(m) Average amp	(n) Cond. angle for max. current			
$E_D = \frac{E}{2\pi}(1 + \cos \alpha)$ $E_a = \frac{E}{2\sqrt{\pi}}(\pi - \alpha + \frac{1}{2}\sin 2\alpha)^{1/2}$	180°	$\frac{E}{\pi R}$	180°	—	—	—	f	
$E_D = \frac{E}{2\pi}(1 + \cos \alpha)$	180°	$\frac{E}{2\pi R}$ (load highly inductive)	180°	$0.54\left(\frac{E}{\pi R}\right)$	210°	No	f	
$E_D = \frac{E}{\pi}(1 + \cos \alpha)$	180°	$\frac{E}{\pi R}$	180°	$0.26\left(\frac{2E}{\pi R}\right)$	148°	No	$2f$	
$E_D = \frac{E}{\pi}(1 + \cos \alpha)$	180°	$\frac{2E}{\pi R}$	360°	$CR_1 = \frac{E}{\pi R}$ $CR_2 = 0.26\left(\frac{2E}{\pi R}\right)$ with highly inductive load	180° 148°	No	$2f$	CR_2 necessary when load is not purely resistive. Frequency limited by recovery characteristics of rectifiers and SCR.
$E_D = \frac{2E}{\pi}\cos \alpha$ (assuming continuous current in load)	180°	$\frac{E}{\pi R}$	180°	—	—	Yes	$2f$	
$E_D = \frac{E}{\pi}(1 + \cos \alpha)$	180°	$\frac{E}{\pi R}$	180°	$CR_1 = \frac{E}{\pi R}$ $CR_2 = 0.26\left(\frac{2E}{\pi R}\right)$	180° 148°	No	$2f$	Without CR_2, SCR's may be unable to turn off an inductive load. Also, CR_2 relieves SCR's from free-wheeling duty. See Sec. 8.5.

Chart 8.1 (cont.)

Circuit		(c)	(d)	Peak reverse voltage		(g)
(a) Name	(b) Connections	Load voltage waveforms	Peak forward voltage on SCR	(e) On SCR	(f) On diode	Max. load voltage $(\alpha = 0)$ E_D = average d-c value E_a = RMS a-c value
(7) Single-phase bridge with 2 SCR's on common a-c line. Resistive or inductive load			E	E	E	$E_D = \dfrac{2E}{\pi}$
(8) Single-phase bridge with 4 SCR's and inductive load			E	E	—	$E_D = \dfrac{2E}{\pi}$
(9) Single-phase bridge with single SCR in d-c circuit. Resistive or inductive load			E	O	E (CR$_1$ and CR$_2$)	$E_D = \dfrac{2E}{\pi}$
(10) Three-phase half-wave with resistive load, or inductive load with free-wheeling rectifier			E (possibly $\sqrt{3}\,E$ if load open and if SCR's have high reverse currents)	$\sqrt{3}\,E$	E	$E_D = \dfrac{3\sqrt{3}\,E}{2\pi}$
(11) Three-phase half-wave with inductive load (no free-wheeling rectifier)			$\sqrt{3}\,E$	$\sqrt{3}\,E$	—	$E_D = \dfrac{3\sqrt{3}\,E}{2\pi}$
(12) Three-phase bridge with 3 SCR's. Resistive load, or inductive load with free-wheeling rectifier			$\sqrt{3}\,E$	$\sqrt{3}\,E$	$\sqrt{3}\,E$	$E_D = \dfrac{3\sqrt{3}\,E}{\pi}$
(13) Three-phase bridge with 6 SCR's. Resistive load, or inductive load with free-wheeling rectifier			$\sqrt{3}\,E$ (1.5E if SCR's shunted by resistance)	$\sqrt{3}\,E$	$\sqrt{3}\,E$	$E_D = \dfrac{3\sqrt{3}\,E}{\pi}$

Chart 8.1 (cont.)

(h) Load voltage vs trigger delay angle α	(j) Trigger angle range full ON to full OFF	Max. steady-state current in SCR		Max. steady-state current in diode rectifier		(p) Ability to pumpback inductive load energy to supply line	(q) Fundamental frequency of load voltage (f = supply frequency)	(r) Notes and comments
		(k) Average amp	(l) Cond. angle	(m) Average amp	(n) Cond. angle for max. current			
$E_D = \frac{E}{\pi}(1 + \cos\alpha)$	180°	$\frac{E}{\pi R}$	180°	$\frac{E}{\pi R}$	180°	No	2f	Diode rectifiers act as free-wheeling path, conduct $(\pi + \alpha)$ degrees with inductive load.
$E_D = \frac{2E}{\pi}\cos\alpha$ (assuming continuous current in load)	180°	$\frac{E}{\pi R}$	180°	—	—	Yes	2f	With resistive load operation is same as circuit (7).
$E_D = \frac{E}{\pi}(1 + \cos\alpha)$	180°	$\frac{2E}{\pi R}$	360°	$CR_1 = \frac{E}{\pi R}$ $CR_2 = 0.16\left(\frac{2E}{\pi R}\right)$	180° 148°	No	2f	CR_2 necessary when load is not purely resistive. Frequency limited by recovery characteristics of rectifiers and SCR's.
$E_D = \frac{3\sqrt{3}\,E}{2\pi}\cos\alpha$ $(0 < \alpha < 30°)$ $E_D = \frac{3E}{2\pi}[1 + \cos(\alpha + 30°)]$ $(30° < \alpha < 150°)$	150°	$\frac{\sqrt{3}\,E}{2\pi R}$	120°	$0.16\left(\frac{3\sqrt{3}\,E}{2\pi R}\right)$	134°	No	3f	
$E_D = \frac{3\sqrt{3}\,E}{2\pi}\cos\alpha$ (assuming continuous current in load)	150°	$\frac{\sqrt{3}\,E}{2\pi R}$	120°	—	—	Yes	3f	
$E_D = \frac{3\sqrt{3}\,E}{2\pi}(1 + \cos\alpha)$	180°	$\frac{\sqrt{3}\,E}{\pi R}$	120°	$CR_1 = \frac{\sqrt{3}\,E}{\pi R}$ $CR_2 = 0.14\left(\frac{3\sqrt{3}\,E}{\pi R}\right)$	120° 132°	No	3f	Without CR_2, SCR's may be unable to turn off an inductive load. Also, CR_2 relieves SCR's from free-wheeling duty.
$E_D = \frac{3\sqrt{3}\,E}{\pi}\cos\alpha$ $(0 < \alpha < 60°)$ $E_D = \frac{3\sqrt{3}\,E}{\pi}\left(1 + \frac{\cos\alpha}{2} - \frac{\sqrt{3}}{2}\sin\alpha\right)$ $(60° < \alpha < 120°)$	120°	$\frac{\sqrt{3}\,E}{\pi R}$	120°	$0.056\left(\frac{3\sqrt{3}\,E}{\pi R}\right)$	212°	No	6f	SCR's require two gate signals 60° apart each cycle, alternately a gate signal duration > 60°

Chart 8.1 (cont.)

Circuit		(c)	(d)	Peak reverse voltage		(g) Max. load voltage ($\alpha = 0$)
(a) Name	(b) Connections	Load voltage waveforms	Peak forward voltage on SCR	(e) On SCR	(f) On diode	E_D = average d-c value E_a = RMS a-c value
(14) Three-phase bridge with 6 SCR's with inductive load			$\sqrt{3}\,E$ (1.5E if SCR's shunted by resistance)	$\sqrt{3}\,E$	—	$E_D = \frac{3\sqrt{3}\,E}{\pi}$
(15) Inverse parallel SCR's with resistive load			E	E	—	$E_a = \frac{E}{\sqrt{2}}$
(16) SCR inside bridge with a-c resistive load			E	0	E	$E_a = \frac{E}{\sqrt{2}}$

During the positive half-cycle of the supply voltage, the SCR anode is positive with respect to its cathode, and the gate can exert control over the SCR conduction characteristics as described in detail in Sec. 5.2. Until the gate is triggered by a proper positive signal from the trigger circuit, the SCR blocks the flow of load current in the forward direction. At some arbitrary delay angle α, a positive trigger signal is applied between gate and cathode which initiates SCR current conduction. Immediately the full supply voltage, minus approximately one volt drop across the SCR, is applied to the load. With a zero reactance source and a purely resistive load, the current waveform after the SCR is triggered will be identical to the applied voltage wave, and of a magnitude dependent on the amplitude of the voltage and the value of load resistance R. As shown in Fig. 8.1(b), load current will flow until it is commutated by reversal of the supply voltage at $\omega t = \pi$. By controlling the trigger delay angle α with respect to the supply voltage by such means as described in Chap. 5 and later in this chapter, we may vary the phase relationship of the start of current flow to the supply voltage and control the load current from a maximum value down to zero—hence the term *phase control*.

Chart 8.1 (cont.)

(h) Load voltage *vs* trigger delay angle α	(j) Trigger angle range full ON to full OFF	Max. steady-state current in SCR		(m) Average amp	(n) Cond. angle for max. current	(p) Ability to pumpback inductive load energy to supply line	(q) Fundamental frequency of load voltage (f = supply frequency)	(r) Notes and comments
		(k) Average amp	(l) Cond. angle	Max. steady-state current in diode rectifier				
$E_D = \frac{3\sqrt{3}\,E}{\pi}\cos\alpha$ (assuming continuous current in load	120°	$\frac{\sqrt{3}\,E}{\pi R}$	120°	—	—	Yes	6f	SCR's require two gate signals 60° apart each cycle, alternately a gate signal duration > 60°.
$E_a = \frac{E}{\sqrt{2\pi}}(\pi - \alpha + \frac{1}{2}\sin 2\alpha)^{1/2}$	180°	$\frac{E_a}{2.2\,R}$ or $\frac{E}{\pi R}$	180°	—	—	—	f	With inductive load, load voltage and current depend on $\omega L/R$ as well as R and α.
$E_a = \frac{E}{\sqrt{2\pi}}(\pi - \alpha + \frac{1}{2}\sin 2\alpha)^{1/2}$	180°	$\frac{E_a}{1.1\,R}$ or $\frac{2E}{\pi R}$	360°	$\frac{E_a}{2.2\,R}$ or $\frac{E}{\pi R}$	180°	—	f	Inductance in d-c circuit must be minimum. Frequency limit determined by recovery characteristics of rectifiers and SCR's. With inductive load, load voltage and current depend on $\omega L/R$ as well as R and α.

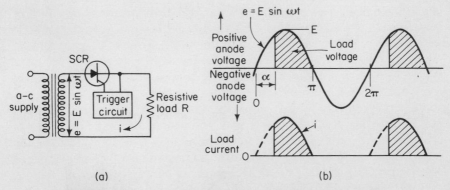

Fig. 8.1 Half-wave phase-controlled SCR with resistive load: (a) circuit; (b) waveforms.

The average d-c voltage E_D across a resistive load in a half-wave circuit as a function of the delay angle α is given as

$$E_D = \frac{\int_\alpha^\pi E \sin \omega t \, d(\omega t)}{\int_0^{2\pi} d(\omega t)} = \frac{E\left[-\cos \omega t\right]_\alpha^\pi}{\left[\omega t\right]_0^{2\pi}},$$

or

$$E_D = \frac{E}{2\pi} (1 + \cos \alpha) \qquad (8.1)$$

Maximum output voltage occurs with zero trigger delay angle. At this condition $\alpha = 0$, and $E_{D_{max}} = E/\pi = 0.318E$ (the same output as for a conventional half-wave diode rectifier with resistive load).

Expressing the average d-c load voltage as the ratio between it and the maximum load voltage at zero delay angle, we obtain

$$\frac{E_D}{E_{D_{max}}} = \frac{\dfrac{E}{2\pi} (1 + \cos \alpha)}{\dfrac{E}{\pi}}$$

$$\frac{E_D}{E_{D_{max}}} = \frac{1 + \cos \alpha}{2}. \qquad (8.2)$$

With resistive load, the average load current I_D is directly proportional to the average load voltage divided by the load resistance:

$$I_D = \frac{E}{2\pi R} (1 + \cos \alpha). \qquad (8.3)$$

In some cases, such as with incandescent lamp and electric heating loads, one is interested in the root-mean-square (rms) value of the load voltage, E_a, where

$$E_a = \left[\frac{\int_\alpha^\pi (E \sin \omega t)^2 \, d(\omega t)}{\int_0^{2\pi} d(\omega t)}\right]^{1/2},$$

or

$$E_a = \frac{E}{2\sqrt{\pi}} \left(\pi - \alpha + \frac{1}{2} \sin 2\alpha\right)^{1/2}. \qquad (8.4)$$

Expressing the rms load voltage as the ratio between it and its maximum value at $\alpha = 0$, we get

$$\frac{E_a}{E_{a_{max}}} = \frac{\dfrac{E}{2\sqrt{\pi}} \left(\pi - \alpha + \dfrac{1}{2} \sin 2\alpha\right)^{1/2}}{\dfrac{E}{2}} = \left(\frac{\pi - \alpha + \dfrac{1}{2} \sin 2\alpha}{\pi}\right)^{1/2}. \qquad (8.5)$$

The variation of average and rms load voltage with delay angle, as expressed in equations (8.2) and (8.5) is shown in Fig. 8.2.

8.2 Full-wave Circuit with Resistive and Inductive Load

Controlled full-wave d-c output may be secured by connecting SCR's into either of the conventional full-wave diode rectifier circuits, i.e., the centertap or the bridge configuration. Figure 8.3 shows the full-wave centertap configuration employing two SCR's to feed a resistive load. The bridge configuration (see Fig. 8.7) is often used when a transformer is undesirable and the magnitude of the supply voltage properly meets the load voltage requirements.

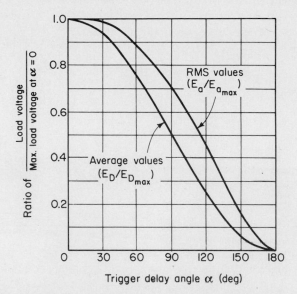

Fig. 8.2 Variation of average and rms load voltage with trigger delay angle in half-wave and full-wave SCR phase-controlled circuits with resistive load.

In Fig. 8.3, SCR_1 will apply voltage to the load if properly triggered during the half-cycle when the top end of the transformer secondary winding is positive (0 to $\omega t = \pi$). Between $\omega t = \pi$ and $\omega t = 2\pi$, the bottom end of the transformer is positive, and SCR_2 will apply voltage to the load if properly triggered. The similarity between the load current and voltage waveforms of Fig. 8.3(b) and those of Fig. 8.1(b) is obvious. Where the half-wave circuit applies a phase-controlled voltage to the load once each cycle, the full-wave circuit applies two such waveshapes each cycle, thus doubling the average voltage and power on the load as well as doubling the fundamental frequency of voltage on the load. Mathematical expressions of the output voltage may be derived in a similar way to the half-wave circuit. The equations and other pertinent data for this circuit and other generally used phase-controlled circuits are tabulated in Chart 8.1. It is interesting to note from these data that, unlike the half-wave circuit, the SCR's may be subjected to unequal forward and reverse blocking voltages. With load connected in this circuit [Chart 8.1(3)], the SCR will be subjected to a reverse voltage peak twice the value of the forward voltage. If triggered at the same delay angle, both SCR's share the load current. Hence, the maximum average current through each SCR is one-half of the maximum average load current.

If inductance is added to the load, some significant changes in the performance of the full-wave circuit take place. For the sake of simple circuit analysis and discussion, assume that the inductance is much larger than the

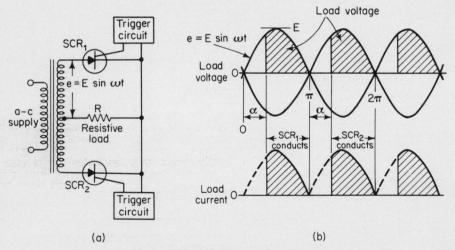

(a)   (b)

Fig. 8.3 Full-wave centertap phase-controlled SCR circuit with resistive load: (a) circuit; (b) waveforms.

"critical" value, which is defined as that value which will cause continuous current to flow in the load. Hence, essentially pure d-c load current will flow regardless of delay angle. In practice, the load current in circuits with even large inductive loads may revert to a discontinuous pulse mode similar to the resistive load case at delay angles larger than approximately 90 deg.

In accordance with the foregoing assumption, the load current is depicted at a continuous level in Fig. 8.4(b). In alternately sharing this load current, each SCR must conduct 180 deg each cycle regardless of the delay angle. As the trigger delay angle α is increased above zero, the continuous load current dictates that each SCR must conduct beyond the point where transformer voltage reverses. This is illustrated by the load voltage waveform in Fig. 8.4(b). SCR$_1$ is triggered at an angle α after time 0, and continues to conduct until SCR_2 is triggered at an angle α 180 deg later. From the point at which it is triggered until transformer voltage reversal at $\omega t = \pi$, SCR_1 delivers positive voltage to the load. Beyond $\omega t = \pi$, SCR_1 delivers negative voltage to the load, as depicted by the shaded area below the zero line. Expressed another way, during this latter part of the cycle SCR_1 returns energy stored in the load inductance to the supply line. The average d-c voltage on the load is the average value of the algebraic sum of the positive and negative voltage-time integrals. The average load current is the average d-c load voltage divided by the load resistance R.

The average d-c voltage, E_D, across an inductive load in the centertap circuit can be expressed as a function of the delay angle α as

$$E_D = \frac{\int_\alpha^{\alpha+\pi} E \sin \omega t \, d(\omega t)}{\int_\alpha^{\alpha+\pi} d(\omega t)} = \frac{E\left[-\cos \omega t\right]_\alpha^{\alpha+\pi}}{\left[\omega t\right]_\alpha^{\alpha+\pi}}$$

$$E_D = \frac{2E}{\pi} \cos \alpha. \tag{8.6}$$

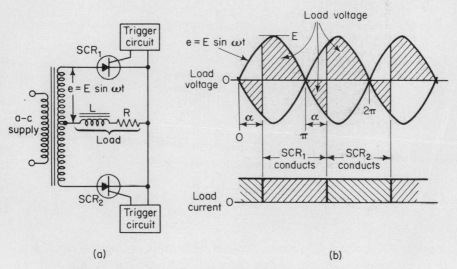

Fig. 8.4 Full-wave centertap phase-controlled SCR circuit with inductive load: (a) circuit; (b) waveforms.

Expressed as the ratio between the d-c load voltage and the maximum value at $\alpha = 0$,

$$\frac{E_D}{E_{D_{max}}} = \frac{\dfrac{2E}{\pi} \cos \alpha}{\dfrac{2E}{\pi}}$$

$$\frac{E_D}{E_{D_{max}}} = \cos \alpha. \tag{8.7}$$

Analysis of equations (8.6) and (8.7) reveals that, with inductive load, the d-c output voltage is zero at a delay angle of 90 deg, and that at a delay angle approaching 180 deg, the direction of energy transfer is wholly from the load back to the supply line. As contrasted to circuits in which the energy stored in an inductive load "free-wheels," as will be discussed later, this "pump-back" action of inductive load energy can be very useful for rapid reduction or momentary reversal of the voltage in the load in such applications as generator, motor, or magnetic clutch excitation, and lifting magnet supplies.

8.3 General Solution for Full-wave Circuits with Inductive Load

Other SCR circuits, including multiphase circuits, can be analyzed for load voltage characteristics versus trigger delay angle α in a manner similar to the preceding examples. The results of these analyses are tabulated in Chart 8.1.

For phase-controlled rectifiers with inductive load (no free-wheeling current paths), Rissik[1] has developed a generalized solution for the load voltage E_D as a function of delay angle in single-way circuits. For a system of p phases, each SCR will conduct $2\pi/p$ rad each cycle. This is illustrated in Fig. 8.5, in which the SCR under consideration is delayed in its triggering by

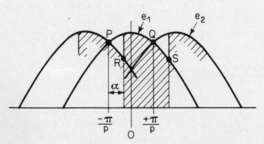

Fig. 8.5 Voltage waveshape in phase-controlled single-way inductive load circuits.

angle α and conducts from point R to point S instead of over the period from P to Q, which would occur with no delay. The load voltage is the average value of e_1 between R and S, that is, the shaded area under the curve divided by the time duration of this segment. The SCR anode voltage to the neutral point is $E \cos \omega t$, in which $-\pi/p < \omega t < +\pi/p$. For single-way circuits, the load voltage is

$$E_D = \frac{\int_{-(\pi/p)+\alpha}^{(\pi/p)+\alpha} E \cos \omega t \, d(\omega t)}{\dfrac{2\pi}{p}} = \frac{pE}{2\pi} \left[\sin \omega t \right]_{-(\pi/p)+\alpha}^{(\pi/p)+\alpha}$$

$$E_D = \frac{pE}{\pi} \sin \frac{\pi}{p} \cos \alpha \quad \text{for single-way circuits,} \tag{8.8}$$

where

$$E = \text{peak value of phase-to-neutral voltage.}$$

For double-way (bridge) circuits, the load voltage consists of the envelope from one side of the line to the opposite side of the line, rather than from line to neutral as in the single-way circuit. Accordingly, the load voltage is twice that of the single-way circuit for a given phase-to-neutral voltage. Expressed in terms of the peak line-to-neutral voltage E, the load voltage in double-way circuits is

$$E_D = \frac{2pE}{\pi} \sin \frac{\pi}{p} \cos \alpha \qquad (8.9)$$

for double-way (bridge) circuits with no free-wheeling paths for load current.

From equations (8.8) and (8.9) it is evident that the output load voltage of SCR phase-controlled circuits with inductive load varies as the cosine of the trigger delay angle regardless of circuit.

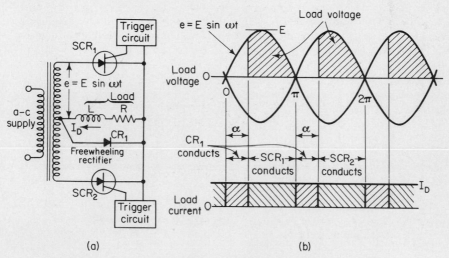

Fig. 8.6 Full-wave centertap phase-controlled SCR circuit with inductive load and free-wheeling rectifier: (a) circuit; (b) wave forms.

8.4 Inductive Loads with "Free-wheeling" Discharge Paths

A different type of circuit action with inductive load occurs if a "free-wheeling" rectifier is connected across the load. For example, rectifier CR_1 in Fig. 8.6(a) acts in a free-wheeling capacity in a single-phase centertap configuration. As in the foregoing sections, a heavily inductive load requires continuous current conduction in the load, as represented by the load-current waveform in Fig. 8.6(b).

SCR$_1$ conducts during the positive half-cycle from the instant at which it is triggered at delay angle α. However, unlike the earlier inductive load case, SCR$_1$ ceases to conduct as the supply voltage reverses at $\omega t = \pi$. As the voltage across the load tries to reverse its polarity, it is clamped at essentially zero by the presence of the free-wheeling rectifier CR_1, and the load current maintained by the load inductance flows through CR_1 until SCR$_2$ is, in turn, triggered. The periods of current flow through the SCR's and CR_1 are illustrated in Fig. 8.6(b). Although the load current has the waveshape characteristic of an inductive load, the load-voltage waveshape and the variation of its average value with delay angle are similar to those of the resistive load mode of operation described in Fig. 8.3. With the free-wheeling diode in place, this type of circuit cannot "pump back" the stored energy of the inductance into the supply line. Instead, by delaying the trigger to or beyond 180 deg, the inductive energy dissipates itself as a discharge current through the free-wheeling rectifier. This current decays at the rate of the L/R time constant of the load, and no amount of phase control can speed the decay.

The maximum steady-state duty on the free-wheeling diode CR_1 in the centertap circuit may be determined as follows. The load current as a function of supply voltage and trigger angle is

$$I_D = \frac{E}{\pi R}(1 + \cos \alpha).$$

Since CR_1 conducts during the delay angle, its share of the average load current is

$$I_{CR_1} = I_D\left(\frac{\alpha}{\pi}\right) = \frac{E}{\pi R}(1 + \cos \alpha)\left(\frac{\alpha}{\pi}\right) = \frac{E}{\pi^2 R}(\alpha + \alpha \cos \alpha).$$

To find the delay angle α at which the maximum value of I_{CR_1} occurs, we set

$$\frac{dI_{CR_1}}{d\alpha} = 0,$$

or

$$1 + \cos \alpha - \alpha \sin \alpha = 0.$$

Solving graphically for α, we obtain $\alpha = 74$ deg. If this value is substituted in the expression for I_{CR_1}, the maximum value is given as

$$I_{CR_1} = \frac{E}{\pi R}(1 + \cos 74°)\left(\frac{74°}{180°}\right),$$

or

$$\text{Maximum } I_{CR_1} = 0.26 I_D. \tag{8.10}$$

Chart 8.1 lists the current duty for free-wheeling rectifiers in this and other commonly used phase-controlled circuits.

8.5 The Single-phase Bridge and Its Alternate Variations

The preceding illustrative examples of resistive load, inductive load, and inductive load with a free-wheeling rectifier typify the three main categories of load for phase-controlled rectifiers. Although the single-phase centertap circuit is illustrated, the same analyses can be extended to other single-phase and multiphase circuits.

Because of its widespread acceptance since the advent of solid-state rectifiers and controlled rectifiers, the single-phase bridge deserves some additional discussion. It has several interesting variations, each with its similarities as well as unique features.

Figure 8.7 illustrates five variations of the single-phase bridge. With purely resistive load, all five circuits behave identically in so far as the load voltage variation with α is concerned. With inductive load, the performance of each circuit is unique. For easy reference the current and voltage duty on the semiconductors in each of the circuits is tabulated in Chart 8.1. Briefly, the characteristics of each circuit are as follows:

1. The circuit in Fig. 8.7(a) employs two SCR's with common cathodes (or common anodes) and diode rectifiers in the other two elements of the bridge. The common-cathode configuration is often desirable when one is triggering both SCR's from a common source without electrical isolation. Let us consider the half-cycle when the anode of SCR_1 is positive. SCR_1 will conduct current from the a-c supply through the load and the diagonally opposite diode CR_2 after it has been triggered at $\omega t = \alpha_1$. At time $\omega t = \pi$, the a-c supply voltage swings through zero. With inductive load, the stored energy in the load at this point starts free-wheeling through the low-impedance path of CR_1 and SCR_1, thus by-passing the a-c supply during this part of the cycle until SCR_2 is triggered at $\omega t = \alpha_2$. The waveforms in Fig. 8.7(a) indicate the conduction periods of each of the SCR's and diode rectifiers.

   With a high L/R ratio in the load, this circuit is handicapped by an inability to turn off the load voltage quickly. For example, if SCR_1 is conducting heavily and gate drive is abruptly removed from both SCR's, the load current will free-wheel through SCR_1 and CR_1 throughout the complete negative half-cycle. When the a-c supply swings positive again at $\omega t = 2\pi$, SCR_1 will already be in conduction as if triggered by the gate at $\alpha = 0$, and will deliver a full half-cycle of voltage to the load. Half-wave free-wheeling operation as in circuit 2 of Chart 8.1 will continue indefinitely until either the a-c or d-c circuit is opened, or until a gate signal on SCR_2 is again applied to commutate SCR_1, thus allowing both SCR's to be gradually phased back to zero output.

2. The instability limitation of circuit 8.7(a) can be remedied by adding a separate free-wheeling rectifier path, represented by CR_3 in Fig. 8.7(b). Since this single diode offers a lower-impedance discharge path for the stored load energy than the combined series impedance of CR_1 and SCR_1 or CR_2 and SCR_2, it will carry the load current during the free-wheeling part of the cycle. The relative conduction periods are indicated in the waveforms of Fig. 8.7(b). Except when $\alpha = 0$, the SCR's and diode rectifiers in the bridge conduct less average current than in the previous circuit. Also, since an SCR is not abruptly subjected to reverse voltage at the end of its conduction period, the commutating duty on the SCR's and bridge diodes is much less severe than in Fig. 8.7(a). However, CR_3 is now subjected to this severe commutating duty.

3. The stable action of circuit 8.7(b) can be duplicated without the need for an additional free-wheeling rectifier diode by connecting both SCR's to one of the a-c lines, as shown in Fig. 8.7(c). In this case, diodes CR_1 and CR_2 provide the free-wheeling path rather than the SCR's. While each of the SCR's conducts $(180 - \alpha)$ deg each cycle, CR_1 and CR_2 each conduct $(180 + \alpha)$ deg. Only the diodes are subject to heavy commutating duty.

4. The relative economics of SCR's versus diode rectifiers may sometimes make the circuit of Fig. 8.7(d) desirable. Here a single SCR in the d-c side of a conventional rectifier bridge (SCR_1) is used to control both halves of the a-c cycle. Even the slightest amount of inductance in the d-c circuit necessitates a free-wheeling rectifier, CR_5, for satisfactory commutation of SCR_1 each half-cycle. Without CR_5, the diodes in the bridge would have to provide free-wheeling action through SCR_1. Current flow through SCR_1 would be continuous, and the gate of SCR_1 would lose control over the circuit after SCR_1 had once been triggered. With CR_5 in the circuit, the current through SCR_1 drops to zero for several microseconds as the a-c supply voltage passes through zero. Ideally, the d-c output voltage across the bridge during reverse recovery of the diodes will swing one or two volts negative. This will apply about one volt negative potential across SCR_1 for a time duration dependent on the reverse recovery characteristics of CR_1 through CR_4. This positive turn-off action on SCR_1 can be used to provide reliable circuit operation well beyond 400 cps if the SCR turn-off time is a low value.

5. None of the four circuits above is capable of pumping back the stored magnetic load energy into the a-c supply, because of the free-wheeling action inherent in each. The free-wheeling path can be eliminated by

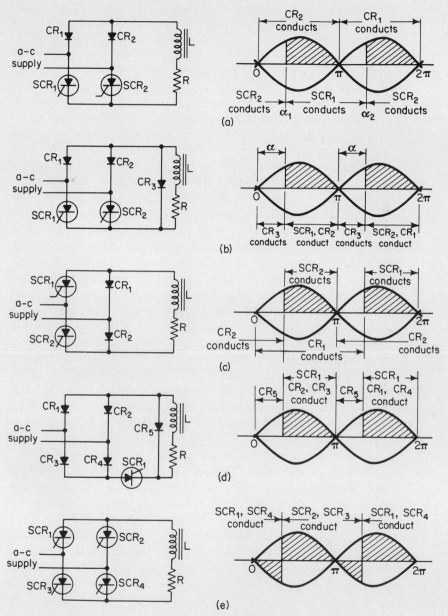

Fig. 8.7 Variations of the phase-controlled bridge with inductive load.

using an SCR in each of the four elements of the bridge, as shown in Fig. 8.7(e). This circuit operates analogously to that in Fig. 8.4, with negative voltage being applied to the load for a part of each cycle, depending on the trigger angle α. This type of circuit is used when the current through a highly inductive load must be quickly "killed" to zero. It should not be confused with reversing or plugging types of circuits, in which the voltage applied to the load can be reversed by additional SCR's without the prerequisite of stored magnetic energy in the load.

8.6 Generation of Harmonics

When operating in a phase-controlled circuit, SCR's function effectively as synchronous switches, and the loading on the a-c supply is of a pulsed or discontinuous nature. The current in both the a-c and d-c systems departs from the sinusoidal waveform typical of most other electrical apparatus operating from an a-c system. Depending on the specific circuit, the nature of both the supply system and the load, and the triggering angle, both voltage and current waveforms may be rich in harmonics of the a-c supply frequency.

Harmonics in the a-c supply may be of concern because of their possible interference effects on other loads on the same electrical system, and on nearby systems such as telephone and other audio circuits, owing to inductive coupling. These effects are seldom troublesome in SCR systems below approximately 100 kw. Interference at radio frequencies is discussed in Sec. 10.8. Another consideration arises from the fact that only the fundamental component of the a-c current wave in conjunction with the sinusoidal supply voltage can supply real power to the load. The harmonics in the system current produce additional losses by virtue of their rms value, and reduce the power factor of the rectifier. Detailed analysis of harmonics in the a-c supply is covered in pp. 284–317 of Ref. 1.

The d-c output of a phase-controlled rectifier circuit is composed of a pure direct current voltage with superimposed a-c harmonics which may be represented by a Fourier series. The output ripple voltage consists only of frequencies which are multiples of both the supply frequency and the number of rectifier phases.[1] Inductance in the d-c circuit reduces the amplitude of the current harmonics. Nearly perfect smoothing of the d-c output current can be obtained by using d-c chokes in series with the load so that the L/R ratio of the d-c circuit becomes very large, or through use of LC filters or active filters, such as series power transistors.

8.7 Current Commutation, Overlap, and Reverse Recovery

The circuit analyses and the formulas expressed in Chart 8.1 are based on the simplifying assumption that, even with inductive loads, the load current switches or commutates instantaneously from one SCR to another when the latter is triggered. This assumption greatly simplifies calculations and, at low frequencies and commercial voltages, generally does not substantially affect the results of these calculations. Actually, the presence of inductance in the a-c supply, the transformer, and the SCR circuitry will not permit the current to switch instantaneously from one SCR to the next.

Figure 8.8 represents a typical phase-controlled circuit in which the total commutating reactance for each SCR is represented as a lumped inductance X_c. SCR_2 is depicted as furnishing current i_2 to the inductive load up to the point $\omega t = (0 + \alpha)$ when SCR_1 is triggered. Because of the inductance in series with the SCR's, i_2 cannot immediately decrease to zero, nor can current i_1 through SCR_1 rise immediately to the load-current level I_D. Yet the load

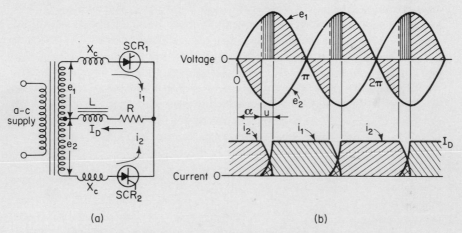

Fig. 8.8 The effects of overlap during commutation of load current: (a) circuit; (b) waveforms.

current I_D must remain essentially constant because of its inductive nature. To satisfy these conditions, i_1 increases on the locus of a short-circuit current, as depicted in Fig. 8.8(b), while i_2 decreases at a rate such that $i_1 + i_2 = I_D$ on an instantaneous basis. When i_1 reaches the load-current level, i_2 reaches zero. SCR_2 shuts off, and SCR_1 alone carries the load current for the remainder of that half-cycle. The interval of dual conduction is called the overlap angle u, and since both SCR's are conducting simultaneously during this interval, the transformer secondary terminals are essentially shorted out. The right-hand terminal of the load is at a voltage which is the mean value between the potentials of the ends of the transformer windings. In this circuit the mean value is at the same voltage as the centertap. Hence, the voltage across the load during the overlap angle is zero, and overlap thus causes a loss in load voltage, represented by the vertically shaded area (see Fig. 8.4 for comparison with the nonoverlap case).

The overlap angle is a function of the commutating reactance X_C and I_C, the direct current commutated from one SCR to the next. In Fig. 8.8, $I_C = I_D$, the d-c load current. It can be shown[2] that the relationship between these factors is

$$\cos (u + \alpha) = \cos \alpha - \frac{I_C X_C}{E \sin \dfrac{\pi}{p}}, \tag{8.11}$$

where

X_C = commutating reactance line-to-neutral in ohms.
E = peak line-to-neutral voltage.
p = number of phases (two in single-phase full wave).

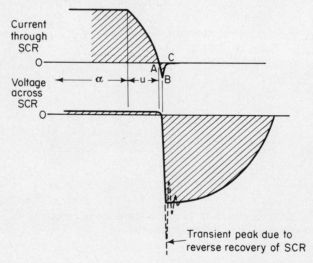

Fig. 8.9 Detail of commutation in phase-controlled SCR circuit.

Likewise, the loss in d-c load voltage E_x owing to overlap† may be expressed as

$$E_x = \frac{I_C X_C p}{2\pi}. \tag{8.12}$$

It should be noted that overlap in the sense used above does not exist in phase-controlled circuits when a free-wheeling rectifier is active in the circuit.

---

† A loss in load voltage also results from resistive voltage drop (copper losses) in the circuit. This voltage drop is directly proportional to the load current and the value of source and circuit resistance.

Phase-controlled circuits, particularly those with inductive loads, often subject the SCR's to severe "commutating duty" when phased back to intermediate triggering angles, such as those illustrated in Fig. 8.8. A detailed enlargement of the current waveshape and the SCR voltage is shown in Fig. 8.9.

At the end of the commutation interval, point A, the current through the outgoing phase reaches zero at a relatively steep rate of change. Under this condition practical SCR's have a substantial number of minority current carriers left in their center-base regions which must be swept out or neutralized by recombination before the SCR will block reverse voltage. Hence, a reverse sweepout current builds up through the SCR for several microseconds, as indicated between points A and B in Fig. 8.9. At point B the SCR regains its blocking ability very abruptly, and the reverse current is forced to essentially zero at point C while the voltage across the SCR jumps to a high negative value (the line-to-line transformer secondary voltage). The abrupt chopping of the reverse current between B and C can lead to dangerous transient reverse voltage peaks and oscillations on the SCR, as indicated by the dashed waveform, owing to the exchange of stored energy between the circuit inductance and capacitance. To correct these transient conditions, "snubber" circuits composed of series resistance and capacitance are often connected across the SCR's.

8.8 D-C Motor Drives

The use of SCR's for control of motor speed is a large subject which includes several other techniques in addition to phase control. Although a detailed discussion is beyond the scope of this book, several factors of general interest can be mentioned about phase control of d-c motors.

Because of the increased form factor of phase-controlled armature current compared to that which occurs in operation of a motor on pure direct current, higher copper losses for a given torque must be expected. Likewise, the harmonic content of the phase-controlled armature voltage waveshape produces additional iron losses in the machine. If objectionable, both of these factors can be minimized by using a d-c choke in series with the motor armature or by increasing the number of phases.

Another factor worthy of consideration arises from the counterelectromotive force (CEMF) of a d-c motor load. With a non-CEMF resistive or inductive load, maximum SCR current flows when the SCR conduction angle of each cycle is maximum ($\alpha = 0$). Provided the SCR is capable of handling the current at the maximum conduction angle into a resistive load, it has no trouble carrying the lower currents which occur at shorter conduction angles. However, a d-c motor may be called on to deliver its maximum torque at very low speeds. This requires the SCR to furnish high average current at a low phased-back d-c voltage. Because of the SCR's current-rating dependence on conduction angle (Fig. 4.26), this condition of high current during a short conduction angle (high form factor) thus becomes the limiting SCR rating in contrast to the linear resistive type of load. Here again, a smoothing choke in series with the motor can spread out the conduction angle for a given torque requirement and hence can increase the current-handling capability of a given SCR.

Motor loads, as well as certain filament-type loads, are characterized by heavy inrush currents if full voltage is suddenly applied to them. "Soft-start" and current limiting circuits[3] can be used to phase back the armature voltage during the starting interval or on overloads, thus protecting the SCR as well as the motor from damage.

8.9 Triggering Phase-controlled Circuits

Fundamental types of SCR trigger circuits for phase control were covered in Sec. 5.5. For the sake of basic discussion, these circuits generally employed manual or mechanical control in the form of a potentiometer to vary the phase of the SCR trigger signal. Substitution of a proper sensing resistor for the potentiometer allows these circuits to be controlled by light, temperature, pressure, humidity, etc. Many of these trigger circuits can also be controlled by low-level electrical signals, thus allowing them to be used as amplifiers and in closed-loop or feedback control systems. Regulated power supplies, temperature controls, and adjustable-speed motor drives are typical of such applications.

This section deals with the control and transfer characteristics of a few of the more common SCR trigger circuits.

8.9.1 SATURABLE-REACTOR TRIGGER CIRCUITS

Section 5.5.4 describes the fundamental principles of typical saturable-reactor and magnetic-amplifier triggering circuits for SCR's. The various magnetic triggering circuits are unusually well adapted to phase control of SCR's because of the reset mechanism inherent or easily available in a-c systems, and because the integrating effects of saturating and reset circuits yield generally desirable transfer-characteristic relationships between the control signal and the load voltage. See Fig. 8.10. These types of circuits are also particularly useful where several electrically isolated control signals must be added algebraically, the total signal being used to impart the triggering-angle intelligence to the SCR. A number of standard packaged magnetic-trigger circuits are commercially available for SCR's.

Magnetic-trigger circuits of the type shown in Fig. 5.27 apply a long-duration signal to the SCR gate each cycle instead of the short type of pulse generated by a unijunction transistor. An extended gate signal is desirable when SCR's are operated in highly inductive circuits which require considerable time for the load current to build up to the latching and holding current requirements of the SCR after it is triggered. This avoids the need for special dummy resistive loads or *RC* networks across the load that are often required in inductive circuits when one is operating SCR's with pulsed rather than extended gate signals.

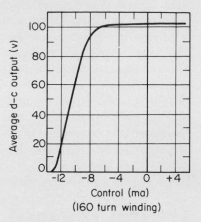

Fig. 8.10 Transfer characteristics of a magnetic-type trigger for SCR's [courtesy of Magnetics, Inc.].

The circuit in Fig. 5.27 derives its voltage and phase reference across the a-c line rather than across the SCR. This is necessary when inverse parallel SCR's (circuit 15, Chart 8.1) are being used to phase-control a-c power to highly inductive loads, such as transformer primary windings, solenoids, or some a-c motors. Erratic triggering and saturation of the magnetic load may occur if the trigger voltage and phase reference are taken across the SCR's rather than across the a-c line.

Figure 5.41 shows a semiconductor circuit which operates analogously to the magnetic trigger circuit and hence can be used for satisfactory SCR triggering even in highly inductive circuits. This circuit can employ a unijunction transistor oscillator to trigger small "pilot" SCR's which provide phase-controlled maintained gate signals to the main-power SCR's. The unijunction transistor, in turn, can be controlled by one of the methods described in the following section.

8.9.2 Unijunction Transistor Trigger Circuits

Because of its unique combination of economy, simplicity, compactness, low power consumption, and high effective power gain, the unijunction transistor (UJT) has been widely adopted for a great variety of phase-control triggering applications. Section 5.5.7 describes the fundamental characteristics and operation of the UJT, as well as several manually controlled circuits using the UJT.

In using the UJT, the circuit designer has a number of basic circuit arrangements from which to choose, each yielding its own specific control transfer characteristics. All of these circuits are variations of the UJT in its basic relaxation oscillator circuit, and for the sake of illustration are shown here in a single-phase half-wave circuit. The same control transfer characteristics apply for full-wave single-phase circuits with resistive a-c or d-c loads, or for inductive load circuits with a free-wheeling rectifier across the load.

Series resistance control: Figure 8.11(a) illustrates one of the simplest UJT trigger circuits, in which the trigger angle is controlled by varying resistor R in the charging circuit to capacitor C. This circuit is suitable for manual control of the average load voltage E_D, or for those circuits where such elements as thermistors or photosensitive resistors can be substituted for R.

Figure 8.11(b) shows the load voltage as a function of the RC time constant and supply line frequency for several values of the UJT intrinsic standoff ratio η. In equation form, this transfer characteristic can be expressed as[4]

$$\frac{E_D}{E_{D_{\max}}} = \frac{1}{2}\left[\cos\left(2\pi f RC \ln \frac{1}{1-\eta}\right) + 1\right].   (8.13)$$

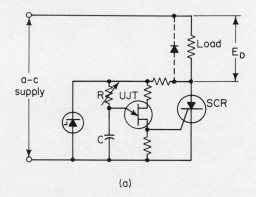

(a)

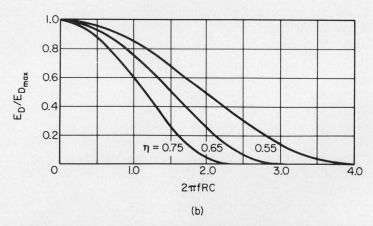

(b)

Fig. 8.11 Phase control with unijunction transistor using series resistance control for half- and full-wave circuits: (a) half-wave circuit; (b) control transfer characteristic.

Series transistor control: For electrical control of the UJT trigger angle, a transistor operating in a heavily degenerative common-emitter mode may be inserted in place of the timing resistor of Fig. 8.11. This arrangement is shown in Fig. 8.12(a). This circuit and the others discussed in this section can be readily analyzed with several simplifying assumptions that yield practical results: (1) the circuit for synchronizing the UJT with the voltage on the SCR anode is such that timing is initiated simultaneously with the point at which the SCR anode voltage swings positive through zero; (2) the SCR acts as a perfect switch; (3) leakage currents of all transistors and capacitors are zero;

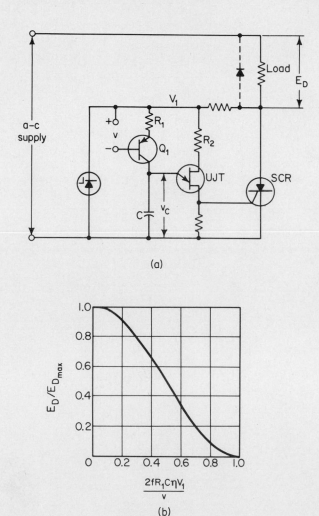

(a)

(b)

Fig. 8.12 Phase control with unijunction transistor using series transistor control for half-wave and full-wave circuits: (a) half-wave circuit; (b) control transfer characteristic.

(4) transistor current gain is sufficiently high that collector current can be assumed to be equal to emitter current; and (5) the UJT is perfectly temperature-compensated by proper resistance in base two.

In Fig. 8.12(a), capacitor C is charged by the collector current of transistor Q_1. For this common-emitter configuration, the collector current i_c of Q_1 is

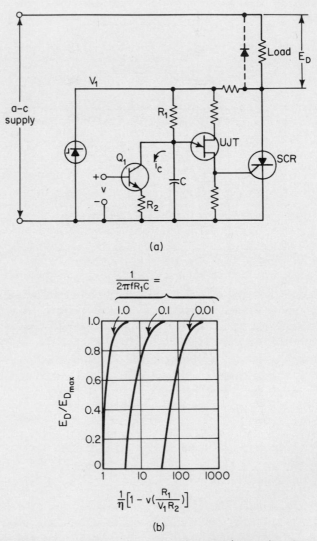

(a)

(b)

Fig. 8.13 Phase control with unijunction transistor using shunt transistor control for half-wave and full-wave circuits: (a) half-wave circuit; (b) control transfer characteristic.

v/R_1, where v is the control signal applied to the circuit. Accordingly, the voltage v_c across capacitor C can be expressed as

$$v_c = \frac{i_c t}{C} = \frac{vt}{R_1 C},$$

where t is the time in seconds from the start of the charging cycle. The UJT triggers at $\omega t = \alpha$ when v_c reaches ηV_1 (Sec. 5.5.7). This occurs at time $t = \alpha/2\pi f$, where α is the trigger angle. Thus,

$$v_c = \eta V_1 = \frac{vt}{R_1 C} = \frac{v\alpha}{2\pi f R_1 C}.$$

Solving for α, we have

$$\alpha = \frac{2\pi f R_1 C \eta V_1}{v}.$$

From equation (8.2), the variation of load voltage for half-wave circuits (as well as full-wave circuits) with resistive load is

$$\frac{E_D}{E_{D_{\max}}} = \frac{1 + \cos \alpha}{2}.$$

Substituting for α, we get

$$\frac{E_D}{E_{D_{\max}}} = \frac{1}{2} + \frac{1}{2} \cos \left(\frac{2\pi f R_1 C \eta V_1}{v} \right). \tag{8.14}$$

This transfer characteristic is shown in Fig. 8.12(b).

Shunt transistor control: Higher control power gain at the expense of linearity can be achieved with the UJT by connecting the control transistor across the timing capacitor instead of in series with it. Shunt transistor control is illustrated by Q_1 in Fig. 8.13(a). A signal v on the base of Q_1 causes collector current i_c to be diverted from C, thus increasing the time α required for the capacitor to charge to the triggering point.

The transfer characteristic of this type of circuit can be expressed as[4]

$$\frac{E_D}{E_{D_{\max}}} = \frac{1}{2} \left\{ \cos \left[2\pi f R_1 C \ln \frac{(V_1 R_2 - vR_1)}{(V_1 R_2 - vR_1 - \eta V_1 R_2)} \right] + 1 \right\}. \tag{8.15}$$

This is shown in graphical form in Fig. 8.13(b). Note that, as the control signal v increases, the output voltage decreases, with the maximum gain occurring near minimum output.

Linear UJT control: The circuit of Fig. 8.14(a) is useful for those applications that require linear control characteristics over the complete range from zero to full output. Figure 8.14(b) depicts the linearity of this approach.

Capacitor C_1 is charged from a sine wave current source so that its voltage, v_{C_1}, is a cosine function with respect to the SCR anode voltage. In

Fig. 8.14(a), the current source is derived by proper selection of R_1 and C_1. A suitable transistor drive can also be used for this purpose. Capacitor C_1 is large compared to C_2 and C_3. Accordingly,

$$v_{C_1} = \frac{1}{C_1} \int_0^\alpha I_p \sin \omega t \, dt = \frac{I_p}{\omega C_1} (1 - \cos \alpha),$$

where $I_p \sin \omega t$ is the charging current to C_1.

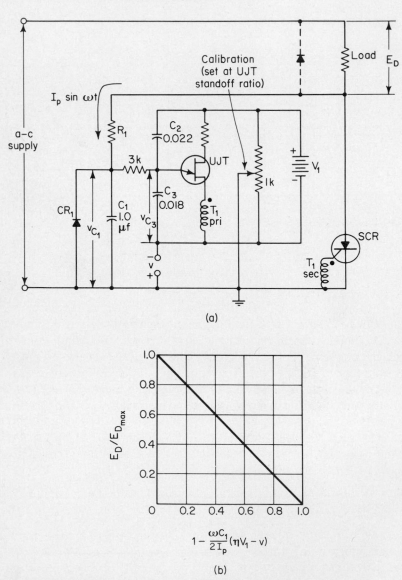

(a)

(b)

Fig. 8.14 Linear phase control using unijunction transistor: (a) half-wave circuit; (b) control transfer characteristic.

The UJT triggers at angle α, when the voltage between the UJT emitter and base one, v_{C_3}, reaches the peak-point voltage ηV_1 of the UJT. The UJT trigger circuit is held below system ground by the control signal voltage v, so

$$v_{C_3} = v + v_{C_1}.$$

At the instant of triggering, the preceding equations give

$$v_{C_3} = v + v_{C_1} = v + \frac{I_p}{\omega C_1}(1 - \cos \alpha) = \eta V_1.$$

Solving for $\cos \alpha$, we get

$$\cos \alpha = 1 - \frac{\omega C_1}{I_p}(\eta V_1 - v).$$

From equation (8.2), the variation of load voltage for half- and full-wave circuits with resistive load, or for inductive load with a free-wheeling rectifier, is

$$\frac{E_D}{E_{D_{\max}}} = \frac{1 + \cos \alpha}{2}.$$

Substitution for $\cos \alpha$ yields

$$\frac{E_D}{E_{D_{\max}}} = \frac{1 + \left[1 - \dfrac{\omega C_1}{I_p}(\eta V_1 - v)\right]}{2},$$

or

$$\frac{E_D}{E_{D_{\max}}} = 1 - \frac{\omega C_1}{2 I_p}(\eta V_1 - v). \tag{8.16}$$

The linear variation of load voltage with control signal v is plotted in Fig. 8.14(b). Note that 100 per cent output voltage is developed when $v = \eta V_1$. For zero output when $v = 0$, the current source and the capacitor C_1 must be selected so that $2 I_p / \omega C_1 = \eta V_1$.

During the negative half-cycle of the a-c supply, diode CR_1 establishes a zero voltage on C_1 in preparation for the next timing cycle. The circuit of Fig. 8.14(a) can be adapted to single-phase full-wave operation by charging C_1 from a full-wave rectified current source with suitable means for discharging C_1 after each SCR has been triggered. Other UJT circuit configurations are possible for linear control transfer characteristics.[5]

REFERENCES

1. H. Rissik, *Mercury-Arc Current Convertors*. London: Sir Isaac Pitman & Sons, Ltd., 1941, pp. 182, 284.

2. E. F. Christensen, C. H. Willis, and C. C. Herskind, "Analysis of Rectifier Circuits," *A.I.E.E. Trans.*, Vol. **63** (1944).

3. *Silicon Controlled Rectifier Manual*, 2nd ed. General Electric Company, Auburn, N.Y., 1962, pp. 119–20.

4. F. W. Gutzwiller, "An All-Solid-State Phase Controlled Rectifier System," A.I.E.E. Conference Paper CP 59-217, presented at Winter General Meeting, New York, February, 1959.

5. E. K. Howell, "Better SCR Phase Control In Control Systems," *Electronic Design*, February 3, 1964, pp. 34–39.

6. W. P. Overbeck, "Critical Inductance and Control Rectifiers," *Proc. I.R.E.*, Vol. **27**, No. 10 (October, 1939), pp. 655–59.

CHAPTER 9

POWER INVERTERS AND D-C CHOPPERS

The SCR has a wide field of application as a power switch in circuits that convert direct current to alternating current (often called "inverters") or to direct current at a different voltage level (converters). Circuits of a similar nature are also used to convert alternating current of one frequency to alternating current at another frequency. Although many different SCR inverter and converter circuits have been proposed and used for these specific purposes, all circuits have one particularly important characteristic in common: they include circuit means for turning off or commutating the current through the SCR's so that they regain their forward blocking ability after conduction in each cycle.

In circuits operating from an a-c line such as those discussed in the previous chapter, SCR commutation is accomplished by the natural reversal of the a-c power system. Line commutation of this type can also be used for those inverters that convert and transfer power from a d-c supply into a stiff a-c system. In this case the a-c system on the output is used to commutate or turn off the SCR's in the inverter. For example, a phase-controlled rectifier circuit like that in Fig. 8.4 delivers power from the inductive d-c load to the a-c supply twice each cycle. If a d-c source is connected in the load in proper polarity, and if the SCR's are triggered at a delay angle greater than 90 deg, this circuit will deliver (invert) a net flow of power from the d-c source to the a-c system on a continuous basis. However, care must be taken not to trigger the SCR's at delay angles greater than 180 deg. Triggering beyond 180 deg will result in the a-c system's being connected to the d-c source in such polarity that the flow of SCR current will be aided rather than opposed, thus allowing a short-circuit current of damaging proportions to build up in the d-c system. Further discussion in this chapter will be confined to those types of circuits which are *not* connected to a stiff a-c system and which are commutated instead by suitable load characteristics and special turn-off circuitry.

Chapter 6 discusses the basic criteria for turning off an SCR and presents several fundamental circuits besides line commutation for accomplishing SCR turn-off. Inverter and chopper circuits operating on a cyclical basis use any one of these or similar turn-off schemes. The optimum type of turn-off circuit for a particular application depends on electrical considerations, such as frequency, efficiency, regulation, SCR switching characteristics, the possibility of open- and short-circuited load conditions, and the starting and stopping duty. In addition, the bulk and cost of circuit components may be deciding factors in the choice of an inverter or chopper circuit.

Satisfactory operation of SCR's in inverter and chopper circuits depends largely on the length of time (t_c) that the circuit applies reverse voltage to the SCR to turn it off during each cycle. Provided that the circuit applies reverse voltage to the SCR for a time longer than the critical turn-off time characteristic of the SCR (t_{OFF}), the SCR gate can regain control of forward blocking ability. If the circuit turn-off time decreases below the critical turn-off time of the SCR, the SCR will fail to block forward voltage in the following half-cycle. In most inverter circuits this leads to a short-circuit condition which requires prompt shut-down of the circuit to prevent damage.

The inverter and chopper circuits that are described below have been selected because of their fundamental nature and wide applicability. The basic equations apply as well to other circuit arrangements that use the same turn-off principles. In general, the parallel inverter is used for low-frequency applications (below approximately 2 kc) and the series inverter for high frequencies (above approximately 1 kc). Rectification of the a-c output of these types of inverter circuits provides efficient d-c to d-c conversion. Likewise, an a-c input can be rectified to furnish d-c power to an inverter, thus providing frequency-changing action. In this latter case, a capacitor between rectifier and inverter is generally used to provide a low-impedance path for high-frequency components in the inverter and to accept power from the inverter during brief intervals in each cycle.

9.1 The Basic Parallel Inverter

Figure 9.1 illustrates the basic parallel inverter, so called because the commutating capacitor C is connected effectively in parallel with the load (in this case, the primary of a transformer feeding the load). Power is supplied to the inverter from a d-c source E, and alternating current is delivered to the load through a transformer which, for the purpose of analysis, has a secondary winding with the same number of turns as each side of centertap on the primary. Step-up or step-down of voltage may be secured by suitable variation of this turns ratio. A d-c choke L_1 is connected in series with the d-c source. It is assumed to be large enough to cause continuous current to flow from the d-c supply. The trigger circuit applies a positive gate signal to each SCR alternately and thus determines the frequency of the alternating current output.

It is assumed that SCR_1 is conducting and SCR_2 blocking; a portion of the d-c supply voltage, e, is applied to the left-hand side of the transformer. Autotransformer action charges capacitor C to a voltage $2e$, with positive polarity on the right-hand

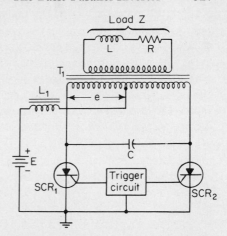

Fig. 9.1 Single-phase parallel inverter with reactive load.

side of the capacitor. When a trigger signal is applied to the gate of SCR_2, it switches into conduction and applies the commutating capacitor C across SCR_1 in such a polarity that SCR_1 is abruptly turned off by this negative voltage. Capacitor C discharges through the d-c source at a rate depending on the load current already flowing in L_1. With current flowing from left to right through the right-hand side of the transformer primary and SCR_2, voltage on the transformer now reverses and charges capacitor C to the opposite polarity. When SCR_1 is again triggered, SCR_2 is commutated by capacitor C, and the circuit reverts to its original state. In this manner, current is alternately conducted through each half of the transformer primary, creating an alternating flux and an a-c voltage in the secondary.

Figure 9.2 illustrates the voltage and current waveforms in the basic parallel inverter when it is operating with continuous current from the d-c supply.† Current alternately flows through each SCR and approximates a square wave. Each SCR delivers one-half the average current supplied by the d-c source. The short current peak at the end of each conduction period in Fig. 9.2(b) is the reverse recovery transient that sweeps carriers out of the end regions of the *p-n-p-n* structure until the SCR gains its reverse blocking ability. The reverse recovery current flows through the incoming SCR in the forward direction and shows itself as a positive pulse on the leading edge of the current waveshape. Under loaded conditions, the load voltage [solid line in Fig. 9.2(c)] approaches a square wave. As load current is reduced, the

† For an analysis of this circuit when the d-c supply current flows in pulses, see C. F. Wagner, "Parallel Inverters with Resistive Load," *Electrical Engineering* (November, 1935), pp. 1227–35.

commutating capacitor C takes longer to reverse its charge each cycle, and the load voltage assumes a triangular waveform of higher amplitude, as indicated by the dashed lines in Figs. 9.2(c) and 9.2(d). For a transformer turns ratio of 1:1 between all three windings, the blocking voltage across each SCR is twice the load voltage as indicated in Fig. 9.2(d). The circuit turn-off time t_c increases at light loads. The peak voltage that the SCR must block also increases simultaneously and can reach several times the d-c supply voltage. Heavy overloads or short circuits that momentarily reduce the circuit turn-off

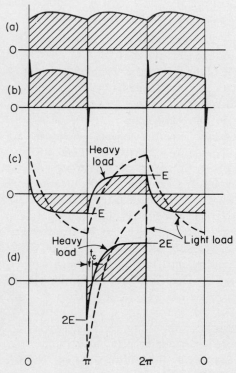

Fig. 9.2 Voltage and current waveforms in basic parallel inverter (Fig. 9.1): (a) d-c supply current, (b) current through SCR_1, (c) load voltage, and (d) voltage across SCR_1.

time below the turn-off time characteristic of the SCR prevent the SCR from turning off at the end of its half-cycle of conduction. With both SCR's conducting simultaneously under this condition, the transformer does not support voltage, and a high fault current builds up until the d-c source is interrupted by external means.

Wagner[1] has developed equations and curves showing the main relationships in the basic parallel-inverter circuit with inductive load and no feedback of reactive energy. Figure 9.3 shows the circuit turn-off time as a function of load and commutating parameters for this type of inverter circuit with sufficient inductance to maintain constant d-c current from the source. Circuit turn-off time t_c must be longer than the turn-off time of the SCR's under worst conditions of current and temperature to maintain satisfactory circuit operation. Note that inductive loads require considerable commutating capacitance, regardless of the SCR turn-off time characteristics. The basic parallel inverter actually requires sufficient commutating capacitance to overcompensate for any lagging power factor load.

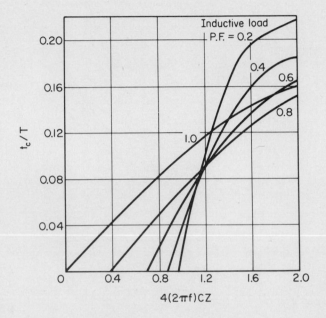

C = commutating capacitance (farad).
Z = load impedance referred to primary (ohms) = $\sqrt{R^2 + (\omega L)^2}$.
T = time for one cycle (sec) $1/f$.
t_c = circuit turn-off time (sec).
P.F. = power factor (R/Z).

Fig. 9.3 Turn-off time characteristics for basic parallel inverter with continuous d-c current.

Peak SCR voltage in both the forward and reverse directions is plotted in Fig. 9.4 for various circuit conditions. This set of curves is adapted from Wagner's analysis. As load impedance increases, SCR voltage mounts rapidly, so it is obvious that a minimum load must be maintained on the inverter to keep the SCR's functioning properly.

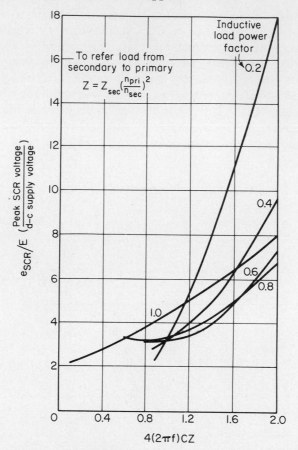

Fig. 9.4 Peak forward and reverse voltage on SCR in basic parallel inverter (Fig. 9.1).

9.2 Parallel Inverter with Reactive Feedback

Minor modifications of the basic parallel inverter can overcome several limitations of the foregoing circuit. Figure 9.5 illustrates this improved circuit, which was described by McMurray and Shattuck.[2] Although it superficially resembles the basic parallel inverter of Fig. 9.1, its method of commutation is quite different. The addition of the feedback diodes CR_1 and CR_2 permits this circuit to operate reliably into widely varying reactive loads without the need for large values of commutating capacitance C. Likewise, the voltage applied to the SCR's is held to a value slightly greater than $2E$, not only over wide load-power-factor changes, but also from no load to full load.

In Fig. 9.5 the d-c choke is moved to the cathode circuit of the SCR's and is selected to resonate with the commutating capacitor C to provide a negative interval of voltage on the SCR anode that is somewhat longer than the turn-off time required for the SCR. Choke L_1 is no longer a source of continuous current, and it and capacitor C are smaller in value than is needed for the previously described basic parallel inverter under similar lagging power-factor load conditions.

Consider one-half cycle of operation of this circuit when it is operating into an inductive load. Assume that SCR_1 is in conduction and that the current has reached a constant value through it and L_1. The anode of SCR_2 and the right-hand plate of C will attain twice the d-c supply voltage E above ground

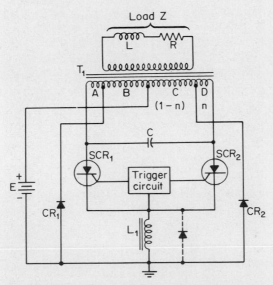

Fig. 9.5 Parallel inverter with feedback of reactive energy.

owing to the autotransformer action of T_1. Triggering of SCR_2 connects C across SCR_1 in the reverse direction, turning it off. At the same time, voltage $2E$ is also applied across choke L_1. Capacitor C discharges in oscillatory fashion through L_1, CR_1, and the extreme left-hand part of the primary winding of T_1. As capacitor C resonantly reverses its charge, the anode of SCR_2 starts to swing negative with respect to ground. This forces diode CR_2 into conduction to discharge the energy ($\frac{1}{2}LI^2$) now stored in L_1. Current flow now continues through SCR_2, CR_2, and the extreme right-hand side of the transformer primary. Autotransformer action between sections C and D serves to return part of the stored energy in L_1 to the d-c supply, thus minimizing losses.

With the brief commutating interval complete (typically in the order of 10 to 25 μsec) and with SCR_1 now turned off, the inductive load attempts to maintain load current in the direction it had been flowing prior to commutation, for a period of time depending on the load power factor. During this part of the cycle SCR$_2$ turns off, and current continues to flow from right to left in the transformer primary, the path now being section C of the primary, the d-c source, and CR_2. This action returns reactive load energy to the d-c supply. When this inductive current reaches zero, SCR$_2$ can again be triggered and current established in the opposite direction through transformer and load. Now CR_2 blocks while SCR$_2$ conducts to complete the new half-cycle until SCR$_1$ is triggered again.

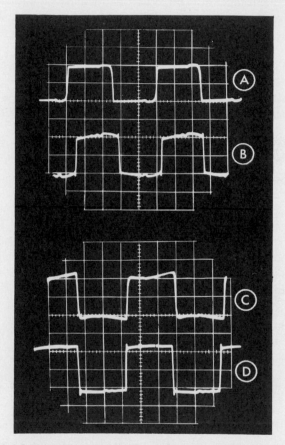

Fig. 9.6 Load voltage waveforms at 400 cps for SCR inverter of type shown in Fig. 9.5 ($n = 0$): (a) load power factor = 1.0; (b) load power factor = 0.7 lagging; (c) load power factor = 0.7 leading; (d) load open circuit. Horizontal scale = 500 μsec/cm. Vertical scale = 100 v/cm.

In order to provide the double triggering necessary for each SCR every half-cycle when the circuit operates into inductive load, the trigger signal must consist of a series of pulses or a square wave rather than a single short pulse. Typical trigger circuits for this type of inverter are shown in Fig. 5.34.

On capacitive load, the feedback diodes CR_1 and CR_2 conduct reactive current before, rather than after, the half-cycle of voltage ends. With resistive load, the feedback diodes conduct only during the brief interval when an SCR is being commutated by the reversal of voltage on C.

To minimize overshoot of the load voltage and forward SCR blocking voltage at the beginning of each half-cycle and to achieve optimum regulation of load voltage, the two primary halves of the transformer must be closely coupled through use of such design techniques as bifilar winding. With close coupling between both primary windings, it is evident from inspection of the circuit in Fig. 9.5 that the voltage across section B and section C on the primary cannot exceed the d-c source voltage E. Any voltage in excess of this value is clamped by current flow into the d-c source through one of the feedback diodes depending on polarity of the a-c voltage. Figure 9.6 shows load-voltage waveforms in a typical inverter circuit of this type under various load- and power-factor conditions. The excellent load regulation of this type of circuit is evident from these oscillograms.

Peak forward voltage on the SCR's is limited to $2E/(1 - n)$, where n is the ratio of the number of transformer primary end turns, indicated by n in Fig. 9.5, to the total turns in one half of the primary. If the cathode of the feedback diode is connected directly to the adjacent SCR anode so that $n = 0$, SCR blocking voltage requirements are $2E$, the minimum value, and the load-voltage waveform best approximates a square wave. However, with $n = 0$ there is no longer any mechanism for pumping back trapped energy in L_1 to the d-c supply at the end of the commutating interval. Instead, this energy is dissipated as a circulating current in the SCR's and feedback diodes, reducing efficiency, particularly at high frequencies. On the other hand, operation with a feedback tap where $0.1 < n < 0.2$ minimizes losses caused by circulating currents.

Under resistive load, each SCR conducts essentially a full half-cycle or 180 electrical deg, and the average current through each SCR is one-half the average load current. With reactive loads, the feedback diodes conduct the part of each cycle when the load voltage is out of phase with the load current, and SCR current is reduced accordingly. The average current $I_{F(AV)}$ through each SCR can be approximated as follows:

$$I_{F(AV)} = \frac{ER}{2Z^2}, \tag{9.1}$$

where

R = load resistance referred to one-half of the primary winding (ohms).

Z = total load impedance referred to one-half of the primary winding (ohms).

The conduction angle of each SCR is approximately $(180° - \arccos R/Z)$ each cycle.

McMurray and Shattuck[2] have analytically determined the values of the commutating parameters, C and L_1, for maximum efficiency (minimum trapped energy in L_1) over a wide range of power factors. These parameters are

$$C = \frac{t_{\text{OFF}}I_c}{1.7E} \text{ farad,} \qquad (9.2)$$

$$L_1 = \frac{t_{\text{OFF}}E}{0.425I_c} \text{ h,} \qquad (9.3)$$

where

t_{OFF} = maximum turn-off time of SCR, seconds.

I_c = maximum value of load current (referred to primary) at instant of commutation, amperes.

Like the basic parallel inverter, heavy overloads or short circuits that exceed the ability of C to commutate the SCR's lead to conduction of both SCR's simultaneously and to a resulting fault condition.

For satisfactory operation, the transformer core must sustain a full half-cycle of voltage without saturating. Unless precautions are taken,

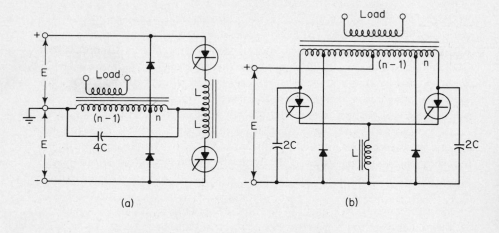

(a)   (b)

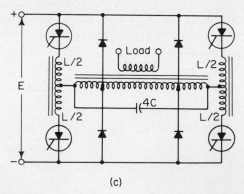

(c)

Fig. 9.7 Alternate circuit arrangements of the parallel commutated inverter with provision for feedback of reactive load energy.

transformer saturation may also cause starting problems if the first half-cycle is in the same direction as the last half-cycle prior to the previous inverter shutdown.

Several alternate solutions can be used to overcome the possibility of transformer saturation under this condition. The transformer can be designed to operate at less than half of saturation flux density, or an air gap may be introduced to provide a low residual flux. Also, the SCR gating circuit can be arranged to start the inverter at an initially higher frequency, or to start it in a polarity direction opposite to the direction of the residual flux.

Efficiencies of 85 per cent or better are readily available at conventional power voltages and frequencies. Figure 9.7 illustrates three other variations of the parallel commutated inverter with provision for feedback of reactive load energy.

9.3 The Series Inverter

As the operating frequency of a simple parallel power inverter is increased above about 1000 cps, efficiency begins to fall sharply as switching and commutation losses mount. For efficient inverter operation at frequencies in the ultrasonic range, the series inverter has several advantages over the parallel type. As used here, the term *series inverter* refers to circuits in which the commutating capacitor operates effectively in series with the load. Hence, current flowing into and out of the commutating capacitor traverses the load and thereby delivers energy to it, rather than being wasted. The commutating energy is not trapped or dissipated in circuit elements. If the inverter is properly designed, the SCR's switch at a point in the cycle where load current is at a low value, thus minimizing switching losses in the SCR. These factors enhance operating efficiency of the series inverter at high frequency. Furthermore, the turn-off time of the SCR may be a substantial part (10 per cent to 25 per cent) of the full cycle, and the rate of rise of forward voltage after the turn-off interval is relatively low and thus compatible with the characteristics of typical SCR's. With little additional circuitry the series inverter may be made short- and open-circuit proof, and, with proper design, the output voltage approximates a sine wave without additional filtering.

A major handicap of the series inverter is the high kva rating required of the reactive components in comparison with the load. This shortcoming is minimized at higher frequencies, where inductive and capacitive values can be low for a given kva requirement.

9.3.1 OPERATION OF THE BASIC SERIES INVERTER

Series-inverter action may be achieved through several different circuit arrangements. As pointed out already, all essentially connect the commutating capacitor in series with the load. The circuit of Fig. 9.8(a) will be used for the purpose of discussion. It is a simple prototype with many practical applications. The load, often the primary of a transformer, is connected between a

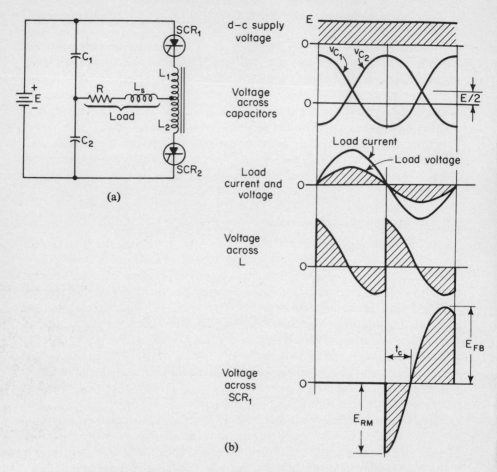

Fig. 9.8 (a) Basic series inverter circuit; (b) waveforms of series inverter operating at resonant frequency with resistive load; (c) waveforms of series inverter operating at one half of resonant frequency with resistive load.

centertapped choke and a capacitor divider. For the purpose of analysis, perfect magnetic coupling is assumed between the two halves of the choke, and the two commutating capacitors C_1 and C_2 are assumed to be equal. Also, the d-c supply has low internal impedance. The SCR's are alternately triggered from an external circuit which determines the operating frequency of the inverter. Removal of this trigger signal shuts down the inverter, as contrasted to the basic parallel inverter, where loss of trigger signal causes a short circuit across the d-c supply.

When SCR_1 is triggered, positive voltage is applied to the right-hand side of the load. In the most generally used mode of operation, a half-cycle current

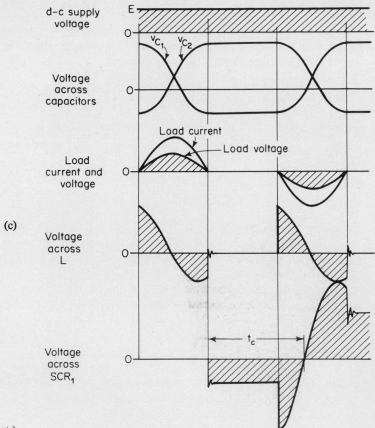

d-c supply voltage

Voltage across capacitors

Load current and voltage

(c)

Voltage across L

Voltage across SCR₁

Fig. 9.8 (cont.)

pulse, of a duration depending on the resonant frequency of the inductive and capacitive circuit elements, flows through the load. When the current through the load tries to reverse, owing to the series resonant action, SCR_1 becomes reverse-biased and turns off. At this point SCR_2 is triggered, applying positive voltage to the left-hand side of the load. Simultaneously a voltage is developed across the bottom section of the choke of such polarity to drive the cathode of SCR_1 more positive with respect to its anode. This prevents the two SCR's from conducting simultaneously and provides positive commutation of the SCR's under wide load variations.

Figure 9.8(b) shows the basic voltage and current waveshapes of the series inverter when it is operating at its natural resonant frequency with resistive load.

The natural resonant frequency f_0 of the circuit can be determined by classical circuit analysis:

$$f_0 = \frac{1}{2\pi}\sqrt{\frac{1}{2LC_1} - \frac{R^2}{4L^2}}, \tag{9.4}$$

where

$$L = L_1 + L_s.$$

Thompson[3] has developed an equation for the circuit turn-off time t_c applied to the SCR's when triggering occurs at the natural resonant frequency f_0. Again, this assumes perfect coupling between L_1 and L_2.

$$\exp\left(-\omega t_c/2Q\right)\cos\left(\omega t_c + \varphi\right) = \frac{1 - \exp(-\pi/2Q)}{2K_1 A}, \qquad (9.5)$$

where

$$\omega = 2\pi f_0$$

$$Q = \frac{\omega L}{R}$$

$$K_1 = \frac{L_1}{(L_1 + L_s)}$$

$$\varphi = \arctan \frac{1}{2Q}$$

$$A = \sqrt{1 + \frac{1}{4Q^2}}.$$

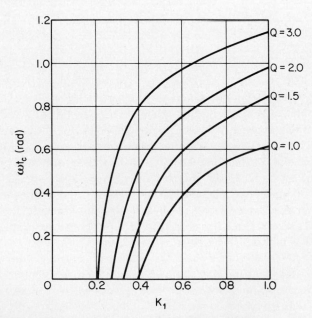

Fig. 9.9 Variation of circuit turn-off time t_c with Q and K_1 in series inverter.

This equation is plotted in Fig. 9.9 for convenience. Thompson also developed solutions for the peak forward voltage V_{FM} applied to the SCR's and the average forward current $I_{F(AV)}$ through each SCR:

$$E_{FM} = E\left[\frac{1 - \exp{(-\pi/2Q)}[1 - 2K_1 A \exp{(\varphi/2Q)}]}{1 - \exp{(-\pi/2Q)}}\right], \qquad (9.6)$$

where

$E = $ d-c supply voltage.

$$I_{F(AV)} = \frac{E[1 + \exp{(-\pi/2Q)}]}{2\pi\omega L[1 - \exp{(-\pi/2Q)}]\left(1 + \dfrac{1}{4Q^2}\right)}. \qquad (9.7)$$

Average load voltage can be determined by multiplying twice the SCR current by the load impedance. The foregoing reference also analyzes this type of circuit when coupling between L_1 and L_2 is less than unity.

9.3.2 ALTERNATE MODES OF OPERATION OF SERIES INVERTER

The series inverter associated with the waveforms in Fig. 9.8(b) is triggered at the instant the current through the previously conducting SCR reaches zero. This results in perfect continuity of the a-c current wave from one half-cycle to the next. However, two alternate modes of operation are possible.

If the trigger frequency is less than the natural resonant frequency f_0 of the circuit, the load current flows in discontinuous pulses as indicated in Fig. 9.8(c). Between pulses no load current flows, and the circuit remains in a stand-by condition with voltages across the capacitors and SCR's static. During this interval the "outgoing" SCR is reverse-biased by the resonant charge on its associated capacitor. Note the increased turn-off time t_c in Fig. 9.8(c) because of this delay action compared to that in Fig. 9.8(b). Variation of the trigger frequency can be used to regulate the average load voltage over a considerable range in practical circuits.

If the trigger frequency is raised above the natural circuit frequency, the SCR's are turned off by the action of the centertapped choke before the natural reversal of load current. The current in this mode of operation approaches a square wave. The range of frequency is limited by the turn-off time requirements of the SCR, since this type of operation shortens the period of reverse SCR bias considerably in comparison with the other two modes of operation.

The basic series inverter is limited in the range of load it can handle without additional circuitry. For resonant action to be effective in turning off the SCR, the quantity under the radical in equation (9.4) must be real, and the load resistance R must, therefore, be less than $\sqrt{2L/C_1}$. Without special precautions, the inverter will develop a short circuit across the d-c supply under high-load-impedance or open-circuit conditions. At the other extreme, if load resistance R is decreased toward short-circuit conditions, circuit Q becomes very high and can lead to excessive voltage on the SCR's, as indicated by analysis of equation (9.6).

Dummy or bleeder loads can be used to alleviate the open-circuit condition. A small value of capacitance across the load has also been successfully used to permit the inverter to continue operation with an open load. Figure 9.10 illustrates a feedback circuit to stabilize operation at no load without introducing the inefficiencies of a bleeder resistance. Transformer T_1 is connected across the load as indicated. Its turns ratio is selected so that under

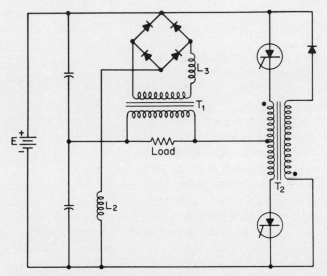

Fig. 9.10 Feedback circuits to permit stable operation under open- and short-circuit conditions and variable power factor.

no-load conditions, sufficient current is pumped back through the rectifier bridge into the d-c supply to maintain stable operation. This action also serves to clip and hence to regulate the load voltage. Inductors L_2 or L_3 limit the feedback current. In inverter circuits where the load consists of a step-up or step-down transformer, the feedback winding may be incorporated as an additional winding on the same core.

A similar type of feedback winding on the centertapped choke may be used to limit voltage on the SCR's during short-circuit conditions. The modified choke is shown in Fig. 9.10 as T_2. With the phasing shown, transformer T_2 will provide current feedback into the d-c supply when the forward voltage on the SCR's exceeds a value determined by the turns ratio of the transformer. By thus effectively lowering the Q of the resonant circuit, the reverse as well as the forward blocking voltage requirements on the SCR's are lessened. With feedback circuits of the type discussed above, the SCR series inverter can be operated stably and efficiently over a wide range of power factor and from short-circuit to open-load conditions.

Figure 9.11 illustrates two other variations of the series inverter circuit with equivalent circuit values for use in the foregoing equations.

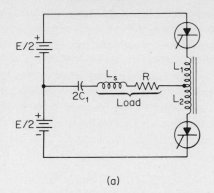

(a)

9.4 Inverter Variations

Many other SCR inverter techniques are discussed in the literature. Some employ other types of SCR commutation techniques.[4] Others interconnect several single-phase inverters to secure multiphase outputs. Several successful techniques have been developed to regulate the a-c output voltage. These include phase control of the output, pulse-width control of the main SCR inverter elements,[5] use of a ferro-resonant regulating transformer in the inverter output, and combining the outputs of

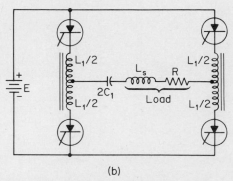

(b)

Fig. 9.11 Alternate circuit arrangements for the series commutated inverter.

two inverters with variable phase relationship between their respective voltages.[6] In order to provide sinusoidal output voltage from an inverter, techniques have also been developed to reduce the harmonic content by selective filtering[7] and by switching the inverter SCR's with proper timing so that harmonic generation in the inverter is minimized.[8]

9.5 Pulse Modulators

SCR's are often used as the switching element in pulse modulators in such applications as driving magnetrons and klystrons. The line-type modulator in Fig. 9.12 is typical of this type of circuit.[9] In its operation the pulse modulator may be likened in several respects to the resonant action of the series inverter. When the circuit is energized from the d-c supply, the capacitors in the pulse-forming network (PFN) charge up resonantly to $2E$ v through the charging choke. The hold-off rectifier CR_1 maintains the voltage on the PFN until SCR is triggered. This discharges the PFN into the pulse transformer load in a short pulse with a shape depending on the electrical characteristics of the PFN. With a slight mismatch between PFN and load, the capacitors in the PFN will reverse their voltage slightly at the end of the discharge pulse, reverse-biasing the SCR momentarily and turning it off. A shunt rectifier CR_2 is sometimes used to return part of the excess energy resonantly to the PFN in proper polarity. CR_2 also reduces the severity of commutating duty on SCR.

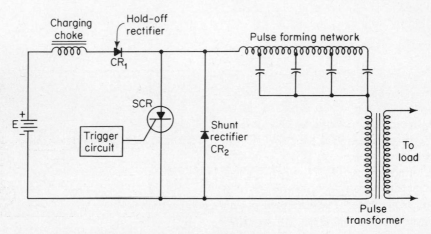

Fig. 9.12 Typical line-type pulse modulator.

During the short discharge interval, the charging choke prevents current in the d-c supply from building up to a level that would keep SCR in the conducting state. Its inductance L should be chosen so that $\pi\sqrt{LC_{PFN}}$ is much longer than the discharge pulse width but less than the repetition period of the modulator (C_{PFN} = total capacitance in PFN).

Low duty-cycle applications of this type subject the SCR to high junction temperature even though the average anode current may be quite low. In switching very quickly from its high voltage-blocking state to high current conduction, the SCR is subjected to severe peak heating at its junctions (Sec. 2.6.3). If excessive, this instantaneous switching dissipation occurring at a localized part of the SCR pellet near the gate connection may damage the SCR. Where necessary, a small saturable reactor in series with the SCR may be used to delay the current rise for a few microseconds until the SCR anode voltage has dropped to a low level and a large part of the junction area is in conduction.

When voltage exceeds the capabilities of a single SCR, additional SCR's may be connected in series, as discussed in Sec. 10.4.

9.6 D-C Choppers

The advantageous characteristics of the SCR as a near-perfect power switch can also be used to convert direct current from a given input voltage to direct current at a lower voltage in a nearly lossless manner. In this mode of operation the SCR performs as a so-called "chopper," which in some respects is analogous to the use of SCR's in phase control of a-c circuits. In Fig. 9.13, which illustrates the general principle of chopping with a switch as the power control element, the shaded area represents voltage applied to the load when the switch is closed. During the intervening period when the switch is open, no voltage is applied to the load.

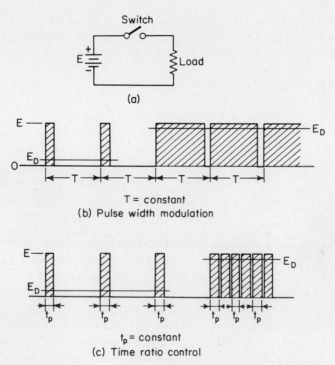

(a)

T = constant
(b) Pulse width modulation

t_p = constant
(c) Time ratio control

Fig. 9.13 Principle of pulse width modulation and time ratio control.

Two distinct modes of operation are possible. In Fig. 9.13(b) the period T between successive switch closings is maintained constant, and the average voltage on the load, E_D, is regulated by varying the time during each period that the switch is closed. By narrowing the pulse width, as on the left-hand side, the average load voltage is low. By widening the pulse width, as on the right, the average load voltage is raised. In the other mode of operation, Fig.

9.13(c), the pulse width is maintained constant, and the load voltage is regulated by varying the repetition rate of switch closing. With a low repetition rate, as on the left, E_D is low. At a high repetition rate, as on the right, E_D is raised. A combination mode of operation is, of course, also possible. In all cases the use of a switch such as the SCR provides inherently highly efficient control of load power. Typical applications are in speed control of d-c motors operating from fixed d-c supplies, regulated power supplies, and lighting and temperature control on d-c systems.

The SCR can perform the chopping function in any one of many circuits. Four such circuits will be discussed here. One of the simplest circuits uses the basic SCR flip-flop or latching relay presented earlier in Fig. 7.8. In this circuit, voltage is applied to the load whenever SCR_1 is in conduction. When SCR_2 is triggered, SCR_1 turns off and voltage is removed from the load. By suitable triggering circuitry, the average voltage on the load may be varied steplessly from full ON to full OFF. Filtering of the load pulses can be accomplished by using the self-inductance of the load or a separate choke in series with the load in connection with a free-wheeling diode CR_1 to maintain load current when the associated SCR is open.

Maximum repetition rate of the switch is limited by the time required to recharge the commutating capacitor C during the ON interval. The time constant of R_2C should be substantially less than the shortest ON time of the chopper. Capacitor C, on the other hand, must be large enough to commutate the maximum load current as defined in equations (7.5) and (7.6).

The chopper circuit in Fig. 9.14 eliminates the capacitor charging and stand-by losses that occur in the circuit of Fig. 7.8 by substituting series resonant charging of the commutating capacitor. This type of commutation also permits higher operating frequency of the chopper, which in turn reduces the size of filter elements and improves system response time. When SCR_1 is triggered, d-c supply voltage is applied to the load. This sudden step function of voltage at the bottom of choke L_1 causes capacitor C to charge through L_1 and CR_1 so that its bottom plate becomes nearly E v positive with respect to its top plate. Once charged, diode CR_1 maintains this voltage on C. D-C voltage is applied to the load as long as SCR_1 conducts. When SCR_2 is triggered, capacitor C is connected across SCR_1 in

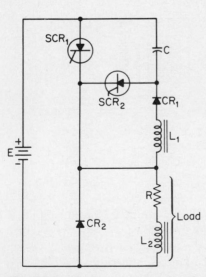

Fig. 9.14 D-C chopper using cathode pulse turn-off of SCR.

the proper polarity to turn it off, thus removing voltage from the load. Current in the load inductance L_2 discharges through the free-wheeling rectifier CR_2. Suitable triggering circuitry on SCR_1 and SCR_2 permits variation of both the repetition rate and the pulse width.

Since SCR_2 handles only the commutating energy, it may generally be lower in rating than SCR_1. The minimum allowable repetition rate is governed by the length of time that capacitor C can maintain the commutating voltage before it leaks off through SCR_2 and CR_1.

The time required to build up a commutating charge on C is $\pi\sqrt{L_1 C}$ sec, and should be less than the shortest ON time of SCR_1. Capacitor C must be sufficiently large to handle the maximum load current while maintaining reverse voltage on SCR_1 during turn-off time. Its size can be determined from equations (7.5) and (7.6), as in the case of the flip-flop discussed earlier. Some additional safety factor in capacitor size should be allowed to compensate for reverse recovery current in SCR_1 and some losses in building up the commutation charge on C.

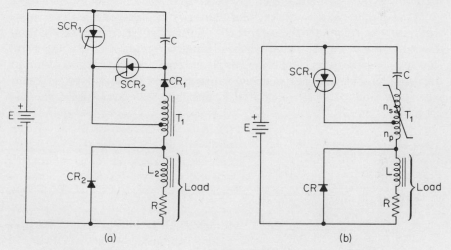

Fig. 9.15 Alternate d-c chopper circuits: (a) load-sensitive cathode pulse turn-off; (b) "Morgan" circuit.

Figure 9.15 shows two other d-c chopper circuits. Figure 9.15(a) is very similar to Fig. 9.14 except that a current transformer is substituted for L_1. Capacitor C is thus charged not only by resonant action, as described earlier, but also by the autotransformer action of load current flowing through the bottom winding of the transformer. Increased loads therefore develop a higher commutating voltage on C, particularly when starting the chopper. Load-compensating action can be emphasized by using another SCR in place of diode CR_1. If this SCR is triggered simultaneously with SCR_1, the commutating voltage on capacitor C builds up resonantly to a higher value than with a diode clamp. Such a circuit arrangement can, therefore, success-fully switch higher currents, or, conversely, can operate satisfactorily with smaller values of commutating capacitance C.

Figure 9.15(b) uses a saturable current transformer to function both as a load-sensitive autotransformer and the commutating switch, thus eliminating the need for SCR_2 and CR_1. While SCR_1 is off, capacitor C charges to the line voltage through the load. When SCR_1 is triggered, the full voltage on C is connected across the top winding of the reactor, n_s. After a short period of time this causes the reactor to saturate in the negative direction and resonantly reverse the charge on C. Load current flowing through the lower winding, n_P, then reverses the flux in the core and charges the lower plate of C to a still higher d-c voltage by autotransformer action. After a period of time depend-ing on the volt-second capacity of the saturable reactor, the reversed voltage on n_s saturates the reactor in the positive direction, connecting the charge on capacitor C across SCR_1 in the proper polarity to turn it off.

This cycle repeats so that a pulse of supply voltage is applied to the load each time SCR_1 is triggered. Pulse width is determined mainly by the supply voltage E and the number of secondary turns n_s in conjunction with the cross section of the square-loop iron core.[10,11] For a given reactor and a fixed trigger frequency, load voltage remains essentially constant as the input d-c supply voltage is varied. With the supply voltage fixed, load voltage varies directly with the trigger frequency. Operation over a 10:1 load-voltage range is possible, and efficiencies over 90 per cent have been achieved in practical circuits.

References

1. C. F. Wagner, "Parallel Inverter with Inductive Load," *Electrical Engineering* (September, 1936), pp. 970–80.

2. W. McMurray and D. P. Shattuck, "A Silicon Controlled Rectifier with Improved Commutation," *A.I.E.E. Trans.*, Part I, *Communication and Electronics* (November, 1961), pp. 531–42.

3. R. Thompson, "An Audio-Frequency High-Power Generator Employing Silicon Controlled Rectifiers," Institution of Electrical Engineers, Paper No. 3889E, May, 1962, pp. 249–58.

4. T. G. Wilson, E. T. Moore, I. M. H. Babaa, "Regulated DC to DC SCR Converter Employing Nonlinear Two Core Transformer," I.E.E.E. Conference Paper 63-1090, June, 1963.

5. Dwight Jones, "Variable Pulse Width Inverter," *Electronic Equipment Engineering* (November, 1961), pp. 29–30.

6. C. W. Flairty, "A 50 KVA Adjustable-Frequency 24-Phase Controlled Rectifier Inverter," *Direct Current* (December, 1961), pp. 278–82.

7. R. R. Ott, "A Filter for Silicon Controlled Rectifier Commutation and Harmonic Attenuation in High Power Inverters," A.I.E.E. *Communication and Electronics* (May, 1963), pp. 259–62.

8. F. G. Turnbull, "Selected Harmonic Reduction in Static DC-AC Inverters," I.E.E.E. Trans., Paper 63-1011, June, 1963.

9. G. N. Glasoe and J. V. Lebacqz, *Pulse Generators*. New York: McGraw-Hill Book Co., Inc., 1948.

10. Glenn E. Snyder, "Silicon Controlled Rectifier High Voltage Power Supply," A.I.E.E. Conference Paper CP 61-865, June, 1961.

11. W. McMurray, "SCR DC to DC Power Converters," Paper 11-3, 1963. Proceedings of the Intermag Conference (I.E.E.E.), Washington, D.C., April, 1963.

12. B. D. Bedford and R. G. Hoft, "*Principles of Inverter Circuits*." New York: Wiley, 1964.

CHAPTER 10

GENERAL APPLICATION CONSIDERATIONS

Several of the preceding chapters have discussed the SCR as a device, whereas other chapters have discussed some of the basic circuits in which SCR's are used. A successful application requires a happy marriage of these two areas of knowledge: the semiconductor device and the circuit. This chapter reviews some of the general considerations necessary in successfully applying the SCR device to the practical circuit or system.

10.1 Check List for SCR Selection

The circuit designer has a large variety of SCR types, covering a wide range of speed and power, from which to make his selection for an application. For a judicious selection, his choice should be predicated on a number of technical factors consistent with the economic and reliability aspects of his application. Fundamentally, none of the SCR ratings should be exceeded. However, sound engineering economics dictates that the designer should not apply the SCR too conservatively for his requirements, either. Customarily, SCR ratings and characteristics are specified as maximum or minimum limits, and the circuit designer must determine which of the parameters in his application is the limiting one. Because of the varying safety factors and conservatism of different industries that use the SCR, SCR specifications seldom incorporate arbitrary application safety factors, thus properly reserving this discretion for the individual circuit designer.

The following check list itemizes some of the major technical points that should be considered in selection of an SCR for a particular application:

1. Level of reliability and quality consistent with economic factors.
2. Load current: continuous, overload, and fault conditions. Also, rate-of-rise of current after triggering.
3. Blocking voltage: recurrent and transient peaks in both forward and reverse directions.
4. Temperature and cooling methods.
5. Triggering requirements and gate sensitivity.
6. Turn-off time and ability to block under fast rate-of-rise of voltage (dv/dt).
7. Possible alternate use of p-n-p-n devices with gate turn-off gain, bilateral switching action, or light-triggering.

Several of these items have been specifically covered earlier. The remaining items and other general application considerations are discussed in the following material.

10.2 Cooling the SCR

High temperature, which inherently limits the performance of any semi-conductor material, is one of an SCR's worst enemies. Although a properly designed and fabricated SCR can satisfactorily operate at its maximum rated junction temperature indefinitely, operation at temperatures in excess of this rating can lead to the following problems:

1. Increase in blocking currents. This leads to thermal runaway of the SCR. In some cases, such as static switches, high blocking current can cause circuit malfunction.
2. Deterioration of surface stability and device blocking and triggering characteristics.
3. Melting of alloys and solders in joints and in the junction "sandwich."
4. Thermal fatigue where the SCR is not specifically fabricated to withstand this phenomenon.
5. Misfiring and loss of forward blocking ability.
6. Increased turn-off time.
7. Reduced safety factor for overloads and faults.

These are some of the reasons which establish the need for adequate cooling and dissipation of the internal thermal losses of the SCR. These thermal losses are generated by blocking currents, the voltage drop during conduction, the gate signal, and the dissipation during switching on and off. Chapter 4 discusses the mechanisms of internal heat generation and transfer. The heating losses, which are generally measured in watts, raise the junction temperature above the surrounding medium as the heat flows out to its surroundings. To dissipate this heat with a minimum rise in junction temperature, lead-mounted SCR's below approximately one ampere load-current rating are often directly soldered into a circuit without the need for any

(a)

(b)

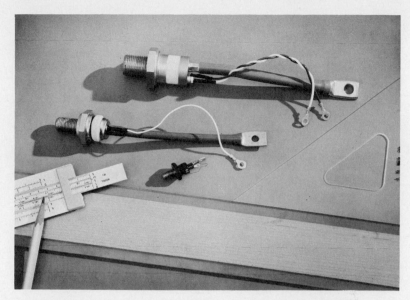

(c)

Fig. 10.1 (a) Lead-mounted SCR's; (b) fin-mounted SCR's; (c) stud-mounted SCR's [courtesy of General Electric Company].

additional cooling or heatsinking provisions. SCR's of this type [Fig. 10.1(a)] rely on their own housings to dissipate heat by radiation and convection to the surrounding ambient, and on their leads to conduct heat to adjacent components. To optimize radiation heat transfer, SCR's of this type are often given a flat painted finish to achieve high emissivity.

Above about one ampere rating, SCR's are generally mounted to a fin or other type of heat sink capable of passing the heat losses on to the surrounding air or to water in the case of a liquid-cooled SCR. Typical examples of commercially available stacks of finned SCR's for air-cooling are shown in Fig. 10.1(b).

Many of the medium- and high-current SCR types are also available in stud-mounted versions which the equipment designer can mount to a heat sink of his own design [see Fig. 10.1(c)]. This may be desirable because of space or form restrictions, or because of the use of a cooling medium other than air. This type of SCR generally employs a copper stud with a machine thread for making mechanical and thermal contact to the heat sink. Other types are available for pressing into a hole in the heat sink. The heat sink itself may consist of a bus bar, chassis, liquid cooling system, cold plate, or cooling fin.

For an optimum cooling job, the stud-mounted SCR must be mounted to the heat sink in a manner that achieves a low and stable thermal resistance of the contact between stud and heat sink. When an aluminum heat sink is used, a good grade of corrosion-inhibitor should be used in the joint to minimize the possibility of galvanic corrosion between stud and heat sink. Because of the unequal coefficients of thermal expansion of copper and aluminum, joints between these two materials may also work loose under wide temperature swings owing to thermal ratcheting effects. Special assembly techniques, including the use of belleville spring washers, can be used to overcome this possible problem.

To ensure an adequate thermal contact between stud and heat sink, the mating surfaces must be flat and free of burrs or other high spots. Where the stud is screwed into a tapped hole, the hole must be square with the surface. Special attention and care should be given to the manufacturer's recommended torque specifications for attaching the stud. Insufficient torque leads to a poor thermal contact, and excessive torque can cause permanent impairment of the SCR electrical characteristics, owing to mechanical stresses on its junctions. A torque wrench should always be used for this type of assembly.

To minimize the effects of poor thermal transfer through the inevitable voids in the thermal contact between stud and heat sink, it is customary to apply a layer of silicone grease or other commercial joint preparation to the surfaces before joining. In low- and medium-power applications, a thin layer of mica, beryllia, or other electrical insulation can be inserted between the surfaces to provide a thermal path, yet allow electrical isolation between heat sink and SCR. However, this increases the temperature gradient across the joint.

10.3 Cooling-fin Design

Practical cooling-fin designs can best be based on a judicious blending of both theoretical and practical aspects because of the several approximations and fringe effects encountered in this area. It is customary to calculate a fin design by use of equations and nomograms such as those shown in the following paragraphs, and then to adjust and refine to a final design based on experience and prototype measurements.

The rate of heat flow from fin to ambient can be expressed as follows.

$$p = hA\eta(\Delta T), \tag{10.1}$$

where

p = rate of heat flow, w
h = total heat-transfer coefficient of the fin, w/in.^{2} °C
A = surface area of fin, in.^{2}
η = fin effectiveness factor, defined below
ΔT = temperature difference between hottest point on fin and ambient, °C.

A brief discussion on each of the factors in equation (10.1) will reveal the variables on which they depend. The area A of the fin includes both sides and the effective area of the edges. The heat-transfer coefficient h is the sum of both the radiation and convection (free or forced) coefficients for the particular fin design; that is, $h = h_r + h_c$.

10.3.1 RADIATION HEAT TRANSFER

For stacked painted fins with surface emissivity of 0.9 or more and operating up to 200°C, the radiation coefficient (h_r) can be closely approximated by this equation:†

$$h_r = 1.47 \times 10^{-10}\epsilon(1 - F)\left(\frac{T_S + T_A}{2} + 273\right)^3 \frac{w}{in.^{2}°C}, \qquad (10.2)$$

where

ϵ = surface emissivity
F = shielding factor owing to stacking ($F = 0$ for single unstacked fins)
T_S = surface temperature of cooling fin, °C.
T_A = ambient temperature, °C.

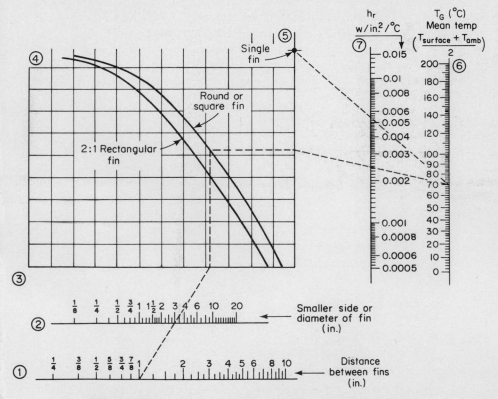

Fig. 10.2 Radiation nomogram for single and stacked flat painted fins (emissivity = 0.9).

† This equation is derived from Equations 31-3 and 31-90 in M. Jakob, *Heat Transfer* (New York: John Wiley & Sons, Inc., 1957), Vol. II.

Surface emissivity ϵ is a function of the surface finish. At one extreme, bright metallic finishes have an emissivity factor between 0.05 and 0.10, whereas at the other, flat oil-painted surfaces have an emissivity as high as 0.96. In free convection-cooled applications, where the radiation component of the total heat transfer is substantial, it is, therefore, desirable to maximize radiation heat transfer by painting or anodizing the fin surface.

Figure 10.2 presents equation (10.2) in the form of a nomogram which takes into account the detrimental effects of stacking cooling fins along a perpendicular axis. The dashed lines on this nomogram represent a solution for the case in which a stack composed of 3 by 3 in. square painted fins at one inch spacing and in a 40°C ambient operates at a surface temperature of 100°C. The radiation heat-transfer coefficient h_r is found to be 0.0024 w/in.^{2} °C

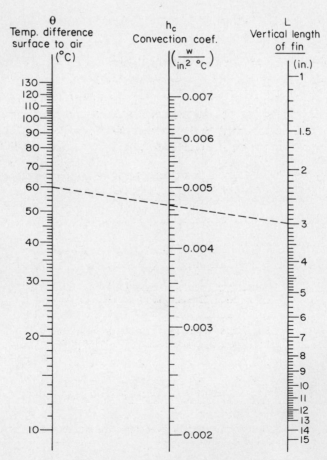

Fig. 10.3 Free convection nomogram for vertical cooling fins in sea level air.

and the heat transferred by radiation, p_r, is $h_r A(\Delta T) = (0.0024 \text{ w/in.}^2 \text{ °C})$ (3 by 3 in.^{2})(2 sides)(100 − 40°C) = 2.6 w per fin. For a single unstacked fin under the same conditions, $h_r = 0.0054 \text{ w/in.}^2 \text{ °C}$ and $p_r = 5.8$ w per fin.

10.3.2 Free or Natural Convection

For vertical fins surrounded by air at sea level and at surface temperatures up to 800°C, the free-convection heat-transfer coefficient h_c can be approximated by the following equation, which assumes laminar flow of the cooling medium.[1]

$$h_c = 0.00221 \left(\frac{\Delta T}{L}\right)^{0.25} \text{ w/in.}^2 \text{ °C,} \tag{10.3}$$

where

ΔT = temperature difference between surface and ambient air, °C.
L = vertical length of fin, in.

Since any degree of turbulent flow increases heat transfer, this solution is conservative. This equation also remains conservative for fin spacing down to approximately $\sqrt[4]{L}$ in. For convenience, Fig. 10.3 presents equation (10.3) in the form of a nomogram. The dashed line represents a solution for a 3 by 3 in. square cooling fin mounted vertically in a 40°C ambient and operating at 100°C surface temperature. The solution shows a free-convection heat-transfer coefficient h_c of 0.0047 w/in.^{2} °C.

Altitude derating factors for the free-convection heat-transfer coefficient are shown in Fig. 10.4 for fins measuring one-half inch to two feet vertically.

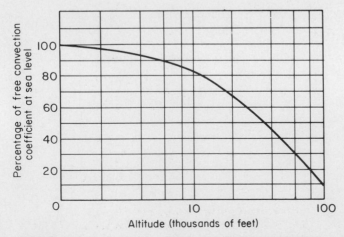

Fig. 10.4 Effect of altitude on free-convection heat transfer.

10.3.3 FORCED CONVECTION

When air is moved over cooling fins by external mechanical means, such as fans or compressors, heat transfer is improved and the convection heat-transfer coefficient h_c can be approximated by the following equation:†

$$h_c = 11.2\sqrt{\frac{V}{L}} \times 10^{-4} \text{ w/in.}^2 \text{ °C,} \tag{10.4}$$

where

V = free-stream linear-cooling air velocity across fin surface, ft/min.
L = length of fin parallel to air flow, in.

This equation is based on laminar (nonturbulent) air flow which exists for smooth fin lengths L less than C/V, where C is a constant given in Table 10.1 for various air temperatures. For $L > C/V$, air flow becomes turbulent, and

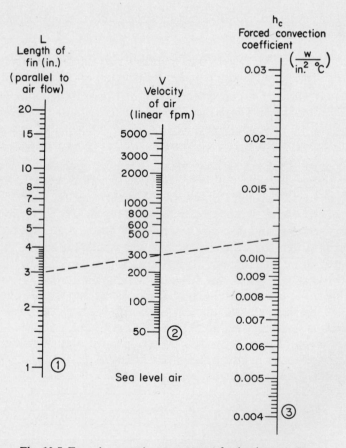

Fig. 10.5 Forced convection nomogram for laminar air flow.

† This is accurate within one per cent of Equation (7.48), p. 149, of Ref. 1.

heat transfer is thereby improved at the expense of increased power requirements on the blower or fan. Minimum fin spacing for the above equation is $B\sqrt{L/V}$, where B is also a constant given in Table 10.1.

TABLE 10.1. Laminar flow limitations.

Air temperature	B	C
25°C	3.4	37,000
55°C	3.8	45,000
85°C	4.1	52,000
125°C	4.5	63,000
150°C	4.7	70,000

Figure 10.5 presents a nomogram for convenience in solving the forced-convection equation, (10.4). The dashed line represents a solution for a 3 by 3 in. square fin exposed to 40°C ambient air being moved across the fin at 300 lin ft per min. The forced-convection heat-transfer coefficient h_c is found to be 0.011 w/in.^{2} °C.

10.3.4 FIN EFFECTIVENESS

For fins made of thin material, the temperature of the fin decreases as distance from the heat source (the SCR) increases, owing to the effects of surface cooling. Thus calculations of heat transfer, such as the preceding examples, that are based on the assumption that the entire fin is at a uniformly high temperature, are optimistic and should be corrected for the poorer heat transfer which exists at the cooler extremities of the fin. The correction factor is fin effectiveness η, and its correction function on the total heat transfer is defined in equation (10.1). Fin effectiveness depends on the length, thickness, and shape of the fin, on the total heat-transfer coefficient h, and on the thermal conductivity k of the fin material. It can be computed by means of the nomogram in Fig. 10.6. The typical sequence of proceeding through the nomogram is indicated by the encircled numbers adjacent to the scales. The dashed lines represent a solution for an SCR with an effective stud hex diameter of 0.59 in. mounted on a 3 by 3 in. square painted aluminum fin, $\frac{1}{64}$ in. thick, and with a total heat-transfer coefficient of 0.0134 w/in.^{2} °C. This solution yields a fin effectiveness factor $\eta = 0.67$.

10.4 Series Operation of SCR's

Where the circuit voltage exceeds the voltage rating of single SCR's, it becomes necessary to operate two or more SCR's in series. Successful operation in this manner requires that careful attention be given to several factors.

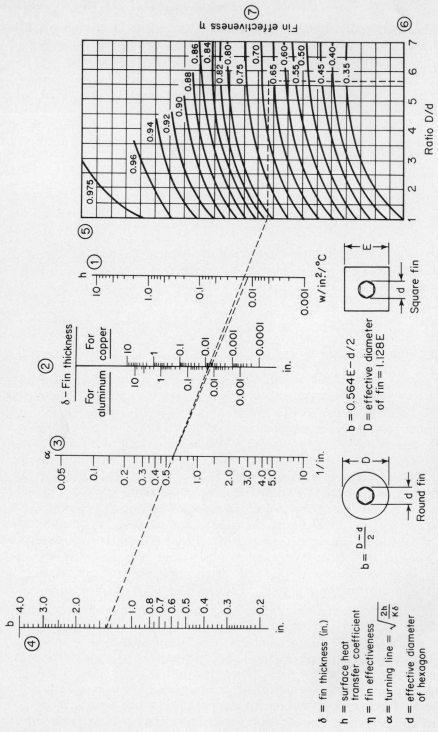

Fig. 10.6 Fin effectiveness nomogram for flat fin of uniform thickness.

Fin effectiveness η

⑦

⑥

Ratio D/d

0.975 0.96 0.94 0.92 0.90 0.88 0.86 0.84 0.82 0.80 0.75 0.70 0.65 0.60 0.55 0.50 0.45 0.40 0.35

⑤

h ①

w/in².°C

δ – Fin thickness

| For aluminum | For copper |

②

in.

α ③

1/in.

b ④

in.

Square fin

$b = 0.564E - d/2$

D = effective diameter of fin = $1.128E$

Round fin

$b = \dfrac{D - d}{2}$

δ = fin thickness (in.)

h = surface heat transfer coefficient

η = fin effectiveness

α = turning line = $\sqrt{\dfrac{2h}{K\delta}}$

d = effective diameter of hexagon

Unless the lowest SCR breakover current, $I_{(BR)F}$, is substantially greater than the highest forward leakage current expected in the string, it is mandatory that some form of forced voltage-sharing be used across each SCR. Figure 10.7 illustrates the characteristics of two typical SCR's operated in series without any external forced voltage-sharing. The forward leakage current i_{FX} must be identical through both SCR's. As the total voltage is raised across the pair, the leakage current i_{FX} increases, so its ordinate in Fig. 10.7 intersects the E-I characteristic of each SCR at voltage points which add up to the total

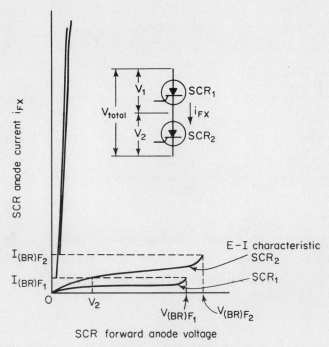

Fig. 10.7 Series operation of SCR's without forced sharing of anode voltage.

voltage V_{total}. When i_{FX} reaches $I_{(BR)F_1}$, the breakover current of SCR$_1$, the total voltage V_{total} is ($V_{(BR)F_1} + V_2$). Any further increase in total voltage will cause SCR$_1$ to switch into its conducting state, impressing the total voltage on SCR$_2$ alone, and thus causing it to switch on also.

In order to realize the full forward blocking voltage capabilities of series-connected SCR's, either one or more of the following circuit elements can be connected across each SCR to match its equivalent blocking characteristic to other SCR's in the string and hence to provide equal distribution of the forward blocking voltage. Because they do not switch in their reverse direction, series SCR's generally are less critical of reverse voltage equalization than in the forward direction. Therefore, the forward voltage equalizing means will usually suffice for the reverse direction as well.

Shunt resistance: For randomly chosen SCR's, maximum voltage will occur across an SCR if it has essentially zero leakage current, and all the other SCR's in series with it have maximum leakage current. In order to keep the voltage on the zero-leakage SCR below its forward voltage rating V_{FXM}, a resistor R can be connected across it so that the total circuit current I_T flowing through the resistor will not develop a voltage greater than V_{FXM}, as illustrated in Fig. 10.8; i.e.,

$$I_T = \frac{V_{FXM}}{R}.$$

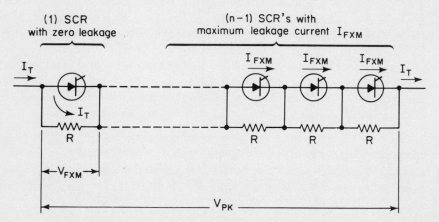

Fig. 10.8 Use of resistors for equalizing voltage across series-connected SCR's.

The current through the identical resistors in shunt with the other SCR's is I_T less the maximum instantaneous leakage current I_{FXM} in these SCR's. For the worst mismatch case, the total blocking-voltage capability of the string V_{PK} is

$$V_{PK} = I_T R + (n - 1)(I_T - I_{FXM})R,$$

where n is the number of series-connected SCR's.

This equation can be solved for the maximum shunt resistance R that will limit the voltage across any SCR to V_{FXM} by substituting for I_T:

$$R = \frac{nV_{FXM} - V_{PK}}{(n - 1)I_{FXM}}. \tag{10.5}$$

Shunt capacitors: For high-frequency operation and during the transient conditions of switching and commutation, capacitors are more effective than resistance in maintaining equal voltage distribution across series SCR's.

Adequate values of shunt capacitance swamp out differences between SCR self-capacitances and recovery characteristics, as well as inequalities between distributed circuit capacitances. Values on the order of 0.01 to 0.1 μf are typical. Since a shunt capacitor discharges through its SCR during the turn-on interval and may cause excessive switching dissipation in the SCR, the switching current should be limited by adding a small amount of resistance in series with each capacitor. This resistance also serves to suppress oscillation of circuit inductance with the capacitor at the end of the commutation interval[2] (Fig. 8.9).

Avalanche (*Zener*) *diodes:* In applications such as pulse modulators, where the current through parallel resistors is intolerable because of the low duty cycle, properly selected high-voltage avalanche diodes may be substituted for the resistors. The avalanche voltage of the diode connected across each SCR should be less than rated voltage V_{FXM} of the SCR, and the diode should be capable of handling the maximum peak blocking current anticipated for that type SCR. With this combination, the maximum current of the series/parallel array of SCR's and avalanche diodes during the blocking state is only slightly higher than the peak blocking current of the worst SCR. If reverse voltage is applied to the string, avalanche or conventional diodes of opposite polarity can be inserted in series with the existing avalanche diodes.

Reactors: Tapped autotransformers with suitable reset means have been successfully used across series strings of SCR's.[3] With a common magnetic circuit and an equal number of turns across each SCR, such a circuit imposes equal voltage distribution across each SCR in an essentially lossless manner.

10.4.1 TRIGGERING METHODS FOR SERIES SCR's

Since the cathodes of SCR's in series operate at different voltage levels, the trigger circuit for each SCR must be electrically isolated from the others. This isolation can be accomplished magnetically or capacitively, or by relying on other means than gate-triggering.

Magnetic isolation methods consist of a single transformer with multiple insulated secondary windings connected to each individual SCR gate, or separate transformers with their primaries in parallel and individual secondaries connected to the respective SCR's. The interwinding insulation must be capable of sustaining the circuit voltage, and the rise time of the gate signal in the secondaries should be at least several amperes per microsecond in order to trigger all SCR's simultaneously. Sufficient resistance should be added to each gate circuit to prevent unequal loading of the trigger signal owing to variation between gate input characteristics. For pulse-trigger applications, capacitance can be used in series with each gate for equalizing purposes. Capacitance tends to supply a constant charge to each SCR gate regardless of gate input characteristics.

Where the main anode supply frequency and rates of voltage rise are not excessive, "slave" triggering by capacitive coupling to one or more of the series SCR's can be used. The circuit shown in Fig. 10.9 uses capacitor coupling to slave-trigger SCR_2 whenever SCR_1 is triggered from a conven-

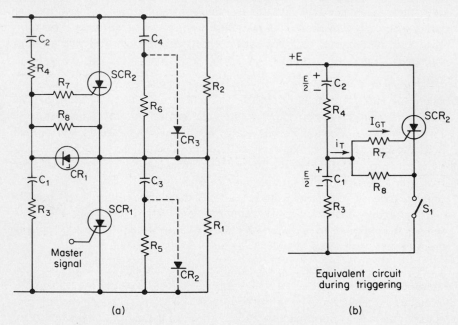

(a)   (b)

Fig. 10.9 Triggering series-connected SCR's by slave-gating.

tional source. In the forward blocking state, SCR_1 and SCR_2 are forced to share the total voltage by means of resistors R_1 and R_2 and capacitors C_3 and C_4. Capacitors C_1 and C_2 also charge to the line voltage. When an appropriate "master" signal triggers SCR_1, its anode voltage starts to decrease very rapidly. Capacitor C_1 discharges accordingly through R_7 and R_8, while the voltage on C_2 starts to increase as distributed circuit capacitance momentarily tries to maintain constant voltage across the pair of SCR's. The respective discharge and charge currents in C_1 and C_2 flow into the gate of SCR_2, triggering it very shortly after the initial trigger to SCR_1. Note that capacitors C_1 through C_4 form a bridge with the gate of SCR_2 across diagonal corners of the bridge. If the capacitors are correctly chosen so that the bridge is balanced, line voltage fluctuations will not cause current to flow in the gate of SCR_2. SCR_2 will be triggered only if SCR_1 is triggered first. CR_1 protects the gate of SCR_2 from excessive forward and reverse voltage. Damping resistors in series with the capacitors limit switching current losses in the SCR's. Diodes CR_2 and CR_3 are optional additions in parallel with resistors R_5 and R_6. They make C_3 and C_4 more effective in reducing the rate of rise of forward voltage (dv/dt) on the SCR's while allowing R_5 and R_6 to limit the discharge current from the capacitors into the SCR's when they are triggered. R_7 limits peak gate current into SCR_2, and R_8 prevents low-level circulating currents mistriggering SCR_2. For the case of two SCR's connected in series, the optimum value of the trigger-coupling capacitors C_1 and C_2 can be approximated if one makes several simplifying assumptions: $C_1 = C_2$; SCR_1 switches on linearly in one microsecond; and the voltage drop of trigger current I_{GT} through the series-parallel array of R_3, R_4, and R_7 is insignificant compared to E, the minimum total blocking voltage at which triggering should occur. Figure 10.9(b) illustrates the equivalent circuit with S_1 representing SCR_1 during the turn-on interval.

With C_1 and C_2 each charged to $E/2$ v, as shown in Fig. 10.9(b),

$$i_T = \frac{dq}{dt} = \frac{E(C_1 + C_2)}{2 \times 10^{-6}},$$

$$i_T = (C_1)E \times 10^6 \text{ amp.}$$

If we assume that the gate voltage of SCR_2 is negligible compared to the voltage drop across R_7, current i_T splits between the gate of SCR_2 and the shunt resistor R_8 so that the trigger current

$$I_{GT} = \left(\frac{R_8}{R_7 + R_8}\right)i_T = \left(\frac{R_8}{R_7 + R_8}\right)(C_1)E \times 10^6,$$

or

$$C_1 = C_2 \geq \frac{(R_7 + R_8)I_{GT}}{(R_8)E} \times 10^{-6} \text{ f.} \tag{10.6}$$

In practice C_1 and C_2 should be several times larger than this calculated value in order to accelerate the switching action of SCR_2. On the other hand, excessive values of capacitance for this purpose may lead to random triggering of SCR_2 owing to line transient disturbances.

For successful operation in series, all SCR's in the string should have reasonably similar switching-speed characteristics to prevent gross inequalities in voltage during the switching process. The circuit design must be based on the ability of the particular SCR type to withstand without damage the momentary high peak forward blocking voltage to which the slowest-switching SCR in the string is subjected.

Other means of triggering series SCR's are possible when suitable devices are available, such as

1. Slave-gating of *p-n-p-n* diode switches by exceeding their breakover voltage or *dv/dt* capabilities.
2. Triggering long series strings of light-activated switches (Sec. 5.3) by a suitable flash of light from a xenon tube or equivalent.

10.5 Parallel Operation of SCR's

Operation of SCR's in parallel becomes necessary when an application requires current in excess of the single capabilities of the largest commercially available SCR's. It is generally more economical and practical to use a single SCR with a high current rating when available than two or more lower-rated SCR's in parallel.

Parallel operation requires certain precautions, owing to the variation in conduction characteristics between SCR's of the same type. Figure 4.2 illustrated the logarithmic relationship of current and forward voltage drop (ON voltage) in a typical SCR. It is evident that even a slight difference in voltage is accompanied by a wide variation in anode current. Since SCR's connected directly in parallel must have equal voltage drops, their characteristics must be essentially identical if the SCR's are to share the load current equally. SCR manufacturers can generally supply SCR's with matched characteristics for operation directly in parallel with as little as 10 to 20 per cent derating of the individual currents to allow for tolerances and thermal effects. For this type of operation, care must be taken to assure equal circuit resistance and reactance in the parallel SCR paths, and it is good practice to mount parallel SCR's on a common heat sink to minimize current unbalance resulting from thermal differences between SCR's. When parallel matched SCR's are being operated in inductive circuits where current build-up through the SCR's takes more than a few microseconds, the gate-trigger signal should be of a sustained rather than a pulsed type. Otherwise, the possibility exists that one or more of the parallel SCR's will not have latched into conduction when the gate signal terminates. These SCR's will, therefore, not conduct for the remainder of the cycle, overloading the other parallel units.

A more flexible approach is to force the SCR's to share the load current by external-circuit means. Both resistors and reactors have been successfully used for this purpose, the latter, of course, being a more efficient technique than the former. Figure 10.10 illustrates how two reactor windings on a common magnetic core T_1 can be connected to two parallel SCR's to achieve uniform current-sharing. When SCR_1 is triggered, voltage is developed across the reactor as shown. This reactor voltage provides both gate and anode

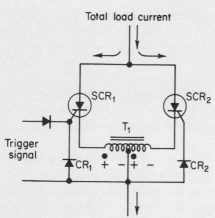

Fig. 10.10 Use of paralleling reactor to force current sharing between parallel SCR's.

voltage to turn on SCR_2. After both SCR's have switched into conduction, the reactor will essentially balance inequalities in current-sharing by developing a voltage that tends to buck down the higher of the two SCR currents and to increase the lesser of the two. Practical designs of this type can equalize currents within ten per cent of each other, even with unmatched SCR's.

Although both SCR's can also be gate-triggered from a common source, the slave-gating arrangement in Fig. 10.10 has the advantage that, if either SCR drops out of conduction on a momentary dip in load current, the paralleling reactor will develop a gate signal to retrigger it again through CR_1 or CR_2. When a retriggering circuit is not used for parallel SCR's, it is desirable to use a square-wave gate signal rather than a narrow pulse to ensure that all parallel SCR's share the load throughout the cycle.

In single-phase circuits, the paralleling reactor core should be capable of supporting $\Delta V/2f$ volt-seconds without saturating, where f = supply frequency and ΔV = maximum voltage mismatch between SCR's at peak load current. To reset the flux in the core after each cycle, either an airgap or a reset winding should be provided. Additional reactors in a chain connection can be used for paralleling more than two SCR's.[4]

10.6 Transient Voltage Protection

Adequate protection of SCR's against transient circuit conditions is just as important to high system reliability as the use of quality components. Unless properly protected, a random circuit transient can cause circuit malfunction just as readily as a defective SCR or other component. Protection concerns three main problem areas: overvoltage, overcurrent, and the general subject of interference and interaction between SCR's and other circuits or components. These subjects will be discussed in turn.

Overvoltage is one of the single greatest causes of failure of semiconductor power devices, since the great majority of electrical systems have transient voltage peaks well in excess of the working or cyclical peaks of the supply voltage. Transient peaks that are five to ten times the recurrent peak circuit voltage are not uncommon in conventional circuits if no means of suppression is present. The high blocking impedance of SCR's often aggravates transient voltage conditions by preventing discharge of stored circuit energy through low-impedance circuits. Transient voltage conditions often lead to permanent semiconductor device damage if the device is unable to absorb high momentary levels of power in the blocking state and if other transient suppression means are not available.

Fundamentally, voltage transients arise from system or circuit disturbances, such as switching. Very often the source of potential trouble is magnetic energy ($\frac{1}{2}LI^2$) stored in an inductive circuit element. This energy is suddenly released when a switch opens and tries to bring the current I to zero quickly. A typical case occurs when primary switching of a transformer interrupts the magnetizing current, causing a very high secondary voltage peak as the flux in the transformer core collapses.[5] Fast switching of the SCR can lead to transient voltages well in excess of normal when commutating duty is aggravated by the hole-storage phenomenon illustrated in Fig. 8.9. Voltage transients are generally at their worst in circuits operating at no load, particularly when no low-impedance path exists for high-frequency components of the transient. This is the case when SCR's are being worked into an inductive load.

The durations of destructive voltage transients range from several milliseconds down to a fraction of a microsecond. Because of their usually intermittent and random nature, detection and measurement require use of sensitive and fast equipment. High-speed oscilloscopes and transient-voltage indicators are the most useful types of equipment for this purpose.

When transient-voltage problems occur, the most economical solution usually lies both in selecting SCR's with greater ability to withstand transient voltage or energy and in taking suitable steps to reduce the amplitude of the transients. From the semiconductor-device standpoint, either an SCR with higher voltage rating or else one that has the ability to dissipate transient energy itself can be selected. Often a conventional diode rectifier in series with the SCR will help the SCR withstand reverse voltage transients.

The reduction of transient amplitude can be accomplished by any of the following alternatives:

1. Changing the location of the switching elements or the sequence of switching. An example is to perform switching in the transformer secondary instead of the primary or load circuits, or to interlock switching so that the secondary is always opened before the primary.
2. Changing the speed of current interruption by the switching elements. For instance, from a transient-voltage viewpoint it is desirable to use a conventional relay or contactor rather than a vacuum switch, since the former devices interrupt current more gradually.
3. Providing additional energy-storage or -dissipation means in the circuit. Typical examples are capacitors and nonlinear resistance such as the General Electric Thyrector selenium voltage suppressor. Capacitive filters are commonly used for low-energy, high-frequency types of transients. They are connected directly across the SCR's or across the input lines to the SCR circuit. Some series resistance is generally necessary to dampen oscillation owing to the capacitance and distributed circuit inductance and to limit the switching duty on the SCR. For general control circuits, properly applied Thyrector voltage suppressors are effective in holding transients below 200 per cent of the recurrent peak voltage of the circuit.
4. SCR's and other semiconductor devices that have so-called "controlled avalanche" blocking characteristics[6] minimize and often eliminate

the need for separate transient-voltage suppressors. By virtue of their ability to dissipate large transient energy levels within their bulk without exceeding the voltage at which destructive surface breakdown occurs across their junctions, these types of SCR's and diode rectifiers not only protect themselves but also protect other circuit elements by limiting the buildup of transient voltage in the circuit.

10.7 Overcurrent Protection

Because of the relatively low thermal capacity of semiconductor devices like the SCR, protection against overcurrents is often more critical than for other types of electrical components. Overcurrent conditions in SCR circuits generally occur for either of two reasons:

1. Short circuits or overloads in the load. This can result from such causes as carelessness with a screwdriver, failure of a component in the load, or stalling of a motor load.
2. Failure by shorting of one of the SCR's or associated semiconductor devices. When an SCR shorts or fails to block, a heavy short circuit is often imposed on the remaining good semiconductor devices during at least part of the cycle.

Just how effective a system must be to protect against these possibilities depends on the balance of many technical and economic factors.[7] If an SCR with sufficiently high current rating is used, conventional overcurrent protective means may be adequate. Higher performance and speed of the protective system are necessary when SCR's are operated near their maximum ratings on a continuous basis. The element of risk also enters the selection of a well-engineered overcurrent protective system. If the possibility of a specific fault condition is very remote, it may be good judgment to forego protection for that condition if the protective device costs are comparable to the cost of what is being protected, or if the protective device introduces another source of possible failure.

Besides the considerations mentioned, the type of overcurrent protection that should be used for a particular application depends on whether or not the fault or overload is current-limited.

10.7.1 CURRENT-LIMITED OVERLOADS

In this type of fault, sufficient impedance remains in the circuit during the fault to limit the fault current below the one-to-three-cycle surge rating of the SCR being protected. Typical examples of this type of overload occur in machine tool drives where a motor is stalled by a breakdown of the tool, or in other systems where a short circuit occurs in the load at a remote point fed through a relatively high-impedance cable. Protection against this type of fault is reasonably simple, since it can make use of conventional overcurrent protective elements, such as fuses, contactors, and circuit breakers, provided that they are properly co-ordinated to clear the overload or fault before the SCR surge rating is exceeded. The SCR blocking characteristics themselves may also be conveniently used for protecting against this type of fault condition. By suitable feedback in the SCR trigger circuitry to detect the presence of an overcurrent condition, the gate-trigger signal can be removed from the SCR so that it blocks on the next cycle and thus removes voltage from the fault.

10.7.2 NON-CURRENT-LIMITED (STIFF) FAULTS

This refers to the type of fault where there is negligible impedance to limit the flow of fault current. Specifically, the resulting fault current exceeds the one-half-cycle surge rating of the SCR. Hence, conventional fuses, circuit breakers, and SCR gate-blocking schemes are too slow for satisfactory protection, since they wait for the current to reach zero no sooner than the end of the first half-cycle before interrupting the current flow. Instead, a so-called "current-limiting" device is required that is capable of interrupting the fault current *before* it reaches its first peak, generally within a few milliseconds.

Special current-limiting fuses of this type are available. Their action is illustrated in Fig. 10.11. If a fault occurs at point A, a fault current builds up, as indicated by the dashed line, if no current-limiting device is used. A properly selected fuse, however, melts at point B and introduces its arc in series with the fault. At point C the arcing ceases and the fault current is interrupted. Use of I^2t ratings[7] is convenient for selecting the correct current-limiting fuse for protecting an SCR. So long as the clearing I^2t of the fuse is less than the I^2t rating of the SCR, the designer has assurance that the fuse will interrupt any stiff fault without damage to the SCR.

Suitable SCR circuits may act as current-limiting circuit breakers capable of interrupting a fault current within 50 μsec of its inception. A basic circuit capable of this performance is described in Sec. 7.7. An SCR may also be used for extremely fast protective service by operating it as a shorting device (electronic crowbar) across the supply line ahead of the circuit or device to be protected.[8] Suitable simple circuitry senses the buildup of a fault current and triggers the SCR, allowing the SCR to divert fault current from the circuit to be protected until conventional fuses or breakers can function.

The foregoing overcurrent protective approaches de-energize the system when a fault occurs in an SCR or other component. In some types of application, such as highly reliable military systems and continuous industrial processes, such a service interruption cannot be tolerated. When the added cost and complexity is warranted, systems can be devised to maintain the output or service even if a semiconductor device or other component fails. Such systems consist of the necessary redundancy of components in addition to suitable means for disconnecting and isolating faulty sections of the circuit.[9]

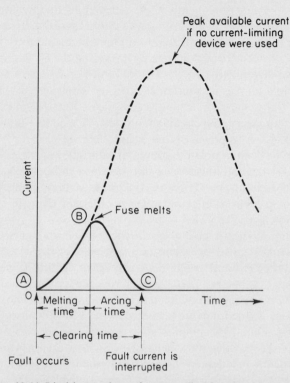

Fig. 10.11 Limiting action of current-limiting fuse in an a-c circuit.

10.8 Interference, Interaction, and Mistriggering

As a switch, the SCR turns on currents in about one microsecond, provided that no other circuit elements limit the rate of rise of the current. Current rate-of-change (di/dt) values from one to 100 amp/μsec are not uncommon in resistive and capacitive circuits. Such fast rates-of-rise of current induce voltages in nearby circuits and may cause notches in the supply-voltage waveform. Sudden wavefronts of this type can generate oscillations in distributed circuit reactances at frequencies in the megacycle range and can cause troublesome radio-frequency interference (RFI) problems in nearby circuits and equipments if not properly handled. High-frequency interference of this type can be transmitted by both conduction and radiation. It may be accompanied by audible noise at the fundamental or a harmonic of the operating frequency of the SCR circuit.

The most basic approach to this type of interference problem consists of limiting the rate-of-rise of current through the SCR. Lumped inductance in series with the supply or load, depending on the circuit, is an effective "brute force" approach. Saturable reactors with nonsquare loop core material can perform the same function in much smaller weight and volume by being effective only during the switching interval, then saturating smoothly and thus removing themselves from the circuit. One can also avoid a fast rate-of-rise of current in a-c switching circuits by triggering the SCR's at the instant when system voltage is zero.

Often possible sources of interference can be connected on the secondary of the power transformer or behind a low-pass filter to isolate conducted interference. If necessary, the circuit should also be installed inside grounded electrostatic shielding to prevent radiated interference.

In addition to being a possible source of interference, the SCR may also be acted upon by external interference, switching on unintentionally and thus causing possible circuit malfunction. Interference may come from many sources, including other SCR's, and will act on either the gate or anode (or on both) to mistrigger the SCR.

Mistriggering on the anode is caused either by voltage transients in excess of the breakover voltage or by momentary fast rates-of-rise of anode voltage. These effects can be reduced or eliminated by selecting SCR's with high dv/dt withstand capability, by use of RC filters across the SCR, by use of negative gate bias, or by operating the SCR on a stiff low-reactance line.

The gate circuit can also cause misfiring of the SCR if spurious signals are picked up in this circuit. A common source of undesired gate signals comes from the inductively coupled pulse of a nearby SCR switching into conduction. Mistriggering owing to these effects can be eliminated by judicious part and lead placement, by shielding or twisting gate-signal leads, by keeping both leads of a power circuit together and thus avoiding inductive loops, and by loading down the gate of the SCR with appropriate shunt resistance and capacitance.

References

1. W. H. Giedt, *Principles of Engineering Heat Transfer*. Princeton, N.J.: D. Van Nostrand Co., 1957, p. 218.

2. I. Somos, "Switching Characteristics of Silicon Power-Controlled Rectifiers, I—Turn-On Action," *A.I.E.E. Communication and Electronics*, Vol. **80**, Part I (1961), pp. 320–26.

3. E. W. Manteuffel and T. A. Phillips, "The Shunt-Loaded Magnetic Amplifier —II," *A.I.E.E. Communication and Electronics*, Vol. **81**, Part I (1962), pp. 451–52.

4. I. K. Dortort, "Current Balancing Reactors for Semiconductor Rectifiers," *A.I.E.E. Communication and Electronics*, Part I (1958), pp. 452–56.

5. F. W. Gutzwiller, "Rectifier Voltage Transients: Cause, Detection, Reduction," *Electrical Manufacturing* (December, 1959), pp. 167–73.

6. F. W. Gutzwiller, "More Reliability With Controlled Avalanche Rectifiers," *Electronics* (March 29, 1963), pp. 38–41.

7. F. W. Gutzwiller, "Overcurrent Protection of Semiconductor Rectifiers," *Electrical Manufacturing* (April, 1959), pp. 106–14.

8. F. W. Gutzwiller, "Using the Silicon Controlled Rectifier for Protection," *Electro-Technology* (October, 1961), pp. 130–32.

9. *Silicon Controlled Rectifier Manual*, 2nd ed. General Electric Company, Rectifier Components Department, Auburn, N.Y., 1961, p. 195.

APPENDIX A

TURN-ON CRITERION FOR *p-n-p-n* DEVICES

In the usual manner, we shall define the d-c alpha of a transistor as the ratio of collector current which flows as a result of emitter current.[1,2] Thus we have

$$I_C = \alpha I_E + I_{CBO},\qquad\qquad (A.1)$$

where I_{CBO} is the thermally generated current which is collected. The small-signal alpha α_s is derived from equation (A.1) by differentiating with respect to emitter current I_E. Thus we get

$$\alpha_s = \frac{dI_C}{dI_E} = \alpha + I_E \frac{d\alpha}{dI_E}.\qquad\qquad (A.2)$$

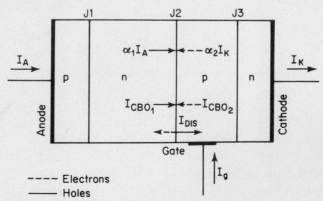

Fig. A.1 Schematic of *p-n-p-n* device.

In Fig. A.1, we see that the current flow across junction $J2$ consists of holes and electrons collected from the adjacent bases, where $\alpha_1 I_A$ is the current resulting from diffusion of holes which were injected by junction $J1$, $\alpha_2 I_K$ is the current owing to electrons diffusing from $J3$, I_{CBO_2} and I_{CBO_1} are the thermally generated currents collected by $J2$, and I_{DIS} is the displacement current resulting from any change in voltage across the capacitance of junction $J2$. Proceeding in the same manner as Moll, et al.,[2] we see that the anode current must be equal to that across $J2$; consequently,

$$I_A = \alpha_1 I_A + \alpha_2 I_K + I_{co} + I_{DIS}, \tag{A.3}$$

where $I_{co} = I_{CBO_1} + I_{CBO_2}$. From Fig. A.1 we see that by Kirchhoff's law

$$I_K = I_A + I_g. \tag{A.4}$$

Using equations (A.3) and (A.4), we can solve for I_A, and obtain an expression very much the same as that developed by others,[2,3] where

$$I_A = \frac{\alpha_1 I_g + I_{co} + I_{DIS}}{1 - \alpha_1 - \alpha_2}. \tag{A.5}$$

Now suppose we increase the gate current I_g by a small amount ΔI_g. This increase will cause the anode current I_A to increase by an amount ΔI_A. With alphas which increase monotonically with emitter current, switching will begin when $\Delta I_A / \Delta I_g \to \infty$. To determine the conditions that must exist for this relation to hold, we differentiate equation (A.3) with respect to I_g. If it is assumed that the problem can be treated as one-dimensional and that changes in alphas with voltage across the devices are negligible, the result is

$$\frac{dI_A}{dI_g} = \alpha_1 \frac{dI_A}{dI_g} + I_A \frac{d\alpha_1}{dI_g} + \alpha_2 \frac{dI_K}{dI_g} + I_K \frac{d\alpha_2}{dI_g}. \tag{A.6}$$

Using the relation of equation (A.2), we note that the small-signal alphas can be expressed in terms of the d-c alphas as follows:

$$\frac{d\alpha_1}{dI_A} = \frac{\alpha_{1s}}{I_A} - \frac{\alpha_1}{I_A} \tag{A.7}$$

and

$$\frac{d\alpha_2}{dI_K} = \frac{\alpha_{2s}}{I_K} - \frac{\alpha_2}{I_K}. \tag{A.8}$$

Furthermore, equations (A.7) and (A.8) can be written in terms of I_g so that

$$\frac{d\alpha_1}{dI_g} = \frac{d\alpha_1}{dI_A}\frac{dI_A}{dI_g} = \frac{\alpha_{1s}}{I_A}\frac{dI_A}{dI_g} - \frac{\alpha_1}{I_A}\frac{dI_A}{dI_g} \tag{A.9}$$

and

$$\frac{d\alpha_2}{dI_g} = \frac{d\alpha_2}{dI_K}\frac{dI_K}{dI_g} = \frac{\alpha_{2s}}{I_K}\frac{dI_K}{dI_g} - \frac{\alpha_2}{I_K}\frac{dI_K}{dI_g}. \tag{A.10}$$

Substituting equations (A.9), (A.10), and (A.4) into (A.6) and solving for dI_A/dI_g, we find that

$$\frac{dI_A}{dI_g} = \frac{\alpha_{2s}}{1 - \alpha_{1s} - \alpha_{2s}}. \tag{A.11}$$

Thus, the condition specified by equation (A.6) is satisfied when $\alpha_{2s} + \alpha_{1s} = 1$. Consequently, I_A becomes unstable and will increase without limit.

By differentiating equation (A.3) with respect to I_{co} and making the same type of substitutions, we can show that

$$\frac{dI_A}{dI_{co}} = \frac{1}{1 - \alpha_{1s} - \alpha_{2s}}, \tag{A.12}$$

if gate current and displacement current are assumed to be invariant with I_{co}. Furthermore, the same procedure can be used to show that

$$\frac{dI_A}{dI_{DIS}} = \frac{1}{1 - \alpha_{1s} - \alpha_{2s}}, \tag{A.13}$$

if the thermally generated current and the gate current are independent of the displacement current. The significance of equations (A.11), (A.12), and (A.13) is that if the sum of the small-signal alphas is unity, i.e., $\alpha_{1s} + \alpha_{2s} = 1$, then an infinitesimal increase in gate current, temperature, or voltage will cause a *p-n-p-n* device to begin switching.

REFERENCES

1. J. J. Ebers and J. L. Moll, "Large Signal Behavior of Junction Transistors," *Proc. I.R.E.*, Vol. **42** (December, 1954), pp. 1761–72.

2. J. L. Moll, M. Tanenbaum, J. M. Goldey, and N. Holonyak, "*P-N-P-N* Transistor Switches," *Proc. I.R.E.*, Vol. **44** (September, 1956), pp. 1174–82.

3. I. M. Mackintosh, "The Electrical Characteristics of Silicon p-n-p-n Triodes," *Proc. I.R.E.*, Vol. **46** (June, 1958), pp. 1229–35.

FORWARD BLOCKING CURRENT

The current which flows through the center junction of a *p-n-p-n* device in the forward blocking state consists of three components, as shown in Fig. B.1.

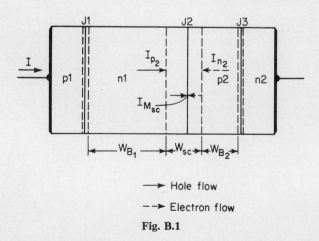

→ Hole flow

– –► Electron flow

Fig. B.1

I_{p_2} = hole current which diffuses from region *n*1 into the space-charge layer of junction *J*2.

I_{n_2} = current caused by electrons which diffuse from region *p*2 into the space-charge layer of *J*2.

I_{Msc} = hole and electron current generated within the space-charge layer of *J*2.

Thus, the total current across the center of junction $J2$ is

$$I_2 = I_{p_2} + I_{n_2} + I_{Msc}. \tag{B.1}$$

Using the methods and nomenclature of Sec. 2.4.4, we can write

$$I_{p_2} = \frac{qD_p p_{n0}}{L_p}\left(\frac{p_1 - p_{n0}}{p_{n0}} \operatorname{csch} \frac{W_{B_1}}{L_p} - \frac{p_2 - p_{n0}}{p_{n0}} \coth \frac{W_{B_1}}{L_p}\right), \tag{B.2}$$

and

$$I_{n_2} = \frac{qD_n n_{p0}}{L_n}\left(\frac{n_3 - n_{p0}}{n_{p0}} \operatorname{csch} \frac{W_{B_2}}{L_n} - \frac{n_2 - n_{p0}}{n_{p0}} \coth \frac{W_{B_2}}{L_n}\right). \tag{B.3}$$

Holes and electrons are generated in the space-charge layer of $J2$ by both thermal agitation and avalanche multiplication. By referring to Secs. 2.3.4 and 2.4.4 we can express the current generated in the space-charge layer of $J2$ as

$$I_{Msc} = (M_p - 1)I_{p_2} + (M_n - 1)I_{n_2}$$

$$+ \frac{qn_i M^* W_{sc}}{2\sqrt{\tau_{p0}\tau_{n0}}\cosh\left[\dfrac{q(V_t - V_i)}{kT} + \dfrac{1}{2}\ln\dfrac{\tau_{p0}}{\tau_{n0}}\right]}. \tag{B.4}$$

Combining equations (B.1), (B.2), (B.3), and (B.4), we obtain

$$I_2 = \frac{qM_p D_p p_{n0}}{L_p}\left(\frac{p_1 - p_{n0}}{p_{n0}} \operatorname{csch} \frac{W_{B_1}}{L_p} - \frac{p_2 - p_{n0}}{p_{n0}} \coth \frac{W_{B_1}}{L_p}\right)$$

$$+ \frac{qM_n D_n n_{n0}}{L_n}\left(\frac{n_3 - n_{p0}}{n_{p0}} \operatorname{csch} \frac{W_{B_2}}{L_n} - \frac{n_2 - n_{p0}}{n_{p0}} \coth \frac{W_{B_2}}{L_n}\right)$$

$$+ \frac{qn_i M^* W_{sc}}{2\sqrt{\tau_{p0}\tau_{n0}}\cosh\left[\dfrac{q(V_t - V_i)}{kT} + \dfrac{1}{2}\ln\dfrac{\tau_{p0}}{\tau_{n0}}\right]}. \tag{B.5}$$

At the two emitter junctions $J1$ and $J3$, the emitter efficiencies are, by definition, the injected minority-carrier current divided by the total current through the junction

$$\gamma_1(I_1) \equiv \frac{I_{p_1}}{I_1}, \tag{B.6}$$

$$\gamma_3(I_3) \equiv \frac{I_{n_3}}{I_3}, \tag{B.7}$$

With no gate current, $I_1 = I_2 = I_3$. Therefore,

$$\gamma_1(I_1)I_2 = I_{p_1}, \tag{B.8}$$

$$\gamma_3(I_3)I_2 = I_{n_3}. \tag{B.9}$$

Again we refer to Sec. 2.4.4 to write

$$I_{p_1} = \frac{qD_p p_{n0}}{L_p}\left(\frac{p_1 - p_{n0}}{p_{n0}} \coth \frac{W_{B_1}}{L_p} - \frac{p_2 - p_{n0}}{p_{n0}} \operatorname{csch} \frac{W_{B_1}}{L_p}\right), \quad \text{(B.10)}$$

$$I_{n_3} = \frac{qD_n n_{p0}}{L_n}\left(\frac{n_3 - n_{p0}}{n_{p0}} \coth \frac{W_{B_2}}{L_n} - \frac{n_2 - n_{p0}}{n_{p0}} \operatorname{csch} \frac{W_{B_2}}{L_n}\right). \quad \text{(B.11)}$$

By combining equations (B.5), (B.8), (B.9), (B.10), and (B.11) to eliminate $(p_1 - p_{n0})/p_{n0}$ and $(n_3 - n_{p0})/n_{p0}$, we can obtain an expression for current:

$$I_2 = \frac{\dfrac{qn_i M^* W_{sc}}{2\sqrt{\tau_{n0}\tau_{p0}} \cosh\left[\dfrac{q(V_t - V_i)}{kT} - \dfrac{1}{2}\ln\dfrac{\tau_{p0}}{\tau_{n0}}\right]}}{1 - \gamma_1(I_1)M_p \operatorname{sech}\dfrac{W_{B_1}}{L_p} - \gamma_3(I_3)M_n \operatorname{sech}\dfrac{W_{B_2}}{L_n}}$$

$$- \frac{\dfrac{(qD_p M_p)(p_2 - p_{n0})}{L_p}\tanh\dfrac{W_{B_1}}{L_p} + \dfrac{(qD_n M_n)(n_2 - n_{p0})}{L_n}\tanh\dfrac{W_{B_2}}{L_n}}{1 - \gamma_1(I_1)M_p \operatorname{sech}\dfrac{W_{B_1}}{L_p} - \gamma_3(I_3)M_n \operatorname{sech}\dfrac{W_{B_2}}{L_n}}. \quad \text{(B.12)}$$

In the forward blocking state $p_2 \ll n_{n0}$, and $n_2 \ll n_{p0}$ so equation (B.12) can be rewritten in the form

$$I = \frac{I_d + I_{sc}}{1 - \alpha_1 - \alpha_2}, \quad \text{(B.13)}$$

where

$$I_d = \frac{qD_p M_p p_{n0}}{L_p}\tanh\frac{W_{B_1}}{L_p} + \frac{qD_n M_n n_{p0}}{L_n}\tanh\frac{W_{B_2}}{L_n} \quad \text{(B.14)}$$

$$I_{sc} = \frac{qn_i M^* W_s}{2\sqrt{\tau_{p0}\tau_{n0}}\cosh\left[\dfrac{q(V_t - V_i)}{kT} - \dfrac{1}{2}\ln\dfrac{\tau_{p0}}{\tau_{n0}}\right]} \quad \text{(B.15)}$$

$$\alpha_1 = \gamma_1(I_1)M_p \operatorname{sech}\frac{W_{B_1}}{L_p} \quad \text{(B.16)}$$

$$\alpha_2 = \gamma_3(I_3)M_n \operatorname{sech}\frac{W_{B_2}}{L_n}. \quad \text{(B.17)}$$

Note that equation (B.13) is identical with equation (2.71) of Chap. 2.

INDEX

DATE DUE

OCT 10 '73			
JUN 12 '78			
20 APR '81			
2 MAY '83			
12 MAY '83			
APR 3 0 1984			
MAY '85			
MAY 4 '88			
DEC 29 '88			
APR 22 '91			
GAYLORD			PRINTED IN U.S.A